MODERN CONCEPTS IN CHEMISTRY

EDITORS

Bryce Crawford, Jr., University of Minnesota
W. D. McElroy, Johns Hopkins University
Charles C. Price, University of Pennsylvania

HAROLD S. JOHNSTON, Ph.D., California Institute of Technology, is Dean of the College of Chemistry, University of California, Berkeley. He previously taught at Stanford University and the California Institute of Technology. Dr. Johnston has written widely on fast gas phase reactions, kinetic isotope effects, photochemistry, and reaction rates of oxides of nitrogen.

GAS PHASE
REACTION RATE
THEORY

HAROLD S. JOHNSTON

UNIVERSITY OF CALIFORNIA, BERKELEY

THE RONALD PRESS COMPANY • NEW YORK

Library of Congress Catalog Card Number: 66-21855
PRINTED IN THE UNITED STATES OF AMERICA

Preface

One might say: Write down Schroedinger's equation, including the time, for all nuclei and electrons of interest and derive rate phenomena from there. Exactly this program has been and is being followed by some theorists; a deduction with respect to laboratory observables is occasionally made; but by and large these theories are still high above chemical kinetics. Future generations of kineticists should watch for their cue from these "in principle" theories. On the other hand, fundamental quantum-mechanical treatments of certain simple reactions have been carried through—charge exchange $H + D^+ = H^+ + D$, for example. However, at low, chemically interesting energies, it is still extremely difficult to treat problems as simple as: H $(1s)$ $+$ $H \rightarrow H$ $(2p)$ $+$ H or $H + H \rightarrow H + H^+ + e^-$. At high energies (kilovolts, usually) one can use the Born approximation to treat many simple atomic rate processes. These methods are not yet ready to be applied to low-energy molecular rate processes and are outside the scope of this book.

Molecular kinetics operates at a higher level of abstraction than "fundamental particle" quantum mechanics. The situation is analogous to that in molecular spectroscopy, where atoms are regarded as the "particles" and frequencies are obtained empirically from spectroscopy. The spectroscopist postulates a molecular model including force constants and bond lengths; from this model he derives frequencies to be compared with those observed. In molecular kinetics, the observables are quantities such as rate constants, activation energies, and kinetic isotope effects. The kineticist utilizes data developed in molecular spectroscopy and molecular-structure determinations, and on this basis he constructs models to explain or, preferably, to predict rates.

The observed rate constant is an average over a wide range of molecular properties. The theories of chemical reaction rates, vintage 1923 through 1963, arise from models whose properties are averaged over wide-ranging molecular distribution functions. It happens that the observed average rate constants are not very sensitive to the details of the postulated model.

There are two judgments to this situation. It is a comfort to the chemical engineer, because he should be able fairly accurately to predict kinetic data from almost any internally consistent molecular theory. (But there are limits; see Chapter 13.) On the other hand, this situation is very distressing to the natural philosopher, since he learns very little about what the molecules are doing from observed rate constants.

In unimolecular reaction kinetics, in flash spectroscopy, in experiments with crossed molecular beams, we get a glimpse of the magnificent richness of molecular processes that are averaged over to give the observed rate constant. There is strong reason to believe that we stand at the threshold of a new era in kinetics. By means of ingenious experiments and penetrating analysis, kineticists are going to understand the molecular dynamics of chemical change.

In this book I seek to carry out a review and judgment of the simple theories of chemical kinetics that were developed and used during the last forty years. The field of chemical kinetics as practiced in recent years has been a highly partisan affair. About 1933, collision theory seemed to consist merely of the hard-sphere collision-rate expression and a vague, empirical "steric factor." The methods of quantum mechanics and statistical mechanics were applied to chemical rate problems by a number of people during the period from 1928 to 1935. Certain lines of this work were codified into "activated-complex theory" (Henry Eyring) or "transition-state theory" (M. G. Evans) about 1935. The theory was postulated to be of universal applicability, and enthusiastic practitioners named it "*the* theory of rate processes" or "the theory of *absolute* reaction rates." This enthusiasm won many advocates to the theory. Organic chemists embraced the theory by virtue of the convenient *language* that it gave to them, and they have extended it as a method of notation (Chapter 16). Many productive theoretical studies have been made by means of activated-complex theory. Many graduate students of Henry Eyring have become professors of chemistry. This group and this tradition represent one "party." The zealousness of the activated-complex school, on the other hand, alienated many serious chemists, and generated an opposing "party." They regard activated-complex theory as a scheme of adjustable parameters that can "explain" anything and predict nothing. Collision theorists assert that the postulate of universality was accepted by activated-complex theorists without logical or experimental verification. Today many molecular-beam kineticists regard "the activated complex" with the same disdain as was turned upon the "steric factor" thirty years ago by the hot-blooded young activated-complex kineticist of that day.

I would like to believe that I sit on the fence between activated-complex theory and collision theory, and that I point out good features of each method. The early fury of the activated-complex theorists drove collision theory underground for about twenty years—much to the loss of science, for in this period physicists have used collision methods to make spectacular advances in nuclear theory. It is hoped that the present resurgence by collision theorists will not banish the positive aspects of activated-complex methods. On the other hand, the time is long overdue for some claims of activated-complex theory to be thrown out.

Primarily, this book is directed at seniors and first-year graduate students. The goal is to teach in detail (as opposed to "teach about") certain basic methods in molecular mechanics and chemical kinetics. To this end, the algebraic structure of simple two-atom collision rates and three-atom metathetical reactions is presented in great detail. For other reactions, considerable use is made of graphical presentation in terms of three-atom models. For more complex molecules, the methods are briefly outlined and reference is given to advanced textbooks or journal articles. The examples chosen are frequently taken from my own publications. Several unpublished studies are included. In all cases where experimental data are compared with theory, the theoretical calculations were redone especially for this comparison; and where possible the experimental data have been recalculated. Thus even experienced kineticists will find new material in some chapters, and perhaps they will be amused by new presentations in other chapters. Only a few chemical reactions are discussed in detail; these have been selected to illustrate principles, and no effort has been made to cover the literature.

The material for this book is the product of the course in chemical kinetics that I have taught at Berkeley during the past four years. Each student has a standing offer of an A in the course, regardless of examination grades, if he writes a publishable term paper on some topic in kinetics. Several students have collected on this offer, and to them I am grateful for some of the content of this book. To many of my research students I am deeply grateful for portions of the book. Even more, I am indebted to present and former colleagues at Berkeley for point and counterpoint in the development of these ideas, especially Kenneth Pitzer, Dudley Herschbach, Richard Powell, Bruce Mahan, and Robert Connick. I would like to express profound appreciation to my teachers who brought a philosophical turn of mind to the teaching of chemistry—Roscoe Dickinson, Don Yost, and Richard Tolman.

HAROLD S. JOHNSTON

Berkeley, California
    January, 1966

Contents

GAS PHASE REACTION RATE THEORY

I

Elementary Reactions

The rate of chemical reactions is a very complicated subject. This statement is to be interpreted as a challenge to enthusiastic and vigorous chemists; it is not to be interpreted as a sad sigh of defeat. One way to approach a complicated subject is to resolve it into its components or elements. A chemical change (processes in industry, in biological systems, in the atmosphere, etc.) can often be resolved into a "network" of chemical reactions, each with a balanced chemical equation between reactants and products. Each chemical reaction, if isolated and studied separately, usually is found to consist of a set of steps or "elementary chemical reactions," typically involving unstable or transient intermediate species. For reactants and products, each in a unique quantum state, processes such as collisions, energy transfer, and molecular rearrangements may be classified as "elementary chemical-physical reactions"; and "elementary chemical reactions" are averages of such processes over a wide-ranging molecular distribution function. Thus the actual, complicated world of reaction rates can be analyzed into more and more abstract elements. On the other hand, the field of chemical kinetics as a theoretical and predictive science reverses the order: this chapter will outline how one builds up a "universe of discourse" from "elementary chemical-physical reactions" to "elementary chemical reactions" to "complex or ordinary chemical reactions."

A. ELEMENTARY CHEMICAL–PHYSICAL REACTIONS

In any branch of physical science it is well to keep clearly in mind the distinction between events observed in the laboratory and the mental images or models built up by the observer to explain the facts. In the family of experiments with "beams," the schematic diagram of the apparatus is very simple (for example, Fig. 1), even though operation of the actual laboratory machines requires the highest order of experimental skill.[1] In these experiments, it is easy to state the nature of the observable phenomena, and the relation to atomic and molecular models is unusually direct. It is

3

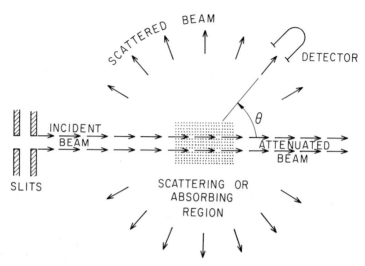

Fig. I-I. Schematic diagram of scattering of a beam from a fixed scattering region.

particularly convenient to define "elementary chemical-physical reactions" in terms of molecular-beam experiments.

(i) Stationary Scattering Region

A schematic diagram of a beam experiment with a stationary target is indicated by Fig. 1. The incident beam is defined by an appropriate system of slits; its intensity I_0 is expressed in terms of the flux of some quantity Q per unit of time t across its cross-sectional area A:

$$I_0 = Q_0/At \qquad \text{quantity/cm}^2\text{-sec} \qquad (1\text{--}1)$$

The beam intensity is a macroscopic concept. It could be expressed in continuous units such as grams per square centimeter per second, ergs per square centimeter per second, or amperes per square centimeter. On the other hand, it could be expressed by means of a particle model, such as photons or atoms or ions per square centimeter per second. The attenuated beam I is described in the same units as the incident beam I_0. The scattered beam spreads out as it leaves the scattering center. The appropriate units are not quantity per unit area but rather quantity per unit solid angle. The total scattered beam per unit time may be written as

$$i = Q_{\text{scattered}}/t \qquad \text{quantity/sec} \qquad (1\text{--}2)$$

In "elastic-scattering" experiments, per unit time the number of scattered particles i plus the number of transmitted particles IA is equal to the number of incident particles I_0A:

$$i = (I_0 - I)A \tag{1-3}$$

The fraction of particles scattered out of the original beam is

$$\text{Fraction scattered} = \frac{I_0 - I}{I_0} \tag{1-4}$$

The original beam has cross-sectional area A. The macroscopic scattering region obstructs or scatters the fraction $(I_0 - I)/I_0$ of the beam, and thus it acts as if it had a "cross-section" of area

$$\Sigma = \frac{I_0 - I}{I_0} A \tag{1-5}$$

Or, in terms of the total scattered beam,

$$\Sigma = i/I_0 \qquad \text{cm}^2 \tag{1-6}$$

Here Σ is the macroscopic "cross-section" offered by the total scattering region. In terms of the quantity Q, it can be seen to be

$$\Sigma = \frac{i}{I_0} = \frac{Q_\text{scattered}}{Q_0} A \tag{1-7}$$

To emphasize the macroscopic nature of the method, note that the intensity of the incident beam could be expressed in units of slugs per acre per week; the total scattered sample could be expressed as slugs per week; and the ratio gives the cross-section of the entire scattering region in units of acres.

Usually one has a particle model for the scattering region. The density of scattering particles is $[n]$ per unit volume, and thus the number of particles in a sample of length L and in a beam of area A is

$$n = [n]AL \tag{1-8}$$

The ratio of the total target cross-section Σ to the total number of particles in the scattering region is some average cross-section per particle; if the sample is thin enough to avoid multiple scattering and to avoid "shadowing" of one particle by another, this average cross-section may be expected to give a fundamental property of the scattering particles:

$$\sigma = \lim_{L \to 0} \frac{\Sigma}{n} \tag{1-9}$$

In terms of Eqs. 5 and 8 this limit is

$$\sigma = \frac{1}{[n]I} \frac{dI}{dL} \tag{1-10}$$

and σ is the cross-section per particle in the scattering region.

To a chemist, one of the most familiar examples of this concept of cross-section is the absorption of monochromatic light by a solute or a gas of known concentration; that is, the Beer-Lambert law is an example of Eq. 10. In integrated form, it is

$$I = I_0 \exp \{-\sigma[n]L\} \qquad (1\text{--}11)$$

In chemical literature, the Beer-Lambert law is often expressed in units of moles per liter and in logarithm to base 10:

$$\log (I_0/I) = \varepsilon[N]L \qquad (1\text{--}12)$$

The relation between these quantities is

$$\sigma = 2303\varepsilon/6.02 \times 10^{23} = 3.82 \times 10^{-21}\varepsilon \text{ cm}^2 \qquad (1\text{--}13)$$

The interaction between incident beam and scattering region may not be elastic. To carry further the example of light absorption: it might be that the incident beam is in part scattered elastically and in part absorbed and re-emitted as fluorescence at a number of different wavelengths. The total cross-section per atom, σ, is based on attenuation of the incident beam (Eq. 10). The cross-section for elastic scattering, σ_E, is based on total scattered light at the same wavelength (Eqs. 9 and 7). The cross-section for fluorescence at wavelength λ, σ_λ, is based on total scattered light at wavelength λ (Eqs. 9 and 6). Thus one may have a scattering cross-section with respect to any observable property p of the scattered beam, σ_p.

For some cases, there arise both conceptual and experimental difficulties in defining the total scattered beam. For scattering that occurs at very small angles, it is difficult to distinguish between the forward, small-angle scattering and the attenuated beam itself. For certain models of the scattering interaction, classical mechanics says that if one had infinitely fine angular resolution of the scattered beam, then the cross-section per particle approaches infinity. However, quantum mechanics removes this infinity in a highly satisfactory manner.

Not only may one define a cross-section with respect to any observable property of the scattered particles, but also one may define a "differential cross-section" for any single placement of the detector. If the incident beam is imagined to be along the Z axis and the scattering region is at the origin, the location of the detector is given by spherical polar angles θ and ϕ. The solid angle that the detector offers to the scattering center is $d\omega$. If the flux of scattered beam (with observable property p) per unit time into this solid angle is $i_p(\theta, \phi) \, d\omega$, then by definition the differential cross-section (for the property p) per scattering particle is

$$\sigma_p(\theta, \phi) \, d\omega = \frac{i_p(\theta, \phi) \, d\omega}{n \, I_0} \qquad (1\text{--}14)$$

Thus for every observable property of the scattered beam, one may observe the differential scattering cross-section for any angular orientation relative to the scattering center. These direct observations give a wealth of data concerning the detailed microscopic interactions of the incident beam and the scattering particles.

(ii) Crossed Molecular Beams

Of especially great interest to chemical kineticists are experiments with crossed molecular beams, schematically indicated by Fig. 2. A generation ago, wise old kineticists warned their students that "one never has collisions

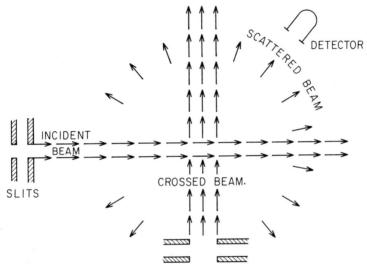

Fig. I–2. Schematic diagram of scattering from crossed beams.

between two crossed molecular beams." In 1955 Datz and Taylor[2] demonstrated that, indeed, one can measure the scattered particles from crossed beams, and they studied the angular distribution of product (KBr) in the reaction

$$K + HBr \rightarrow KBr + H \qquad (1\text{--}15)$$

Problems of intensity are extremely severe. During the last few years there has been rapid development both of experimental techniques and theoretical methods in this field.[1]

In two beams scattered elastically, the scattered beam contains particles from each incident beam. Measurements are made in "laboratory coordinates," but the interactions are most simply described in "center-of-mass coordinates." As two particles approach, it is advantageous to analyze the motion in terms of center-of-mass velocity along line of centers, and the "impact parameter" (see Chapter 7). Regardless of the nature of the interaction, the velocity of the center of mass is the same before and after collision. In center-of-mass coordinates, one can readily obtain relations before and after collision from the principles of conservation of momentum and conservation of energy. If two particles approach in any trajectory other than precisely center-to-center, then the pair has angular momentum, and further powerful deductions can be made from the principle of conservation of angular momentum.

Molecular beams may have a distribution of velocities. However, by ingenious electrical devices one may prepare a beam where all particles have very nearly the same velocity,[3] or by rotating slotted disks one may select a narrow range from the usual thermal spread of velocities. Experiments involving elastic scattering in velocity-selected beams give extraordinarily direct information about the *forces* between molecules.

Crossed molecular beams also give detailed information about inelastic collisions between molecules. Perhaps the simplest inelastic collision is the change in rotational quantum number of a molecule upon collision:

$$A + B \text{ (rotational state } J) \rightarrow A + B \text{ (rotational state } J') \quad (1\text{--}16)$$

Perhaps the next-simplest case is change of vibrational energy, upon collision, from a vibrational state v to v', with perhaps simultaneous change of rotational state:

$$A + B(v, J) \rightarrow A + B(v', J') \quad (1\text{--}17)$$

Systems of inhomogeneous magnetic and electrical fields can be used to separate and distinguish between molecules in different rotational and vibrational states. Also, an inelastic collision might involve change in electronic state (n) of an atom or molecule:

$$A + B(n) \rightarrow A + B(n') \quad (1\text{--}18)$$

In this case, the beam A might be a beam of light, or photons, $h\nu$:

$$h\nu + B(n) \rightarrow B(n') \quad (1\text{--}19)$$

The cases above, Eqs. 16–19, are "energy-transfer" reactions; they are extremely important in all chemical reactions, and their nature can be elucidated directly in molecular-beam experiments.[4]

A type of crossed-beam experiment widely used is ionization of a beam of molecules by a beam of fast electrons in a mass spectrometer:

$$e^- + A \rightarrow A^+ + 2e^- \quad (1\text{--}20)$$

Although this reaction is widely used to make positive ions for mass analysis, specially modified mass spectrometers study the dynamics of this reaction itself.[5]   Mass spectrometers may also be used to study ion-molecule reactions (Chapter 9):

$$A^+ + B \rightarrow A + B^+ \qquad (1\text{--}21)$$

$$A^+ + B \rightarrow C + D^+ \qquad (1\text{--}22)$$

As noted above (Eq. 15), recently there has been considerable success in the measurement of reactions between crossed, neutral molecular beams. An especially interesting series of reactions are those studied by Herschbach[6] and co-workers, between alkali metals and alkyl halides.   Upon reaction of K with CH_3I, C_2H_5I, i-propyl iodide, n-propyl iodide, and n-butyl iodide, the angular distribution of the product KI indicated that the heat of reaction (about 25 kcal) appeared primarily as internal excitation, vibration and rotation; and only 0 to 5 kcal appeared as relative kinetic energy.   Upon reaction of CH_3I with Na, K, Rb, and Cs, it was found that the heat of reaction appeared primarily as internal energy, varying from 80 percent for Na to 95 percent for Cs.

(iii) Elementary Physical Reactions

In the context of chemical kinetics, energy-transfer processes, Eqs. 16–19, are not classified as chemical reactions but rather as physical reactions. An elementary physical reaction is then an inelastic scattering process involving a transition between two energy levels, but there is no qualitative change of molecular structure.

(iv) Elementary Chemical-Physical Reactions

The *ideal* elementary chemical-physical reaction is that of velocity-selected, crossed molecular beams, each in a known single quantum state, to produce products in known single quantum states:

$$A\,(n, v, J) + B\,(n', v', J') \rightarrow C\,(n'', v'', J'') + D\,(n''', v''', J''') \quad (1\text{--}23)$$

So far, this *ideal* crossed-beam experiment has not been carried out, so the definition of an elementary chemical-physical reaction is broadened to include any reasonable approximation to Eq. 23.   The essential feature is that a molecular structure change occurs under conditions such that the usual thermal spread over states is restricted and controlled in some respect. A large fraction of the book *Atomic and Molecular Processes*, edited by D. R. Bates,[5] concerns itself with examples of *elementary physical or elementary chemical-physical reactions.*

B.   ELEMENTARY CHEMICAL REACTIONS

A schematic outline of an apparatus used to study gas-phase chemical reactions is indicated by Fig. 3.   It is indicated to be a bulb in a thermostat, and reactants and products are followed as a function of time by a beam of weak light.   For simple chemical reactions such as

$$N_2O_4 \rightarrow 2NO_2 \qquad (1\text{--}24)$$

$$NO_2 + CO \rightarrow NO + CO_2 \qquad (1\text{--}25)$$

it is clear that a large number of elementary physical and chemical-physical reactions occur.   For example, N_2O_4 is more stable than $2NO_2$ by 14 kcal,

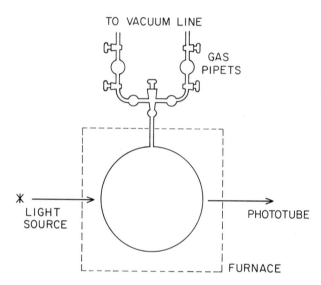

Fig. I–3. Schematic diagram of chemist's reaction flask.

and thus there must be energy-transfer processes to excite the N_2O_4 molecule to a value higher than 14 kcal for reaction to occur.   As a drastic abbreviation for a large number of state-by-state energy-transfer processes (compare Chapter 15), consider the skeleton mechanism of activation by collision with any molecule, M:

$$N_2O_4 + M \xrightarrow{a} N_2O_4^* + M \qquad (1\text{--}26)$$

where the asterisk on N_2O_4 refers to internal energy in the molecule.   Also, there is deactivation by collision,

$$M + N_2O_4^* \xrightarrow{b} N_2O_4 + M \qquad (1\text{--}27)$$

and unimolecular decomposition of the excited molecule,

$$N_2O_4^* \xrightarrow{c} 2NO_2 \qquad (1\text{--}28)$$

From the three reactions, Eqs. 26–28, a set of simultaneous differential equations can be set up and solved for excited reactant $[N_2O_4^*]$ to give a complicated initial behavior and a relatively smooth steady-state solution:

$$\frac{[\mathrm{N_2O_4^*}]}{[\mathrm{N_2O_4}]} = \frac{a[\mathrm{M}]}{b[\mathrm{M}] + c} \tag{1-29}$$

With $[\mathrm{N_2O_4^*}]$ eliminated in terms of its steady-state value, the differential rate of reaction is

$$-\frac{d[\mathrm{N_2O_4}]}{dt} = \frac{ac[\mathrm{M}][\mathrm{N_2O_4}]}{b[\mathrm{M}] + c} \tag{1-30}$$

Thus the observed rate of the simple chemical reaction can be shown to involve several different *kinds* of physical and chemical-physical reactions; and in the example given, it is readily seen that each such process really involves very many quantum states and is thus an average over truly elementary reactions.

As noted above, the observed rate of a chemical reaction involves an average of molecular functions. What sort of distribution functions are the chemical-physical reactions averaged over? The distribution function is already indicated by Eq. 29, and in terms of it two interesting limiting cases can be discussed. If no chemical reaction occurred at all (the rate constants c being zero), the distribution of molecules over excited states would be the equilibrium distribution

$$\frac{[\mathrm{N_2O_4^*}]_{eq}}{[\mathrm{N_2O_4}]} = \frac{a}{b} = P_{eq} \tag{1-31}$$

If the decomposition c is very fast compared to the deactivation rate b, one has the two-step steady-state distribution function

$$\frac{[\mathrm{N_2O_4^*}]}{[\mathrm{N_2O_4}]} = \frac{a[\mathrm{M}]}{c} = P_{ss} \tag{1-32}$$

Equation 29 gives the general case of a three-step steady-state distribution function P. In Chapter 15, every quantum state i of the excited reactant A is formally considered, and the state-by-state distribution function is written as

$$P_i = \frac{[\mathrm{A}_i^*]}{[\mathrm{A}]} = \frac{a_i[\mathrm{M}]}{b_i[\mathrm{M}] + c_i} \tag{1-33}$$

where activation, deactivation, and reaction constants (a_i, b_i, c_i) may be different for each state. The rate of reaction is the rate per state, summed over all states:

$$\mathrm{Rate} = \sum_i c_i[\mathrm{A}_i^*] \tag{1-34}$$

$$= [\mathrm{A}] \sum_i c_i P_i = [\mathrm{A}] \sum_i \frac{a_i c_i[\mathrm{M}]}{b_i[\mathrm{M}] + c_i} \tag{1-35}$$

$$= [\mathrm{A}] \langle c \rangle_{av} \tag{1-36}$$

In Eq. 34 the rate is expressed in terms of elementary chemical-physical rate constants c_i and the actual concentrations of species A_i^* as a function of quantum state. Consideration of the definition of the molecular distribution function (Eq. 33) allows one to replace the detailed molecular concentrations $[A_i^*]$ by the macroscopic concentration of reactant (Eq. 35). The general definition of an average (Eq. 6–6) replaces the detailed molecular rate constants c_i by the average value $\langle c \rangle_{av}$ (Eq. 36) over *all* states of the reactant.

The equilibrium distribution function, Eq. 31, is like any other equilibrium constant: to the ideal-gas approximation it is independent of concentration, but it changes with temperature. The steady-state distribution function, Eq. 33 or 30, is fixed by two macroscopic variables, temperature and concentration. (In an explosion one may have a molecular distribution function, variable in time and space, dependent on numerous variables.) Finally, it is possible to define a "steady distribution function"; it is one that is reproducible and that can be fixed by the investigator by control of a small number of macroscopic variables.

The principle of microscopic reversibility states that "at equilibrium, every process and its exact reverse occur at the same average rate." Thus during a chemical reaction, one *never* has precisely an equilibrium distribution function. Large departures from an equilibrium distribution over states are readily demonstrated in the laboratory, even for slow reactions. For example, the unimolecular isomerization of methyl isocyanide[7] has been studied over a wide range of reactant pressure at one temperature:

$$CH_3NC \rightarrow CH_3CN \tag{1–37}$$

If the distribution function of molecules over excited states always had (approximately) its equilibrium value, then the rate constant, $\text{Rate}/[CH_3NC]$, should be constant with a decrease in pressure. Actually the rate constant decreases markedly (Fig. 4), and *all* of this decrease arises from a different molecular distribution function, Eq. 33, at each different total pressure. However, this distribution function is reproducible, and controllable by means of two macroscopic variables, temperature and pressure.

An *elementary chemical reaction* is a single type of elementary chemical-physical reaction, averaged over a reproducible, steady distribution function. In the example cited above, every state of the N_2O_4 molecule with internal energy above 14 kcal undergoes a different chemical-physical reaction; but they are all of the same type, an excited N_2O_4 molecule dissociating to two NO_2 molecules. The sum of all these processes over the actual steady-state distribution function is an elementary chemical reaction.

In the crossed-beam experiments, there are no collisions between the reactive collision and the detector. The rate of an elementary unimolecular reaction,

$$A_i \rightarrow \text{products}$$

will vary linearly with the number of excited species:

$$- \frac{d\mathrm{A}_i}{dt} = c_i \mathrm{A}_i$$

or the rate per unit volume depends on the concentration of excited species:

$$- \frac{d[\mathrm{A}_i]}{dt} = c_i[\mathrm{A}_i] \tag{1–38}$$

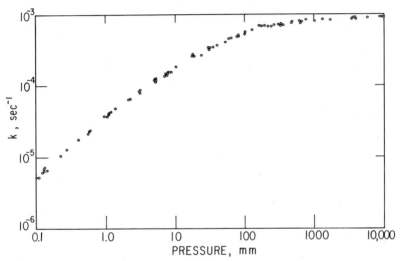

Fig. I–4. Unimolecular isomerization of methyl isocyanide at 230.4°C plotted as log k vs. log p.

This conclusion follows directly from the isolated nature of the reactant after excitation in the crossed beam. Similarly, bimolecular collision rates increase with intensity of each beam, so an elementary bimolecular reaction (Eq. 23) varies linearly with intensity of each beam, and in terms of concentrations,

$$- \frac{d[\mathrm{A}]}{dt} = k[\mathrm{A}][\mathrm{B}] \tag{1–39}$$

In the chemical reaction flask, the products of one elementary chemical reaction may be the reactants of another chemical reaction. The overall observations are disappearance of reactants and appearance of products. How does one know whether a given chemical reaction being studied is a single elementary step or a complex series of reactions? This question is the subject matter of the next section.

C. EXPERIMENTAL CHEMICAL KINETICS

(i) Definitions and Examples

Gas-phase reaction-rate theory is a branch of chemistry. As such, its starting point is an understanding of what is meant by a chemical species and by a balanced chemical reaction. Chemical species include: compounds that can be prepared pure and in bulk, such as O_2, NO, O_3, N_2O_5; compounds that exist always in rapid equilibrium with large amounts of dissociation products, $N_2O_4 \rightleftarrows 2NO_2$; and compounds that exist only in very small amounts or for a short time, such as the nitrate free radical, NO_3, and many other atoms and radicals. The transient species or highly active intermediates are often known from their spectra or they may merely be inferred from the behavior of chemical reactions. There has been a high degree of success of spectroscopic confirmation of free-radical species that were proposed on kinetic grounds. The nitrate free radical, first observed from its visible spectrum, has played a versatile role in reaction mechanisms. To illustrate a number of features of reaction kinetics, a family of reactions involving the oxides of nitrogen is cited below.

Chemical reactions are divided into two classes: laboratory reactions and elementary reactions. Laboratory reactions are macroscopic, observable, stoichiometric relations, such as:

1. $2N_2O_5 = 4NO_2 + O_2$
2. $NO + N_2O_5 = 3NO_2$
3. $2NO_2 + O_3 = N_2O_5 + O_2$
4. $2O_3 + N_2O_5 = 3O_2 + N_2O_5$

A chemical reaction may be written in general form as

$$xA + yB + \cdots = zC + wD + \cdots \tag{1-40}$$

The rate of reaction may be defined either in terms of the rate of decrease in concentration of any reactant or of the rate of increase in concentration of any product. In reading the chemical literature, one must often look very closely to see which definition the author used. However, a general definition of "the rate of reaction" can be given as

$$\mathbf{R} = -\frac{1}{x}\frac{d[A]}{dt} = -\frac{1}{y}\frac{d[B]}{dt} = \frac{1}{z}\frac{d[C]}{dt} = \frac{1}{w}\frac{d[D]}{dt} \tag{1-41}$$

In general, the rate of reaction is a function of the concentrations of reactants, catalysts M, and (in some cases) products:

$$\mathbf{R} = f([A], [B], [C], [D], [M] \cdots) \tag{1-42}$$

In many special cases, the functional relation takes the simple form

$$\mathbf{R} = \mathbf{k}[A]^p[B]^r[M]^s \tag{1-43}$$

In this case p is, by definition, the order with respect to A; r is the order with respect to B; s is the order with respect to the catalyst M; and "the order of the reaction" is $p + r + s$.

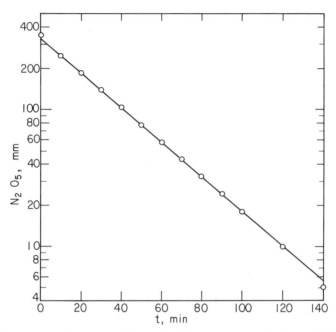

Fig. 1-5. Thermal decomposition of dinitrogen pentoxide during the course of one experiment; test of integrated first-order rate law; data[8] of F. Daniels and E. H. Johnston, *J. Am. Chem. Soc.*, **43**, 53 (1921).

Near room temperature the decomposition of dinitrogen pentoxide (reaction **1**) has been found to follow the first-order rate law

$$-\frac{1}{2}\frac{d[N_2O_5]}{dt} = k_1[N_2O_5] \tag{1-44}$$

The integrated rate equation is

$$-\log\frac{[N_2O_5]}{[N_2O_5]_0} = \frac{2k_1}{2.303}t \tag{1-45}$$

This rate law is illustrated in Fig. 5 by data[8] taken from Farrington Daniels' study of 35 years ago; this reaction has been studied repeatedly since that time. The formation of dinitrogen pentoxide from ozone and nitrogen dioxide (reaction **3**) follows a second-order rate law[9]

$$-\frac{d[O_3]}{dt} = k_3[NO_2][O_3] \qquad (1\text{--}46)$$

for which the integrated rate equation

$$2.303 \log \frac{[NO_2]\,[O_3]_0}{[NO_2]_0\,[O_3]} = ([NO_2]_0 - 2[O_3]_0)k_3 t \qquad (1\text{--}47)$$

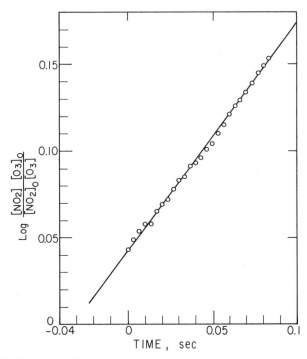

Fig. 1–6. Reaction of ozone with nitrogen dioxide to produce dinitrogen pentoxide; test of integrated second-order rate law; data[9] of H. S. Johnston and D. M. Yost, *J. Chem. Phys.*, **17**, 386 (1949).

is illustrated with experimental data in Fig. 6. The decomposition of ozone as catalyzed by dinitrogen pentoxide follows an interestingly complex rate law; in terms of Eq. 43 the rate expression is

$$\mathbf{R} = k[A]^p[M]^s \qquad (1\text{--}48)$$

During the course of one experiment successive values of ozone define a differential rate

$$-\frac{1}{2}\frac{d[O_3]}{dt} = \mathbf{R}$$

Since the catalyst N_2O_5 remains constant throughout, one notes that a plot of the logarithm of the rate against instantaneous pressure of ozone gives a straight line of slope p:

$$\log \mathbf{R} = p \log [O_3] + \log \mathbf{k} [N_2O_5]^s \qquad (1\text{--}49)$$

Such a plot is shown as Fig. 7, and the reaction is 2/3 order in ozone, over a thousandfold range of ozone pressure.[10]   The empirical rate constant, rate

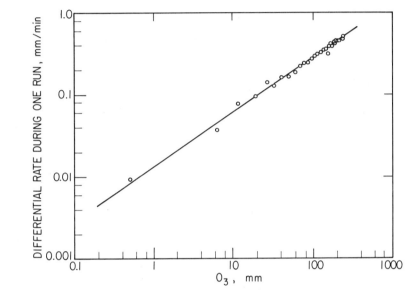

Fig. 1–7. N_2O_5-catalyzed decomposition of ozone; order with respect to ozone during one experiment; data[10] of H. J. Schumacher and G. Sprenger, Z. Physik. Chem., **2B,** 267 (1929) and G. Sprenger, Z. Elektrochem., **37,** 674 (1931).

divided by ozone to the two-thirds power, was found for a number of different experiments; and this quantity gives the order with respect to N_2O_5:

$$\log \mathbf{R}/[O_3]^{2/3} = s \log [N_2O_5] + \log \mathbf{k} \qquad (1\text{--}50)$$

The experimental data (Fig. 8) give 2/3 order with respect to N_2O_5. Thus this reaction is 4/3 order:

$$-\frac{1}{2}\frac{d[O_3]}{dt} = \mathbf{k}_4[O_3]^{2/3}[N_2O_5]^{2/3} \qquad (1\text{--}51)$$

Reaction **2** does not follow Eq. 43, and thus in general it has no order;[11] reaction **2** follows the empirical equation[12]

$$-\frac{d[N_2O_5]}{dt} = \mathbf{k}_2[N_2O_5]\frac{[NO]}{[NO] + \alpha[NO_2]} \qquad (1\text{--}52)$$

This relation is best illustrated by dividing both sides of Eq. 52 by $[N_2O_5]$ and taking the reciprocal:

$$\frac{[N_2O_5]}{R} = \frac{1}{k_2} + \frac{\alpha}{k_2} \frac{[NO_2]}{[NO]} \qquad (1\text{-}53)$$

This rate function is illustrated[12] by Fig. 9. Thus these four examples illustrate that reactions may have integral order (**1** and **3**), fractional order (**4**), or no order (**2**).

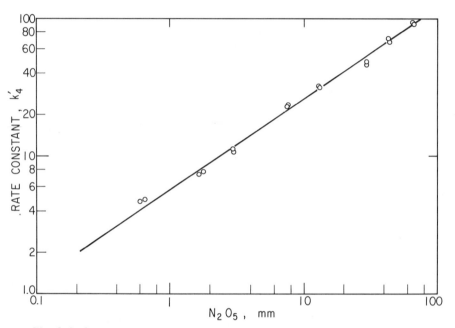

Fig. I–8. Same reaction as Fig. 7; order with respect to N_2O_5 for a series of different experiments: $k_4' = \text{Rate}/[O_3]^{2/3}$.

Figures 5, 6, and 7 show "order with respect to time," that is, the order during a single experiment. Figure 8 shows "order with respect to concentration," that is, the "rate constant" evaluated throughout a single run may have different values when the initial concentrations of reactants or catalysts are varied. Whereas the decomposition of dinitrogen pentoxide is first-order with respect to time under all observed conditions, the first-order rate constant itself becomes first-order in N_2O_5 at pressure below 0.1 mm (Fig. 10); thus at extremely low pressures, reaction **1** becomes second-order:[13]

$$R_1 = k_{01}[N_2O_5]^2 \qquad (1\text{-}54)$$

Whereas reaction **2** is in general very complex (Eq. 53 or Fig. 9), it should be noted that Fig. 9 represents the case where initially the product NO_2 was

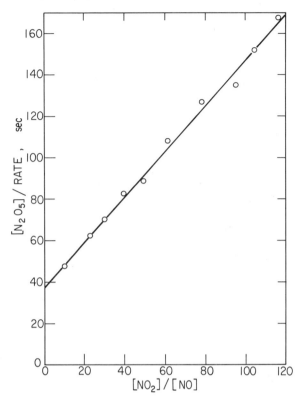

Fig. I-9. Decomposition of N_2O_5 in the presence of NO and in the presence of excess product NO_2; data[12] of I. C. Hisatsune, Bryce Crawford, Jr., and R. A. Ogg, Jr., *J. Am. Chem. Soc.*, **79**, 4648 (1957).

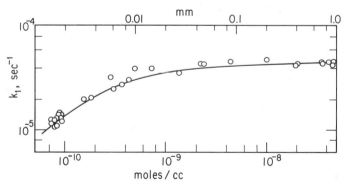

Fig. I-10. Decomposition of N_2O_5 at extremely low pressures; data[13] of J. H. Hodges and E. F. Linhorst, *J. Am. Chem. Soc.*, **56**, 836 (1934); H. C. Ramsperger and R. C. Tolman, *Proc. Natl. Acad. Sci.*, **16**, 6 (1930); H. C. Ramsperger, M. E. Nordberg, and R. C. Tolman, *ibid.*, **15**, 453 (1929).

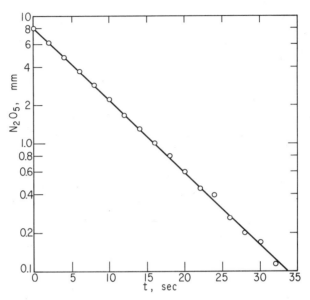

Fig. I–11. Decomposition of N_2O_5 in presence of NO with no added NO_2; first-order rate law for at least 90-percent reaction; data[14] of R. L. Mills and H. S. Johnston, *J. Am. Chem. Soc.*, **73**, 938 (1951).

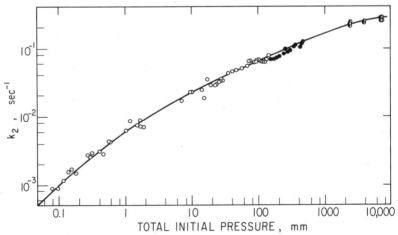

Fig. I–12. Same reaction as Fig. 11; effect of total pressure on first-order rate constant at 27°C; compare Fig. 4.

in tenfold excess over the reactant NO. When NO is in excess of initial N_2O_5 and there is no added NO_2, the rate with respect to time is first-order in N_2O_5 for at least 90 percent of the reaction (Fig. 11). Thus experimental conditions are easily set such that reaction **2** is first-order:[14]

$$\mathbf{R_2} - - \frac{d[N_2O_5]}{dt} = k_2[N_2O_5] \qquad (1\text{--}55)$$

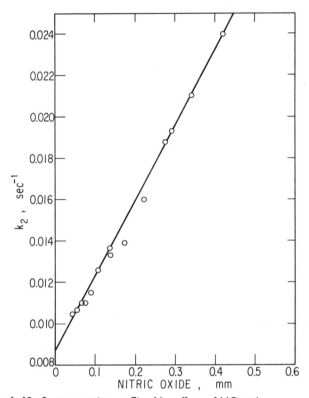

Fig. 1–13. Same reaction as Fig. 11; effect of NO at low pressures.

This rate constant shows a remarkable variation with respect to initial concentration of reactant;[14] Fig. 12 shows the rate constant to vary by a factor of 100 from 0.1 mm to 200 mm of N_2O_5 and to increase by another factor of 3 in the presence of 10 atmospheres of N_2. At very low pressures the first-order rate constant, Eq. 55, increases linearly with nitric oxide (Fig. 13); but also it increases linearly with CO_2, N_2, or even Ar[15] (Fig. 14). Thus the low-pressure, second-order rate constant depends on the identity of the added gas M as well as its pressure:

$$\mathbf{R_{02}} = k_{02M}[N_2O_5][M] \qquad (1\text{--}56)$$

The effect of temperature on the observed rate constant of a reaction is often given by the Arrhenius equation

$$k = A \exp(-E/RT) \tag{1-57}$$

or in logarithmic form

$$\log k = \log A - \frac{E}{2.303R}\frac{1}{T} \tag{1-58}$$

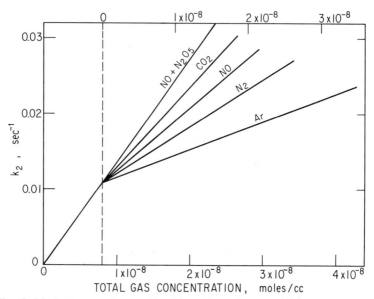

Fig. 1-14. Same reaction as Fig. 11; effect of various foreign gases at low pressures; data[15] of H. S. Johnston, *J. Am. Chem. Soc.*, **75**, 1567 (1953).

Experimental data for reaction **1** between room temperature and 120°C[8,16] are given by Fig. 15. The excellent straight line gives an activation energy **E** of 24.7 kcal/mole. All empirical rate constants defined above were studied over a range of temperature, and the activation energies and **A**-factors were obtained by the various investigators. These experimental data are listed in Table 1.

When a chemical reaction is studied over a wide range of temperature, there may be a change of mechanism, with a complete breakdown of the Arrhenius equation. For example, reaction **1** was studied by Schott and Davidson[17] in a shock tube between 450 and 1100°K in an excess of argon carrier gas. The initial products were not nitrogen dioxide and oxygen; rather, there was a quantitative yield of NO_2 and the nitrate free radical NO_3 (whose spectrum was already known from reaction **4**):

$$N_2O_5 = NO_2 + NO_3 \tag{1-59}$$

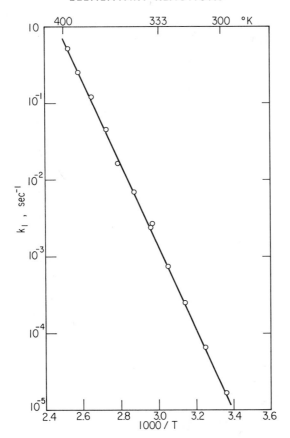

Fig. 1–15. Decomposition of N_2O_5 over moderate range of temperature; the integrated Arrhenius equation; data of Daniels and Johnston (Fig. 5) and of H. S. Johnston and Yu-sheng Tao[16], *J. Am. Chem. Soc.*, **73**, 2948 (1951).

The rate was observed to be first-order with respect to time:

$$-\frac{d[N_2O_5]}{dt} = k_1[N_2O_5][Ar] \tag{1–60}$$

but also first-order with respect to the catalyst argon. The nitrate free radical disappeared according to the rate law

$$-\frac{1}{2}\frac{d[NO_3]}{dt} = e[NO_2][NO_3] + g[NO_3]^2 \tag{1–61}$$

This rate law was demonstrated by studying the rate with respect to the ratio

TABLE I–I

Observed Values of Empirical Rate Constants, and Other Data

Reaction	Quantity Observed	Eq. No.	Range of T (°K)	Range of Total Pressure (mm)	log $\mathbf{A}$*	$\mathbf{E}$ (kcal)	Value* at 300°K	Ref.
(1)	$k_{\infty 1}$	44	298–396	>0.1	13.3†	24.7 ± 0.1	2.3 × 10⁻⁵	8, 16
	$k_{01}/[N_2O_5]$	54	308–338	<0.01	20.3	20.8 ± 2	1.3 × 10⁵	13
	$k_1/[Ar]$	60	450–550	(200)	—	—	2.5 × 10⁴	17
	Intercept at 1, i_{11}	63	600–1100	(200)	12.3	6.4 ± 0.3	—	17
	Intercept at 0, i_{01}	64	600–1100	(200)	11.4	4.4 ± 0.7	1.4 × 10⁸	17
	K	65			‡	20.1 ± 1	2 × 10⁻¹³	17
	$\varepsilon(NO_3)$, 6280 Å	12			‡	—	(3 ± 1) × 10³	17
(2)	$k_{\infty 2}$	55	273–300	>7000	14.8†	21 ± 2	0.29	14
	$k_{02}/[N_2O_5]$	56	300–344	<0.5	19.1	19.3 ± 0.6	1.3 × 10⁵	15
	$k_{02}/[Ar]$	56	300–344	<0.5	—	—	1.7 × 10⁴	15
	Slope, s_2	53	293–303	57–400	16.3†	22.4 ± 2	1.0	12
(3)	k_3	47	293–303	760	12.8	7.0 ± 0.6	4.7 × 10⁷	9
(4)	k_4	51	293–313	100–300	13.8	20.7 ± 1	0.054	10
	K_{ss}	66	293–313	100–300		6.4 ± 0.8	(1 to 3) × 10⁻⁵	10

* cm³/mole-sec unless noted to contrary. $\mathbf{k}$ has same units as $\mathbf{A}$.
† sec⁻¹.
‡ See equation in text for units.

of $[NO_3]/[NO_2]$:

$$\frac{R}{2[NO_2][NO_3]} = e + g\frac{[NO_3]}{[NO_2]} \tag{1-62}$$

With no added NO_2, the maximum value of $[NO_3]/[NO_2]$ is unity, so the value of the intercept at one is

$$\lim_{\substack{NO_3 \to 1 \\ NO_2}} \left\{ \frac{R}{2[NO_2][NO_3]} \right\} = e + g \tag{1-63}$$

With added initial NO_2, the ratio can be made as small as desired, and for zero value of this ratio the observed quantity is

$$\lim_{\substack{NO_3 \to 0 \\ NO_2}} \left\{ \frac{R}{2[NO_2][NO_3]} \right\} = e \tag{1-64}$$

These data are presented as Fig. 16. This degree of scatter is not unusual in shock-tube experiments, where reaction times are of a few microseconds' duration.

Schott and Davidson likewise evaluated the Beer-Lambert constant ε

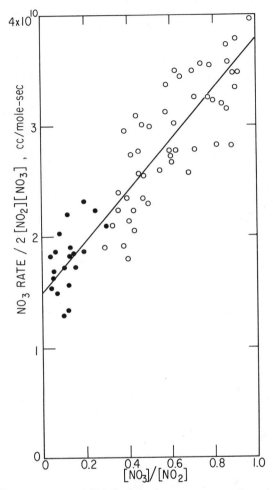

Fig. I-16. Decomposition of N_2O_5 at high temperatures in a shock tube; rate of disappearance of the intermediate radical NO_3; data[17] of Garry Schott and Norman Davidson, *J. Am. Chem. Soc.*, **80**, 1841 (1958).

for light absorption by NO_3, and also the equilibrium constant K for Eq. 59:

$$K = \frac{[NO_2][NO_3]}{[N_2O_5]} \qquad (1\text{-}65)$$

In reaction **4**, the free radical NO_3 has also been observed spectroscopically, and with Schott and Davidson's value of the absorption coefficient ε the observed concentration of NO_3 in the $N_2O_5 + O_3$ system can be evaluated. Schumacher and Sprenger observed NO_3 to vary as the 1/3 power of N_2O_5 and 1/3 power of ozone:

$$[NO_3] = K_{ss}[N_2O_5]^{1/3}[O_3]^{1/3} \qquad (1\text{-}66)$$

This observed steady-state constant, the equilibrium constant of Eq. 65, the absorption coefficient for NO_3, and the rate factors for Eqs. 60–64 are listed in Table 1.

Thus Table 1 contains a wide variety of experimental data on these four reactions. This mass of apparently unrelated data falls into a simple and beautiful pattern when considered in terms of the component elementary chemical reactions.

(ii) Mechanisms of Three Reactions Involving Dinitrogen Pentoxide

The direct observation of the intermediate radical NO_3 by Schott and Davidson in 1958 provided the confirmation of a mechanism[18] that had slowly and painfully evolved over the period 1920–50. The "mechanism" of a complex reaction is the list of elementary chemical reactions postulated to explain the observed rates and products. The decomposition of dinitrogen pentoxide is assumed to involve an elementary unimolecular decomposition,

$$N_2O_5 \xrightarrow{A(M)} NO_2 + NO_3 \qquad (1–67)$$

an elementary bimolecular association,

$$NO_2 + NO_3 \xrightarrow{B(M)} N_2O_5 \qquad (1–68)$$

and two elementary bimolecular reactions,

$$NO_2 + NO_3 \xrightarrow{e} NO + O_2 + NO_2 \qquad (1–69)$$

$$NO + NO_3 \xrightarrow{f} 2NO_2 \qquad (1–70)$$

As noted above (Eqs. 26–36), the rate constant for the elementary unimolecular chemical reaction involves a broad spectrum of energy-transfer processes and elementary chemical-physical dissociations; thus the rate function $A(M)$, constant with respect to time during one reaction, is formally given by

$$A(M) = \sum_i \frac{a_i c_i [M]}{b_i [M] + c_i} \qquad (1–71)$$

Similarly, the bimolecular association constant is

$$B(M) = \sum_i \frac{b_i d_i [M]}{b_i [M] + c_i} \qquad (1–72)$$

where the four detailed molecular rate processes are

$$
\begin{aligned}
N_2O_5 + M &\xrightarrow{a_i} N_2O_{5i}^* + M \\
N_2O_{5i}^* + M &\xrightarrow{b_i} N_2O_5 + M \\
N_2O_{5i}^* &\xrightarrow{c_i} NO_2 + NO_3 \\
NO_2 + NO_3 &\xrightarrow{d_i} N_2O_{5i}^*
\end{aligned}
\qquad (1–73)
$$

(As emphasized in Chapter 15, even these rate constants are averages over states of reactants and products.) The ratio of the two functions A and B is the equilibrium constant for Eq. 59 and is thus independent of energy-transfer catalysts M:

$$K = A/B = [NO_3][NO_2]/[N_2O_5] \qquad (1\text{--}74)$$

The rate of formation of nitrogen dioxide is a convenient variable for expressing the rate of reaction **1** or reaction **2**. From the four-step mechanism (A, B, e, f), the rate is

$$\frac{d[NO_2]}{dt} = A[N_2O_5] - B[NO_2][NO_3] + 2f[NO][NO_3] \qquad (1\text{--}75)$$

In this rate expression there appears the concentration of the free radical NO_3, for which the differential equation is

$$\frac{d[NO_3]}{dt} = A[N_2O_5] - (B + e)[NO_2][NO_3] - f[NO][NO_3] \qquad (1\text{--}76a)$$

At high temperatures the NO_3 concentration is large, and it was observed directly by optical methods. At and near room temperature the NO_3 radical is present at such low concentration that it cannot be observed, and thus the sum of all ways of destroying NO_3 very nearly balances the sum of all ways of forming it, that is,

$$A[N_2O_5] \approx (B + e)[NO_2][NO_3] + f[NO][NO_3] \qquad (1\text{--}76b)$$

This relation is an example of the "steady-state approximation." Another way to state this approximation is that the *net* rate of change of the intermediate is negligible compared to the *gross* rates whereby it is formed and consumed, that is, Eq. 76a is set to zero. (The nature of the steady-state approximation is examined in Appendix A.) When the steady-state approximation for NO_3, Eq. 76b, is substituted in the expression for the formation of nitrogen dioxide, Eq. 75, one finds

$$\frac{d[NO_2]}{dt} = A[N_2O_5]\left\{\frac{e[NO_2] + 3f[NO]}{(B + e)[NO_2] + f[NO]}\right\} \qquad (1\text{--}77)$$

In reaction **1**, nitric oxide is produced by reaction e and consumed by reaction f, and it is present in amounts too small to be measured directly. Thus, one may make the steady-state approximation for nitric oxide in reaction **1**:

$$e[NO_2][NO_3] = f[NO][NO_3] \qquad (1\text{--}78)$$

The rate expression for reaction **1**, derived from the mechanism, is then

$$\mathbf{R_1} = \frac{1}{4}\frac{d[NO_2]}{dt} = k_1[N_2O_5]$$

$$k_1 = Ae/(B + 2e) \qquad (1\text{--}79)$$

For reaction **2**, nitric oxide is one of the added reagents, and one cannot make the steady-state approximation. However, one may make the trial assumption (later confirmed) that the rate constant f is substantially larger than the rate constant e. In this case, the mechanistic rate expression, Eq. 77, reduces to the form of the observed rate, Eq. 52:

$$\mathbf{R_2} = \frac{1}{3}\frac{d[NO_2]}{dt} = A[N_2O_5]\frac{[NO]}{[NO] + (B/f)[NO_2]} \tag{1-80}$$

Thus the intercept of Eq. 52 or Fig. 9 is interpreted as $1/A$ and the slope is $1/Kf$:

$$A = (\text{intercept of Eq. 52})^{-1} \tag{1-81}$$

$$Kf = (\text{slope of Eq. 52})^{-1} \tag{1-82}$$

As noted above, it is very easy to select experimental conditions where $f[NO]$ is very much greater than $B[NO_2]$, so that the observed first-order rate constant for reaction **2** is that of the elementary unimolecular decomposition, Eq. 59:

$$\mathbf{k_2} = A(M) = \sum_i \frac{a_i c_i [M]}{b_i[M] + c_i} \tag{1-83}$$

This rate function has an attainable high-pressure limit (Fig. 12), for which the deactivation rate $b_i[M]$ exceeds the molecular rate constant c_i for all states i that contribute significantly to the reaction:

$$\mathbf{k_{\infty 2}} = \sum \frac{a_i c_i}{b_i} \tag{1-84}$$

$$b_i[M] \gg c_i \tag{1-85}$$

Also, as can be seen from Figs. 12, 13, and 14, this rate function has an attainable low-pressure limit, for which the molecular reaction rate exceeds the deactivation rate for all states i that contribute significantly to the observed reaction:

$$\mathbf{k_{02}} = \sum a_i[M] \tag{1-86}$$

$$b_i[M] \ll c_i \tag{1-87}$$

Thus at the low-pressure limit, the observed rate is that of the physical process, activation by collision.

The behavior of reaction **1** at very low pressures (Fig. 10) is given by the mechanism (Eq. 79). At very low pressures, $B(M)$ becomes less than $2e$, and the rate constant becomes one-half that for reaction **2**:

$$\mathbf{k_{01}} = A(M)/2 \tag{1-88}$$

At high pressures, the ratio of reactions **1** and **2** gives (Eqs. 79 and 83)

$$\frac{k_{\infty 2}}{k_{\infty 1}} = \frac{B_\infty + 2e}{e} = 1.3 \times 10^4 \tag{1-89}$$

where the numerical value is based on Table 1. Thus from Fig. 10 and Eq. 89, one sees that B is very much larger than $2e$ above a pressure of 0.1 mm. Thus the rate constant for reaction **1** becomes

$$\mathbf{k_1} = Ke \qquad \text{above 0.1 mm} \tag{1-90}$$

The high-pressure limit of $B(M)$ is simply the sum of d_i over states, abbreviated as d (compare Eq. 72):

$$B_\infty = 1.3 \times 10^4 e = \sum d_i = d \tag{1-91}$$

At high temperatures in a shock tube, Schott and Davidson observed the rate law (Eq. 61 and Fig. 16)

$$-\frac{1}{2}\frac{d[NO_3]}{dt} = e[NO_2][NO_3] + g[NO_3]^2$$

Thus at high temperatures one must add the additional elementary reaction

$$NO_3 + NO_3 \xrightarrow{g} 2NO_2 + O_2 \tag{1-92}$$

From the value of the rate constant g observed at high temperature and extrapolated to room temperature, one sees that reaction g is negligible in reactions **1** and **2** at ordinary temperature.

The rate constants for deactivation, b_i, do not appear as separate observables in this system. However, in Chapter 15 it is demonstrated (in terms of experiments on chemical activation and of fluorescence quenching, and in terms of a simple, general logical argument) that a highly vibrationally excited polyatomic molecule loses a substantial amount of vibrational energy on almost every close molecular collision. Thus the constants b_i are regarded as all the same b, and they are approximated by the hard-sphere collision constant from the simple theory of bimolecular collisions:

$$b \cong 10^{14} \text{ cc/mole-sec} \tag{1-93}$$

Thus the high-pressure limit of reaction **2** is $b^{-1} \sum a_i c_i$, and the ratio

$$\frac{bk_{\infty 2}}{k_{02}} = \frac{\sum a_i c_i}{\sum a_i} = \langle c \rangle = c \tag{1-94}$$

can be interpreted as the average value of c_i *over the states that react*.

Reaction **3** was observed to be second-order in reactants. The mechanism is simply

$$NO_2 + O_3 \xrightarrow{h} NO_3 + O_2$$
$$NO_3 + NO_2 \xrightarrow{B(M)} N_2O_5 \tag{1-95}$$

GAS PHASE REACTION RATE THEORY

TABLE 1–2

Rate Constants for Elementary Chemical Reactions

Quantity	Derived From	Eq. No.	Value at 300°K	E
$a(N_2O_5)$	k_{01} low P	88	1.3×10^5	20.8 ± 2
$a(N_2O_5)$	k_{02} low P	86	1.3×10^5	19.3 ± 0.6
$a(Ar)$	k_1 high T	60	2.5×10^4	—
$a(Ar)$	k_{02} low P	86	1.7×10^4	—
b	Theory	93	10^{14}	0
$\langle c \rangle_{av}$	$b k_{\infty 2}/k_{02}$	94	2×10^8	2 ± 2
d	$d/e, e$	91	1.6×10^{12}	0 ± 3
e	Ke, K	90, 65	1.2×10^8	4.6 ± 1
e	k_1 high T	61	1.4×10^8	4.4 ± 0.7
f	Kf, K	82, 65	5×10^{12}	2 ± 2
g	k_1 high T	61	6.3×10^6	7.7 ± 1
h	k_3	96	4.7×10^7	7 ± 0.6
K	NO_3 high T	65	2×10^{-13}	20.1 ± 1

Dimensions: moles, cc, sec; kcal.

From the steady-state assumption for NO_3, one finds the observed rate to be that for the elementary reaction h:

$$-\frac{d[O_3]}{dt} = k_3[NO_2][O_3]$$

$$k_3 = h \tag{1–96}$$

Thus from observations on the three reactions **1**, **2**, and **3**, plus the theoretical value for b (Eq. 93), all eight elementary rate constants a, b, c, d, e, f, g, and h can be determined; these are listed in Table 2. The numerical values of the rate constant at 300°K and the activation energy are deduced from the observed quantities listed in Table 1 and the equations deduced from the mechanism. For three cases, an elementary rate constant is found by two completely independent methods, and the agreement is very good.

(iii) Reaction Kinetics as a Predicting Science

In some branches of science, one can *predict* new or different situations. Other branches of science are merely explanatory: one fact, one theory; two facts, two theories; etc. The stage is now set to illustrate that a laboratory reaction may be predicted by way of elementary rate constants measured in completely different systems.

As a matter of historical fact, reaction **4** was studied after reaction **1** but before either reaction **2** or **3**. This presentation ignores the historical sequence and emphasizes that all aspects of reaction **4** *could* have been predicted from the elementary rate constants discovered and measured by way of reactions **1**, **2**, and **3**.

Reaction 4 is the decomposition of ozone, catalyzed by dinitrogen pentoxide. One realizes that, because of the dissociation of N_2O_5, all steps a through h involving N_2O_5, NO_2, NO_3, and ozone must be considered. From the full eight-step mechanism, one estimates the steady-state concentration NO_3, NO_2, and NO. From these steady-state concentrations and the rate constants of Table 2, one calculates the rates of the various reactions: A, B, e, f, g, and h. One example is illustrated in detail. The initial concentrations in moles per cc are assumed to be

$$N_2O_5 = 10^{-7}$$
$$O_3 = 10^{-5} \tag{1-97}$$

From these values, the calculated steady-state concentrations of intermediates are

$$NO_3 = 8.7 \times 10^{-9}$$
$$NO_2 = 2.3 \times 10^{-12} \tag{1-98}$$
$$NO = 6.4 \times 10^{-17}$$

The rates of the various reactions in units of moles per cc per second are

$$\mathbf{R}_A = \mathbf{R}_B = 5 \times 10^{-9}$$
$$\mathbf{R}_e = \mathbf{R}_f = 2.4 \times 10^{-12}$$
$$\mathbf{R}_g = 5.3 \times 10^{-10} \tag{1-99}$$
$$\mathbf{R}_h = 1.1 \times 10^{-9}$$

Thus after one considers the full set of rates, one discovers that two rates, e and f, are negligibly slow; and thus the mechanism consists of steps A, B, g, and h.

The rate of reaction **4** from the mechanism is

$$\mathbf{R}_4 = \frac{1}{2} \frac{d[O_3]}{dt} = \tfrac{1}{2}h[NO_2][O_3] \tag{1-100}$$

From Eq. 98, one sees that the steady-state assumption is fully justified for both NO_3 and NO_2. The differential rate equations incorporating the steady-state assumption are

$$\frac{d[NO_2]}{dt} = A[N_2O_5] - B[NO_2][NO_3] + 2g[NO_3]^2 - h[NO_2][O_3] = 0 \tag{1-101}$$

$$\frac{d[NO_3]}{dt} = A[N_2O_5] - B[NO_2][NO_3] - 2g[NO_3]^2 + h[NO_2][O_3] = 0$$

The summing of these two equations gives

$$A[N_2O_5] = B[NO_2][NO_3] \tag{1-102}$$

and the subtraction of the equations gives

$$2g[NO_3]^2 = h[NO_2][O_3] \qquad (1–103)$$

The steady-state concentrations of the intermediates are

$$[NO_2] = \left(\frac{2g}{h}\right)^{1/3} K^{2/3} \frac{[N_2O_5]^{2/3}}{[O_3]^{1/3}} \qquad (1–104)$$

$$[NO_3] = \left(\frac{Kh}{2g}\right)^{1/3} [O_3]^{1/3}[N_2O_5]^{1/3} \qquad (1–105)$$

The rate expression from the mechanism is thus

$$\mathbf{R_4} = \tfrac{1}{2}\{(Kh)^{2/3}(2g)^{1/3}[N_2O_5]^{2/3}[O_3]^{2/3}\} \qquad (1–106)$$

This elegant rate expression from the mechanism is in exact agreement with that observed, Eq. 51 and Figs. 7 and 8. The steady-state expression for NO_3 derived from the mechanism, Eq. 105, has the same form as that observed, Eq. 66.

TABLE 1–3
Observed and Predicted Quantities for Reaction 4

Quantity	Predicted	Observed
k_4 at 300°K	0.052	0.054
E_4	20.7 $\pm$ 1	20.7 $\pm$ 1
K_{ss}, Eq. 66	9×10^{-5}	$(1 \text{ to } 3) \times 10^{-5}$
E for K_{ss}	6 $\pm$ 1 kcal	6.4 $\pm$ 0.8 kcal

Dimensions: moles, cc, sec; kcal.

Finally, it is of interest to compare the observed value of rate constant **4** with that which can be predicted from the elementary steps deduced from reactions **1**, **2**, and **3**. In Table 3 this comparison is made, and the numerical agreement is excellent. Also in Table 3, a comparison is made between the steady-state concentration of NO_3 as predicted by the mechanism and that observed in system **4**—with, however, the shaky assumption that the spectroscopic slit widths used by Schott and Davidson in Pasadena in 1958 were comparable to those used by Sprenger[10] in Danzig in 1931, so that the Beer-Lambert constant estimated by the former may be used to make quantitative the data of the latter. The observed value of the steady-state constant is of the same order of magnitude as that predicted from the mechanism, but it is substantially lower. The temperature coefficient of the steady-state constant, expressed as an "activation energy," gives excellent agreement between mechanism and experiment.

This example shows wherein reaction kinetics, completely within its

own sphere, is a predictive science.   An elementary reaction can be quantitatively transferred from one system to another.   If one has a complete
enough list of elementary reactions to choose from, one can quantitatively
predict an entire complex reaction (as shown above); but of course, one
can be badly deceived if important elementary steps have been omitted
from the list.   Rate constants and activation energies for *elementary* chemical
reactions should be tabulated in handbooks or other compilations of data.
For such considerations, the *elementary reaction* in kinetics plays a role
comparable to the *pure substance* in tabulations of thermodynamic data.
This analogy should be pressed one step further: kinetic data for unresolved
complex reactions are just as worthless as thermodynamic data for impure
unanalyzed materials.

Having admired this example wherein all elementary rate constants were
deduced from chemical-kinetic observations on other (complex) laboratory
reactions, one should immediately recognize that there are limitations on
how far one can go in deducing elementary rate constants from complex
kinetic data.   An example can be found in the oxidation of methyl radicals.
Methyl radicals rapidly add oxygen[19] to form a chemically activated peroxy
radical:

$$CH_3 + O_2 \rightarrow CH_3OO^*$$

The excited radical may revert to methyl radical and oxygen, decompose to
formaldehyde and hydroxyl radical, or be stabilized by an energy-transfer
collision:

$$CH_3OO^* \rightarrow CH_3 + O_2$$
$$CH_3OO^* \rightarrow H_2CO + HO$$
$$CH_3OO^* + M \rightarrow CH_3OO + M$$

At room temperature the peroxy-methyl radical does not rapidly abstract
hydrogen from other molecules, but it probably undergoes the following
transformation:

$$CH_3OO + CH_3OO \rightarrow CH_3O + CH_3O + O_2$$

Thus a series of about equally fast reactions produces the radicals, CH_3OO,
HO, CH_3O.   These radicals can recombine according to (see Table 4)

$$R_i + R_j \rightarrow R_{ij} \qquad (1\text{--}107)$$

with $CH_3OOOOCH_3$ not being an observed product, but there are still seven
different recombination reactions and six different products.   These radicals
also react, more or less upon every collision, by way of disproportionation
such as

$$CH_3O + CH_3O \rightarrow CH_3OH + H_2CO$$

There is one saturated product and one unsaturated product in these reactions.
In disproportionation reactions, N free radicals give N^2 reactions but only

TABLE I–4

Possible Products from the Recombination of Radicals in the Oxidation of Methyl Radicals

R_j	R_i			
	CH_3	CH_3OO	CH_3O	HO
CH_3	C_2H_6	CH_3OOCH_3	CH_3OCH_3	CH_3OH
CH_3OO		$\times$	$\times$	$\times$
CH_3O			CH_3OOCH_3	CH_3OOH
HO				H_2O_2

$2N$ products, as illustrated by Table 5. Thus, even if one analyzes for all products, the mechanism cannot be deduced if N^2 exceeds $2N$, that is, if the number of free radicals exceeds two. In the present example, CH_2 and O are possible products of disproportion reactions, and these are extremely active intermediates that add and insert in a wide variety of ways. This

TABLE I–5

Possible Products from Radical-Radical Disproportionation in the Oxidation of Methyl Radicals

R_j	R_i			
	CH_3	CH_3OO	CH_3O	HO
CH_3	$CH_4 + CH_2$	$CH_4 + H_2COO$	$CH_4 + H_2CO$	$CH_4 + O$
CH_3OO	$CH_3OOH + CH_2$	$CH_3OOH + H_2COO$	$CH_3OOH + H_2CO$	$CH_3OOH + O$
CH_3O	$CH_3OH + CH_2$	$CH_3OH + H_2COO$	$CH_3OH + H_2CO$	$CH_3OH + O$
HO	$H_2O + CH_2$	$H_2O + H_2COO$	$H_2O + H_2CO$	$H_2O + O$

example is chosen to illustrate that there may be more independent reactions than observable variables, reactants and products. Thus, to understand such a system one must (1) observe directly the intermediate free radicals, (2) study the individual elementary reactions in simpler systems, and (3) make serious use of the theory of elementary reactions in the study of complex systems.

D.   THEORIES OF CHEMICAL KINETICS

An outline of the different "levels of abstraction" in chemical kinetics is:

Complex chemical reactions
    Elementary chemical reactions
      Elementary chemical-physical reactions
      Elementary physical reactions
        Time-dependent quantum mechanics

Complex processes of chemical change are illuminated by anything one can learn (experimental or theoretical) about the component elementary chemical reactions. Similarly, the theory of elementary chemical reactions is illuminated both by experiment and theory in elementary physical processes. There are theories at each of the four levels of abstraction indicated above, and there are strong interactions between all of these levels. This book is primarily oriented toward the theory of elementary chemical reactions— with, however, an interest in problems arising from real chemical situations and in ideas arising from fundamental physical considerations.

In the example cited in section C above, it was shown wherein chemical kinetics is a predicting science, in the sense of transferability of elementary rate constants from one mechanism to another. These predictions are entirely within the field of kinetics. The next and larger question is: By going outside of chemical kinetics to such fields as pure theory, molecular structure, molecular spectroscopy, or thermodynamics, can one predict the rate constants of elementary chemical reactions? The rest of this book is largely devoted to topic-by-topic examination of this question. For some cases such predictions can be made, but there is no simple or single road to this goal.

PROBLEM

Derive the differential rate equation for each of the following laboratory reactions from the mechanism that is given, eliminating all intermediates present in small amounts.

A. Laboratory reaction: $2O_3 = 3O_2$

Mechanism		Intermediate
$O_3 + M \rightarrow O_2 + O + M$	a	O
$O_2 + O + M \rightarrow O_3 + M$	b	
$O_3 + O \rightarrow 2O_2$	c	

B. Laboratory reaction: $4HNO_3(g) \rightarrow 4NO_2 + 2H_2O + O_2$

Mechanism		Intermediates
$HNO_3 \rightarrow HO + NO_2$	a	NO_3
$HO + NO_2 \rightarrow HNO_3$	b	HO
$HO + HNO_3 \rightarrow H_2O + NO_3$	c	NO
$NO_3 + NO_2 \rightarrow NO_2 + O_2 + NO$	d	
$NO_3 + NO \rightarrow 2NO_2$	e	

C. Laboratory reaction: $Br_2 + H_2 = 2HBr$

Mechanism		Intermediates
$Br_2 + M \rightarrow 2Br + M$	a	H
$Br + H_2 \rightarrow HBr + H$	b	Br
$H + HBr \rightarrow H_2 + Br$	c	
$H + Br_2 \rightarrow HBr + Br$	d	
$Br + Br + M \rightarrow Br_2 + M$	e	

HINT: The initiating rate equals the terminating rate of the chain reaction, that is, $R_a = R_e$.

D. Laboratory reaction: $CH_3CHO \rightarrow CH_4 + CO$

Mechanism		Intermediates
$CH_3CHO \rightarrow CH_3 + CHO$	a	CH_3
$CH_3 + CH_3CHO \rightarrow CH_3CO + CH_4$	b	CH_3CO
$CH_3CO \rightarrow CH_3 + CO$	c	
$CH_3 + CH_3 \rightarrow C_2H_6$	d	

where $R_d \ll R_b$ and $R_a = R_d$.

2
Topics in Quantum Mechanics

A. INTRODUCTION TO NEXT SIX CHAPTERS

At this point the subject of chemical kinetics is left aside; the next six chapters constitute a long digression into topics in quantum mechanics, classical mechanics, and statistical mechanics. These six chapters by no means give a complete treatment of these subjects; they give only a summary of those aspects to be used in later chapters. The topics receiving the greatest emphasis are one-dimensional quantum-mechanical barrier penetration, classical-mechanical normal coordinates, molecular partition functions in classical and quantum mechanics, and classical two-body collision theory. The beginning student whose principal contact with these topics has been the undergraduate course in physical chemistry may need to spend considerable time in working through these chapters. For his sake, simple examples are worked out in full detail, problems are presented for further practice, and references to textbooks or monographs are given for advanced treatment of the topics. The advanced student can rapidly scan the equations derived in the next six chapters to note what point of view is being taken, but he may find novel ideas in some of the discussion sections or in some of the figures.

B. DE BROGLIE WAVELENGTH

Every "particle" also has a more or less important "wave" character, and classical mechanics must be replaced or supplemented by the more general quantum mechanics if the de Broglie wavelength

$$\Lambda = h/p = h/mv \qquad (2\text{--}1)$$

is of comparable length to dimensions of the "particle" or the "container." A particle at thermal equilibrium with its surroundings has a range of velocities or moments, and some average value is needed to express the limits of classical mechanics. The "Boltzmann-average" momentum is

$$\langle p \rangle = \int_{-\infty}^{\infty} \exp\left(-p^2/2mkT\right) dp$$
$$= (2\pi mkT)^{1/2} \qquad (2\text{--}2)$$

where k is Boltzmann's constant. Thus the average wavelength of interest is

$$\Lambda = h/(2\pi m k T)^{1/2} = 17.45/(MT)^{1/2} \text{ Å} \qquad (2\text{-}3)$$

where M is molar mass and the numerical value is given in angstrom units. Values of the Boltzmann–de Broglie wavelength as a function of particle mass and temperature are given in Table 1; particles with the mass of an electron m_e, proton m_H, and oxygen atom m_O are given.

TABLE 2–I

De Broglie Wavelengths (Angstrom Units) Based on Boltzmann-Average Momentum at Temperature T

$T°\text{K}$	m_e	m_H	m_O
1	745	17	4.4
10	235	5.5	1.4
100	75	1.7	0.44
300	43	1.0	0.25
500	33	0.78	0.19
1000	23	0.55	0.14
2000	17	0.39	0.10
3000	4.3	0.10	0.025

C.   BARRIER PENETRATION IN ONE DIMENSION

(i) Rectangular Barrier

In classical mechanics, a particle of total energy E approaching a potential-energy barrier of height V^* will pass over the barrier with unit probability if $E > V^*$ and will be reflected with unit probability if $E < V^*$. In quantum mechanics, this is by no means the case. A particle with energy greater than the barrier height may be reflected, and a particle with energy E less than the barrier height has a finite chance of appearing on the other side of the barrier with the same energy E. This nonclassical barrier penetration has been named the "tunnel effect," and the name has been extended to cover the whole quantum-mechanical barrier-crossing problem, above as well as below V^*. Many elementary texts in quantum mechanics include a problem on penetration of rectangular barriers, for which the wave functions are easily obtained, and the problem provides good exercise in the fitting of wave functions at boundaries. Such a calculation is reviewed briefly here.

The potential-energy function V is pictured in Fig. 1. Three regions of the coordinate are distinguished (1, 2, and 3 on the figure). The barrier is of width L. A particle approaches from $-\infty$ with energy E. This energy is shown below the barrier height, but it could equally well be above it.   In the three regions the wave functions are

$$\psi_1 = A \exp(i\alpha x) + B \exp(-i\alpha x)$$
$$\psi_2 = C \exp(\beta x) + D \exp(-\beta x) \qquad (2\text{-}4)$$
$$\psi_3 = E \exp(i\alpha x) + F \exp(-i\alpha x) = E \exp(i\alpha x)$$

where $\alpha = (2\pi/h)(2mE)^{1/2}$

$\qquad \beta = (2\pi/h)[2m(V-E)]^{1/2}$

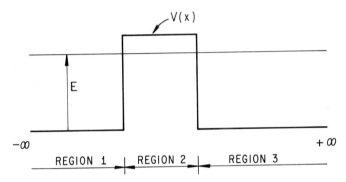

Fig. 2–1. Rectangular potential-energy barrier, V(x), with one representative total energy E of an approaching particle.

The term β is positive if the particle energy is less than the barrier height, and the wave function decreases exponentially in region 2.   The term β is imaginary if the particle energy exceeds the barrier height, and the wave function is an oscillating, free-particle function.   At the discontinuities of the potential-energy function, 0 and L, the wave functions and their first derivatives must be continuous.   Continuity of ψ and $d\psi/dx$ at $x = 0$ gives the relations

$$A + B = C + D$$
$$i\alpha(A - B) = \beta(C - D) \qquad (2\text{-}5)$$

Continuity of ψ and $d\psi/dx$ at $x = L$ gives the further relations

$$C \exp(\beta L) + D \exp(-\beta L) = E \exp(i\alpha L)$$
$$\beta C \exp(\beta L) - \beta D \exp(-\beta L) = i\alpha E \exp(i\alpha L) \qquad (2\text{-}6)$$

The relation needed is the ratio of E to A, since A represents a free particle moving from left to right in region 1 and E represents a free particle of the same energy moving from left to right in region 3.

$$\frac{A}{E} = \frac{\exp(i\alpha L)}{4i\alpha\beta}[(\beta + i\alpha)^2 \exp(-\beta L) - (\beta - i\alpha)^2 \exp(\beta L)]$$

This equation is multiplied by its complex conjugate to give

$$\frac{|A|^2}{|E|^2} = \cosh^2 \beta L + \frac{(\alpha^2 - \beta^2)^2}{4\alpha^2\beta^2} \sinh^2 \beta L \tag{2-7}$$

The reciprocal $|E|^2/|A|^2$ is the probability of tunneling through the barrier per collision, or the "transmission probability."

(ii) Truncated Parabola and Eckart Barrier

R. P. Bell[24] worked out the tunneling problem for a truncated parabolic barrier as shown in Fig. 2. C. Eckart[25] proposed a function for a barrier

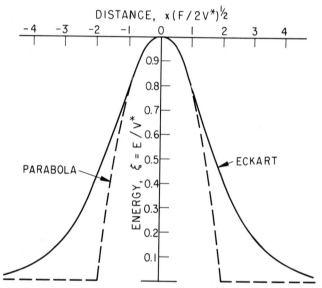

Fig. 2–2. Comparison of symmetrical Eckart potential with corresponding truncated parabola.

that changes smoothly and continuously and for which Schroedinger's equation can be solved exactly. Eckart evaluated in closed form an expression for the probability, $\kappa(E)$, of crossing the barrier for a particle of energy E. In this section the properties of the Eckart function will be reviewed, and there will be presented the results of numerical integration of Eckart's $\kappa(E)$ over a Boltzmann distribution of incident particles with chemically interesting values of energies, masses, and barriers.

Eckart's one-dimensional potential-energy function is

$$V = \frac{Ay}{1 - y} - \frac{By}{(1 - y)^2}$$

$$y = -\exp(2\pi x/L) \tag{2-8}$$

where x is the variable dimension and L is a characteristic length. In dimensionless form, a symmetrical ($A = 0$) Eckart potential is compared with a parabola with the same curvature at the maximum, in Fig. 2. A symmetrical and unsymmetrical Eckart function is given in Fig. 3. It is seen to be flat at both $-\infty$ and $+\infty$. The maximum value is V_1 above the value at $-\infty$ and V_2 above the value at $+\infty$. F^* is the second derivative

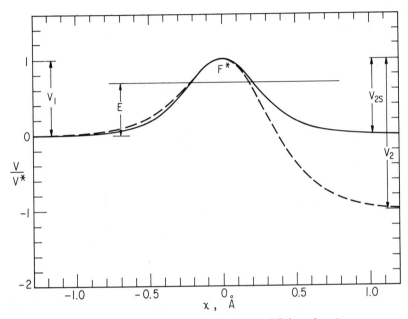

Fig. 2–3. Symmetrical and unsymmetrical Eckart barriers.

of the function at its maximum. The parameters A, B, and L in Eq. 8 are related to V_1, V_2, and F^* in Fig. 3 by

$$A = V_1 - V_2 \tag{2-9}$$

$$B = (V_2^{1/2} + V_1^{1/2})^2 \tag{2-10}$$

$$\frac{L}{2\pi} = \left(\frac{-2}{F^*}\right)^{1/2} \left(\frac{1}{V_1^{1/2}} + \frac{1}{V_2^{1/2}}\right)^{-1} \tag{2-11}$$

The inverse relations are

$$V_1 = (A + B)^2/4B \tag{2-12}$$

$$V_2 = (A - B)^2/4B \tag{2-13}$$

$$F^* = \frac{\pi^2(A^2 - B^2)^2}{2L^2B^3} \tag{2-14}$$

A particle of mass m and energy E approaching the barrier is characterized by the relations

$$\nu^* = (1/2\ \pi)(-F^*/m)^{1/2} \qquad u^* = h\nu^*/kT \qquad (2\text{--}15)$$

$$\alpha_1 = 2\pi V_1/h\nu^* \qquad (2\text{--}16)$$

$$\alpha_2 = 2\pi V_2/h\nu^* \qquad (2\text{--}17)$$

$$\xi = E/V_1 \qquad (2\text{--}18)$$

In these variables, the probability $\kappa(E)$ that a particle starting toward the barrier with energy E at $-\infty$ will pass the barrier and appear later at $+\infty$ with energy E is found by solving Schroedinger's equation for the Eckart function, and the transmission probability is

$$\kappa(E) = 1 - \frac{\cosh 2\pi(a - b) + \cosh 2\pi d}{\cosh 2\pi(a + b) + \cosh 2\pi d} \qquad (2\text{--}19)$$

$$2\pi a = 2[\alpha_1\xi]^{1/2}\left(\frac{1}{\alpha_1^{1/2}} + \frac{1}{\alpha_2^{1/2}}\right)^{-1} \qquad (2\text{--}20)$$

$$2\pi b = 2[(1 + \xi)\alpha_1 - \alpha_2]^{1/2}\left(\frac{1}{\alpha_1^{1/2}} + \frac{1}{\alpha_2^{1/2}}\right)^{-1} \qquad (2\text{--}21)$$

$$2\pi d = 2[\alpha_1\alpha_2 - 2\pi^2/16]^{1/2} \qquad (2\text{--}22)$$

When d is imaginary, the function $\cosh 2\pi |d|$ in Eq. 19 becomes $\cos 2\pi |d|$.

With the aid of Fig. 3 one can readily define a one-dimensional "species Y," one-dimensional "species Z," and a one-dimensional reaction rate. Let Y be any system to the left of the maximum in Fig. 3 and let Z be any system to the right. The partition functions (compare Chapter 6) are

$$f_Y = \int_{-M}^{0} \int_{-\infty}^{\infty} \exp\left(-E/kT\right) dx\,dp/h \qquad (2\text{--}23)$$

$$f_Z = \int_{0}^{M} \int_{-\infty}^{\infty} \exp\left(-E/kT\right) dx\,dp/h \qquad (2\text{--}24)$$

where M is some large, finite distance. Suppose point particles of mass m to be introduced into region Y and withdrawn from region Z in such a way as to maintain a Boltzmann distribution over the region Y. What is the steady-state reaction rate from Y to Z? One selects a point anywhere along x in region Y where the potential energy is essentially constant, and a vertical line is imagined to be there. The rate of reaction for a particular momentum is the left-to-right flux across the line, dn/dt, multiplied by the probability, $\kappa(p)$, that a system with this momentum pass the barrier and appear far to the right in region Z. For a particular momentum, p, the flux across the line is

$$\frac{dn}{dt} = \frac{dn}{dx}\frac{dx}{dt} = \frac{dn}{dx}\frac{p}{m} \qquad (2\text{--}25)$$

and the rate of reaction for the given momentum is

$$\mathbf{R}(n) = \frac{dn}{dx} \kappa(p) \frac{p}{m} \tag{2-26}$$

For a particular cell in phase space, located at the selected value of x and p and of area $dx\,dp$, the fraction of systems is given by Eq. 6–34, and the density of systems along the coordinate is

$$dn/dx = n \exp\left(-E/kT\right) dp/hf_Y \tag{2-27}$$

The total rate is the rate for given momentum integrated over all positive values of momentum,

$$\mathbf{R} = \int_0^\infty \mathbf{R}(p) = \frac{n}{hf_Y} \int_0^\infty \kappa(p) \exp\left(-E/kT\right) p \, dp/m \tag{2-28}$$

In the selected flat region, the energy is all kinetic energy, $E = p^2/2m$, and $dE = p\,dp/m$. The rate of reaction can be expressed as an integral over energy with the transmission probability given by Eq. 19:

$$\mathbf{R}_{qu} = \frac{[Y]}{f'_Y} \frac{1}{h} \int_0^\infty \kappa(E) \exp\left(-E/kT\right) dE \tag{2-29}$$

where $[Y]$ is n_Y per unit volume and f' is the partition function per unit volume. In terms of classical mechanics, $\kappa(E)$ is zero if the energy is less than the barrier height, $E < V_1$ and $\kappa(E)$ is unity if $E > V_1$. Thus the rate according to classical mechanics is

$$\mathbf{R}_{cl} = \frac{[Y]}{f'_Y} \frac{kT}{h} \exp\left(-V_1/kT\right) \tag{2-30}$$

The ratio of quantum-mechanical barrier-crossing rate to classical-mechanical barrier-crossing rate is

$$\Gamma^* = \frac{\mathbf{R}_{qu}}{\mathbf{R}_{cl}} = \frac{\exp\left(V_1/kT\right)}{kT} \int_0^\infty \kappa(E) \exp\left(-E/kT\right) dE \tag{2-31}$$

Upon substitution of Eq. 19 into 31, one obtains a complicated expression not readily integrated by analytic means. Numerical integration with a high-speed electronic computer[26] is readily carried out, however, and results, as a function of u^*, α_1, and α_2, are given in Table 2. For a symmetrical Eckart potential, $\alpha_1 = \alpha_2$, some of the integrals, Eq. 31, are given in graphical form, as discussed below.[27]

The transmission coefficient according to classical mechanics is either zero or one, and this is shown as the *classical* curve in Figs. 4 and 5. The transmission coefficient for a truncated parabola was given by R. P. Bell, and this function is given for various values of α, Eq. 16, in Fig. 4. Eckart's

TABLE 2–2

Computed Barrier-Penetration Quantum Corrections Γ^*
from Unsymmetrical Eckart Barriers, as Function of α_1, α_2,
and u^*

α_1	α_2	u^*								
		2	3	4	5	6	8	10	12	16
0.5	0.5	1.16	1.25	1.34	1.44	1.55	1.80	2.09	2.42	3.26
	1	1.13	1.21	1.29	1.38	1.47	1.68	1.93	2.22	2.94
	2	1.09	1.14	1.20	1.27	1.34	1.51	1.71	1.94	2.53
	4	1.04	1.07	1.11	1.16	1.22	1.35	1.50	1.69	2.16
	8	0.99	1.00	1.03	1.06	1.11	1.21	1.34	1.49	1.88
	12	0.96	0.97	0.99	1.02	1.06	1.15	1.26	1.40	1.76
	16	0.94	0.95	0.97	0.99	1.02	1.11	1.22	1.35	1.68
	20	0.93	0.94	0.95	0.97	1.00	1.08	1.19	1.31	1.64
1	1	1.27	1.43	1.62	1.83	2.09	2.72	3.56	4.68	8.19
	2	1.21	1.35	1.51	1.71	1.93	2.50	3.26	4.28	7.48
	4	1.14	1.24	1.37	1.53	1.71	2.16	2.78	3.60	6.16
	8	1.08	1.16	1.26	1.39	1.54	1.92	2.43	3.12	5.25
	12	1.06	1.12	1.21	1.33	1.46	1.81	2.28	2.91	4.88
	16	1.04	1.10	1.18	1.29	1.42	1.75	2.20	2.80	4.66
	20	1.03	1.08	1.16	1.26	1.39	1.70	2.14	2.72	4.52
2	2	1.32	1.58	1.91	2.34	2.90	4.55	7.34	12.1	34.0
	4	1.26	1.47	1.77	2.18	2.66	4.20	6.85	11.4	33.4
	8	1.19	1.36	1.61	1.93	2.36	3.65	5.87	9.69	28.0
	12	1.16	1.32	1.54	1.84	2.23	3.41	5.44	8.94	25.6
	16	1.14	1.29	1.50	1.78	2.15	3.27	5.20	8.51	24.2
	20	1.12	1.27	1.47	1.74	2.10	3.18	5.03	8.22	23.3
4	4	1.30	1.58	2.02	2.69	3.69	7.60	17.3	42.4	304
	8	1.25	1.51	1.93	2.56	3.56	7.57	18.0	46.7	376
	12	1.22	1.47	1.86	2.59	3.39	7.16	17.0	44.0	354
	16	1.20	1.44	1.81	2.39	3.28	6.88	16.2	41.9	335
	20	1.19	1.42	1.78	2.34	3.20	6.68	15.7	40.3	321
8	8	1.24	1.56	2.04	2.94	4.54	13.8	57.0	307	—
	12	1.22	1.54	2.04	3.00	4.68	15.4	71.7	445	—
	16	1.21	1.53	2.02	2.93	4.65	15.6	74.4	473	—
	20	1.20	1.51	2.00	2.90	4.61	15.5	74.2	474	—
12	12	1.2	1.5	2.1	3.1	5.2	22	162	1970	—
	16	1.2	1.5	2.2	3.1	5.4	25	220	3300	—
	20	1.2	1.5	2.1	3.1	5.4	26	246	3920	—
16	16	1.2	1.5	2.1	3.2	5.7	32	437	—	—
	20	1.2	1.5	2.1	3.2	5.9	37	616	—	—
20	20	1.2	1.5	2.1	3.2	6.1	46	1150	—	—

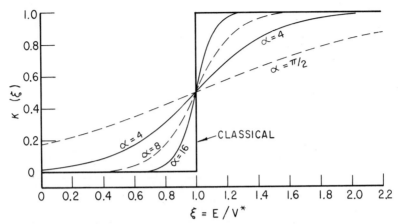

Fig. 2–4. Transmission probability as function of energy for truncated parabola and for various values of $\alpha = V*/2\pi h\nu*$.

transmission coefficient as a function of energy is given by Eq. 19 and for a symmetrical barrier it is compared with the classical function in Fig. 5. A comparison of $\kappa(E)$ for the truncated parabola and symmetrical Eckart potential with equal curvatures at maximum and equal height is obtained from Fig. 4 relative to Fig. 5. The product of the transmission function $\kappa(E)$ and the Boltzmann factor $e^{-E/kT}$ gives the distribution of transmitted systems as a function of energy. Such curves for $\alpha = 8$ and $u*$ equal to $\pi/2$, π, and 2π are shown by Figs. 6, 7, 8. These figures are representative of a barrier height of 6 kcal/mole, a mass about that of a hydrogen atom, and temperatures respectively 1500, 750, and 375°K. The area under one of

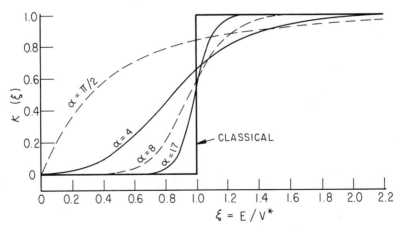

Fig. 2–5. Same as Fig. 4, for symmetrical Eckart barrier.

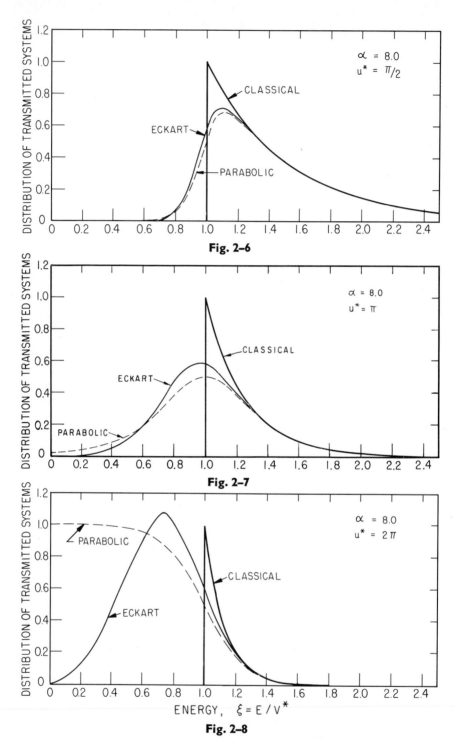

Fig. 2–6

Fig. 2–7

Fig. 2–8

Transmission probability multiplied by Boltzmann factor for truncated parabola and for Eckart barrier, for different values of α and $u* = h\nu*/kT$.

the curves in Figs. 6 to 8 is just the integral given by Eq. 29. The ratio of the area under the Eckart curve to the corresponding classical curve is just $\Gamma^* = \mathbf{R}_{qu}/\mathbf{R}_{cl}$, as given by Eq. 31 and Table 2.

For numerical work, it may be noted that if V^* is in calories/mole and if the imaginary frequency is in cm^{-1}, then

$$\alpha = 2.20 V^*/\omega^* \qquad (2\text{–}32)$$

The quantity u^* is readily expressed in terms of absolute temperature T and ω^* in cm^{-1} as

$$u^* = 1.44\, \omega^*/T \qquad (2\text{–}33)$$

It should be noted, however, that no chemical reaction is truly a one-dimensional rate problem, although certain isomerizations (including internal rotations) may have features resembling this one-dimensional treatment.

3

Kinetic Energy and Effective Mass

A. KINETIC ENERGY

The kinetic energy of an atom of mass m is simply

$$T = \tfrac{1}{2}mv^2 = \tfrac{1}{2}m(\dot{x}^2 + \dot{y}^2 + \dot{z}^2) \tag{3-1}$$

where $\dot{x}$, $\dot{y}$, $\dot{z}$, are components of velocity along the three cartesian axes:

$$\dot{x} = dx/dt \qquad \dot{y} = dy/dt \qquad \dot{z} = dz/dt \tag{3-2}$$

For a diatomic molecule with internuclear distance R and atomic masses m_a and m_b, the kinetic energy is

$$T = \tfrac{1}{2}m_a(\dot{x}_a^2 + \dot{y}_a^2 + \dot{z}_a^2) + \tfrac{1}{2}m_b(\dot{x}_b^2 + \dot{y}_b^2 + \dot{z}_b^2) \tag{3-3}$$

For a molecule with N atoms, regardless of structure, the kinetic energy is

$$T = \sum_{\alpha=1}^{N} \tfrac{1}{2}m_\alpha(\dot{x}_\alpha^2 + \dot{y}_\alpha^2 + \dot{z}_\alpha^2) \tag{3-4}$$

If each atom of a molecule or complex moves in a manner proportional to some progress variable, ρ, then the velocity of each atom,

$$v_\alpha = (\dot{x}_\alpha^2 + \dot{y}_\alpha^2 + \dot{z}_\alpha^2)^{1/2} \tag{3-5}$$

is proportional to the time rate of change of the progress variable:

$$v_1 = A_1\dot{\rho} \qquad v_2 = A_2\dot{\rho}, \cdots v_N = A_N\dot{\rho} \tag{3-6}$$

the kinetic energy of the molecule is

$$T = \frac{1}{2} \sum_{\alpha=1}^{N} m_\alpha A_\alpha^2 \dot{\rho}^2 \tag{3-7}$$

and the "effective mass m" of the "progress variable ρ" is defined as

$$m = \sum m_\alpha A_\alpha^2 \tag{3-8}$$

The simplest example is the translation of a (non-vibrating, non-rotating) molecule. The progress variable is translation of center of mass, the proportionality constants A_α are all unity, and the "effective mass' is the sum of atomic masses, that is, the molecular mass.

A simple case is a non-rotating diatomic molecule vibrating along the z axis with fixed center of mass. The progress variable, $\dot{R}$, is the rate of change of the bond length. The condition that locates the center of mass is

$$m_a(R - w) = m_b w \tag{3-9}$$

where w is the distance of atom b from the center of mass. The condition that retains a fixed center of mass gives the constants A_α:

$$\dot{z}_a = [(R - w)/R]\dot{R} \qquad \dot{z}_b = -[w/R]\dot{R} \tag{3-10}$$

The effective mass for this motion is found to be the "reduced mass" μ:

$$\mu = m_a m_b/(m_a + m_b) \tag{3-11}$$

Another special case is the rotation of a diatomic molecule about the x axis through the counter of mass. The velocities of the atoms are

$$v_a = (\dot{y}_a^2 + \dot{z}_a^2)^{1/2} \qquad v_b = (\dot{y}_b^2 + \dot{z}_b^2)^{1/2} \tag{3-12}$$

The progress variable is the angle Θ and the relations between atomic velocity and progress variable are

$$v_a = (R - w)\dot{\Theta} \qquad v_b = -w\dot{\Theta} \tag{3-13}$$

The effective mass is found to be μR^2, that is, the moment of inertia about the x axis:

$$I_x = \mu R^2 \tag{3-14}$$

A triatomic molecule, a–x–b, that is linear at equilibrium but capable of nonlinear distortions requires nine cartesian coordinates to describe its instantaneous position and nine components of velocity to describe its kinetic energy. Another set of nine coordinates is: three cartesian coordinates of center of mass, X, Y, Z; two coordinates of orientation of the molecule relative to fixed axes in space, Θ_1, Θ_2; two interatomic distances, R_1 and R_2; and two mutually perpendicular angles that give the distortion from linearity Φ and Φ' (Fig. 1). The "effective mass" of various special motions of the linear triatomic molecule will be given, and finally a powerful general method of obtaining such results will be pointed out. The effective mass for translation of the center of mass is of course the molecular mass, $m_a + m_x + m_b = M$. For the special motion of rotation of the molecule about the fixed center of mass, the evaluation of kinetic energy and effective mass follows the method used for the diatomic molecule, though the algebra becomes much more tedious. The condition for center of mass is

$$m_a(R_1 - w) = m_x w + m_b(R_2 + w) \tag{3-15}$$

where w is the distance of the center of mass from the central atom and w is positive if the center of mass lies between a and x. The kinetic energy of rotation is

$$T = \tfrac{1}{2} I(\dot{\Theta}_1^2 + \dot{\Theta}_2^2) \tag{3-16}$$

where the moment of inertia is

$$I = m_a(R_1 - w)^2 + m_x w^2 + m_b(R_2 + w)^2 \tag{3-17}$$

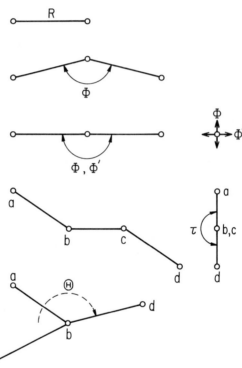

Fig. 3–1. Internal coordinates: R, bond length; Φ, bond angle; τ, torsion angle; Θ, angle between plane abc and bond bd.

and, by substitution of w from Eq. 15 and tedious collection of terms, it may be shown that

$$I = [m_a m_x R_1^2 + m_x m_b R_2^2 + m_a m_b(R_1 + R_2)^2]/M \tag{3-18}$$

A motion of special interest for later applications is that of changes in the bond distances with fixed center of mass and angular variables. A motion has an effective mass for the whole molecule only if there is a defined relation connecting all atoms to one progress variable. Let the ratio of the rate of change of one bond distance to the rate of change of the other bond distance be a parameter c:

$$c = dR_2/dR_1 \qquad (3\text{--}19)$$

The *structure* of the linear molecular is given by a single point in a two-dimensional plot of R_2 against R_1 as in Fig. 2.   A change in structure can be represented by a displacement $d\rho$ on the R_1–R_2 plane, that is, c is the slope

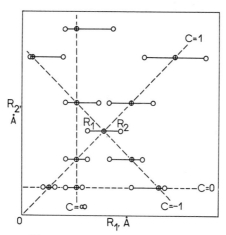

Fig. 3–2. Structure of linear triatomic molecule represented by a point in the R_1–R_2 plane. $\oplus$ locates the position in the R_1–R_2 plane and $\bigcirc$—$\oplus$—$\bigcirc$ represents the relative bond lengths.

of a displacement $d\rho$.   If the linear molecule is oriented along the z axis, the motions of the atoms, subject to fixed center of mass, are given by

$$d\,z_{\mathrm{a}} = dw - dR_1 \qquad dz_x = dw \qquad dz_{\mathrm{b}} = dw + dR_2 \qquad (3\text{--}20)$$

Solving Eq. 15 for w and differentiating, one gets

$$dw = (m_{\mathrm{a}} - cm_{\mathrm{b}})\,dR_1/M \qquad (3\text{--}21)$$

The kinetic energy is simply $T = \tfrac{1}{2}m\dot{\rho}^2 = \tfrac{1}{2}(m_{\mathrm{a}}\dot{z}_{\mathrm{a}}^2 + m_x\dot{z}_x^2 + m_{\mathrm{b}}\dot{z}_{\mathrm{b}})$.   The velocity $\dot{\rho}$ is related to rate of change of bond lengths by

$$\dot{\rho}^2 = \dot{R}_1^2 + \dot{R}_2^2 = (1 + c^2)\dot{R}_1^2 \qquad (3\text{--}22)$$

Cartesian coordinates are eliminated by use of Eqs. 20 and 21, and the "effective mass" of the displacement $d\rho$ of slope c is found to be

$$m_c = \frac{m_{\mathrm{a}}m_{\mathrm{b}}(1 + c)^2 + m_{\mathrm{b}}m_x c^2 + m_{\mathrm{a}}m_x}{M(1 + c^2)} \qquad (3\text{--}23)$$

The variation in "effective mass" with angle in the R_1–R_2 plane is given in Fig. 3 for the triatomic complex: $m_a = 15$, $m_b = 1$ or 2, $m_x = 2$ or 1 (representing the structures H_3C—H—D and H_3C—D—H, where the methyl radical is regarded as one atom). The "effective mass" for a change in structure is uniquely determined by the *slope* of a line on the R_1–R_2 plane, such as in Fig. 2, and it is not a function of position on the plane.

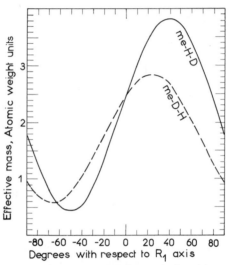

Fig. 3–3. Effective mass for concerted change in bond lengths plotted against the angle whose tangent $c = dR_2/dR_1$.

The linear triatomic molecule is subject to bending in two mutually perpendicular directions, along angles Φ and Φ'. The kinetic energy of the bending vibration is

$$T = \tfrac{1}{2}m(\dot{\phi}^2 + \dot{\phi}'^2) \tag{3–24}$$

The algebraic methods used so far are very tedious for the evaluation of effective mass for this motion. The general method of the next paragraph gives

$$m = m_a m_x m_b R_1^2 R_2^2 / M\,I \tag{3–25}$$

Most of the ideas to be developed later can be understood in terms of the linear three-atom case and the algebraic expressions already derived by straightforward tedious methods. For nonlinear triatomic molecules and for all more complicated molecules, one needs to use the powerful, condensed, vector and matrix methods of E. B. Wilson, Jr.[28] The internal motions of the group of atoms can be represented by a convenient and sufficient set of internal coordinates S, for example, bond lengths and bond angles,

Fig. 1.   The internal kinetic energy (excluding translations and rotations of the molecule as a whole) is given by

$$T = \tfrac{1}{2}\dot{\mathbf{S}}^{t}\mathbf{G}^{-1}\dot{\mathbf{S}} \tag{3-26}$$

where $\dot{\mathbf{S}} = d\mathbf{S}/dt$.   If each internal coordinate moves proportionally to the increase in a defined progress variable ρ, then $\dot{S}_1 = A_1\dot{\rho}$, $\dot{S}_2 = A_2\dot{\rho}$, etc., and in general

$$\dot{\mathbf{S}} = \mathbf{A}\dot{\rho} \qquad \dot{\mathbf{S}}^{t} = \mathbf{A}^{t}\dot{\rho} \tag{3-27}$$

where $\mathbf{S}$ and $\mathbf{A}$ are column matrices and $\mathbf{S}^{t}$ and $\mathbf{A}^{t}$ are the corresponding row matrices.

Insertion of Eq. 27 into Eq. 26 gives

$$T = (1/2)(\mathbf{A}^{t}\mathbf{G}^{-1}\mathbf{A})\dot{\rho}^{2} \tag{3-28}$$

so that the effective mass for the concerted motion ρ is in general

$$m = \mathbf{A}^{t}\mathbf{G}^{-1}\mathbf{A} \tag{3-29}$$

For the linear triatomic molecule, the internal coordinates may be taken as R_1, R_2, Φ and Φ'.   The change of bond lengths in the linear grouping with $c = dR_2/dR_1$ constitutes a special motion ρ, a straight line on Fig. 2, where

$$\mathbf{A}^{t} = [1/(1 + c^2)^{1/2} \qquad c/(1 + c^2)^{1/2}, 0, 0] \tag{3-30}$$

Convenient tables of $\mathbf{G}$-matrix elements are given in Appendix VI of Wilson, Decius, and Cross; a brief table is given in the next section.

These relations apply quite aside from any considerations of potential energy.   Thus the "effectiveness mass" for a given change in internal coordinates is the same whether the motion is a natural vibration of a stable molecule or a portion of a collision or other interaction of unbound atoms.

B.   G-MATRIX ELEMENTS FOR TRIATOMIC MOLECULE

For the triatomic molecule,

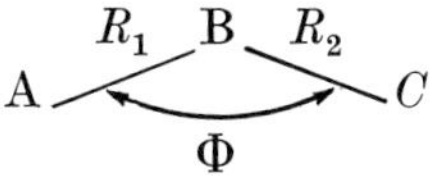

the $\mathbf{G}$-matrix for the bent molecule has the form

$\mathbf{G}$	R_1	R_2	Φ	
R_1	G_{11}	G_{12}	$G_{1\Phi}$	
R_2	G_{21}	G_{22}	$G_{2\Phi}$	(3-31)
Φ	$G_{\Phi1}$	$G_{\Phi2}$	$G_{\Phi\Phi}$	

and for a linear molecule the **G**-matrix is

$$
\begin{array}{c|cccc}
\mathbf{G} & R_1 & R_2 & \Phi & \Phi' \\
\hline
R_1 & G_{11} & G_{12} & 0 & 0 \\
R_2 & G_{21} & G_{22} & 0 & 0 \\
\Phi & 0 & 0 & G_{\Phi\Phi} & 0 \\
\Phi' & 0 & 0 & 0 & G_{\Phi\Phi}
\end{array}
\tag{3-32}
$$

where the elements are obtained from a convenient table in the book by Wilson, Decius, and Cross:[28]

$$
G_{11} = \frac{1}{m_A} + \frac{1}{m_B}
$$

$$
G_{22} = \frac{1}{m_B} + \frac{1}{m_C}
$$

$$
G_{\Phi\Phi} = \frac{1}{m_A R_1^2} + \frac{1}{m_C R_2^2} + \frac{1}{m_B}\left(\frac{1}{R_1^2} + \frac{1}{R_2^2} - \frac{2\cos\Phi}{R_1 R_2}\right)
$$

$$
G_{12} = G_{21} = \frac{1}{m_B}\cos\Phi
\tag{3-33}
$$

$$
G_{1\Phi} = G_{\Phi 1} = -\frac{1}{m_B R_2}\sin\Phi
$$

$$
G_{2\Phi} = G_{\Phi 2} = -\frac{1}{m_B R_1}\sin\Phi
$$

For molecules containing more than three atoms, one should consult Appendix VI of Wilson, Decius, and Cross for the form of the elements of the **G**-matrix.

PROBLEM

For a three-atom linear complex of masses, m_a, m_x, and m_b, the effective mass for the progress variable, $c = dR_2/dR_1$, is given by Eq. 23.

(1) Obtain a general algebraic expression for the values of c to give the extrema of effective mass (maximum and minimum).

(2) Obtain an algebraic expressions for the extrema of effective mass for the case of $m_a = m_b$.

(3) Evaluate the maximum and minimum effective mass for each of the following cases:

	m_a	m_x	m_b
(i)	1	1	1
(ii)	100	1	100
(iii)	1	100	1
(iv)	100	1	1
(v)	100	100	1

4
Potential Energy, V

A. PAIRWISE INTERACTIONS OF ATOMS AND MOLECULES

It is sometimes convenient to single out certain interactions between atoms and molecules, even though actual situations may involve two or more interactions operating at once.

One of the simplest is Coulomb's law:

$$V(R) = Z_1 Z_2 \varepsilon^2 / R \qquad (4-1)$$

where particle 1 has charge $Z_1 \varepsilon$, particle 2 has charge $Z_2 \varepsilon$, R is the separation between the particles, and ε is the charge of a proton.

A spherically symmetrical atom or molecule placed in an electrical field of intensity $\mathbf{E}$ has induced in it a dipole moment $\mathbf{D}$:

$$\mathbf{D} = \alpha \mathbf{E} \qquad (4-2)$$

and the proportionality constant α is defined as the "polarizability." The potential energy between an ion of charge $Z\varepsilon$ and an atom or molecule of polarizability α is

$$V(R) = -Z^2 \varepsilon^2 \alpha / 2 R^4 \qquad (4-3)$$

The polarizability of a hydrogen atom in its ground electronic state can be accurately evaluated from quantum mechanics[20,22]

$$\alpha = (9/2)a_0^3 = 0.678 \times 10^{-24} \ \mathrm{cm}^3 \qquad (4-4)$$

where a_0 is the Bohr radius of the hydrogen atom. For more complex atoms and for molecules, the polarizability can be estimated by approximate quantum-mechanical methods, or from tables of bond and group polarizabilities (Ref. 29, pp. 941–955). The polarizability of a molecule can be experimentally determined by observation of index of refraction as a function of frequency of radiation and extrapolation to zero frequency (Ref. 21, pp. 368–371). Reference 29 (p. 950) gives the polarizability of a number of molecules.

Two hydrogen atoms a large distance apart induce dipole moments in each other, and the resultant "dispersion" or London potential-energy function is found by a straightforward quantum-mechanical treatment (Ref. 20, pp. 384–386; Ref. 29, pp. 1054–1059):

$$V(R) \cong -(13/2)(\varepsilon^2/a_0)(a_0/R)^6 \cdots \qquad (4\text{--}5)$$

When one extends this theoretical treatment to more complex atoms or molecules, the problem becomes highly complicated, and an approximate solution is achieved by a "semiempirical" method. For a complex atom or molecule, quantum-mechanical derivations are made of the polarizability, and parallel derivations are made for the long-range interaction of two such atoms or molecules. In each development intractable sums of integrals appear, and there are close relations between these two sums of integrals. The observable polarizability is identified with the integrals in the one theory and the similar integrals in the other theory are replaced by empirical polarizability. Thus intractable integrals in the theory of intermolecular attractions are "evaluated" by measurements of index of refraction of the substances involved. The result is that spherical molecules at large distances interact as

$$V(R) = -a/R^6 \qquad (4\text{--}6)$$

where the semiempirical constant is

$$a = \frac{3\varepsilon h}{4\pi m_e^{1/2}} \frac{\alpha_1 \alpha_2}{\left(\dfrac{\alpha_1}{N_1}\right)^{1/2} + \left(\dfrac{\alpha_2}{N_2}\right)^{1/2}}$$

$$= \frac{25.0\alpha_1\alpha_2 \times 10^{-60}}{\left(\dfrac{\alpha_1}{N_1}\right)^{1/2} + \left(\dfrac{\alpha_2}{N_2}\right)^{1/2}} \text{ erg-cm}^6 \qquad (4\text{--}7)$$

where α is in units of 10^{-24} cm^3 and N is an "effective number of electrons" of Pitzer.[30]

The constant a in Eq. 6 can also be evaluated by a 100-percent empirical method from gas viscosity or other transport properties. Hirschfelder, Curtiss, and Bird[29] have extensive tables of parameters ε and σ (defined in a subsequent section), evaluated empirically from gas viscosity. The empirical value of the constant a is given in terms of these constants:

$$a = 4\varepsilon\sigma^6 \qquad (4\text{--}8)$$

This situation is fairly typical in chemistry: (1) a good quantum-mechanical theory is well worked out for hydrogen atoms, (2) for more complicated systems a semiempirical theory replaces intractable integrals in an approximate quantum mechanical theory by some empirical parameters, and (3) a 100-percent "empirical theory" evaluates a parameter in one field from observations in an entirely different field.

Molecules may have permanent dipole moments or quadrupole moments, and in these cases interactions between two molecules depend on angular variables that give the orientation of the nonspherical molecules as well as the distance of separation R. An elementary discussion of the various potential-energy functions is given by Ref. 29 (pp. 26–29), which also gives a detailed discussion of these cases (pp. 836–851). The dependence of the potential energy on distance of separation R is as follows:

$$
\begin{array}{lll}
\text{charge-charge} & R^{-1} & \\
\text{charge-dipole} & R^{-2} & \\
\text{charge-quadrupole} & R^{-3} & \text{(4–9)} \\
\text{dipole-dipole} & R^{-3} & \\
\text{dipole-quadrupole} & R^{-4} & \\
\text{quadrupole-quadrupole} & R^{-5} &
\end{array}
$$

The contribution to the dispersion energy as given by Eq. 5 involves only one of several terms. It represents

$$\text{induced-dipole–induced-dipole} \quad R^{-6}$$

Other terms include:

$$
\begin{array}{ll}
\text{induced-dipole–induced-quadrupole} & R^{-8} \\
\text{induced-quadrupole–induced-quadrupole} & R^{-10}
\end{array}
$$

At extremely close distances, all atoms and molecules repel each other very strongly. A semiempirical expression[29] for this repulsion is

$$V(R) = d \exp\left[-f(R/a_0)\right] \qquad (4\text{–}10)$$

where a_0 is the Bohr radius, d is an empirical parameter, and the constant f is approximately

$$f = \left(\frac{2a_0}{\varepsilon^2}\right)^{1/2}(I_1^{1/2} + I_2^{1/2}) = \frac{(I_1^{1/2} + I_2^{1/2})}{3.687} \qquad (4\text{–}11)$$

where I is the ionization energy in electron volts. Another expression often used to represent repulsions is an inverse power law,

$$V = gR^{-j} \qquad (4\text{–}12)$$

where g and j are empirical.

For the complete range of non-bonding interactions between spherically symmetrical atoms or molecules, a convenient empirical function is the Lennard-Jones "6-12 potential":

$$V(R) = 4\varepsilon\left[\left(\frac{\sigma}{R}\right)^{12} - \left(\frac{\sigma}{R}\right)^{6}\right] \qquad (4\text{–}13)$$

where σ is the finite distance where the potential energy is zero, and ε is the absolute value of the depth of the potential well. The relation between the Lennard-Jones constants ε and σ and transport properties of gases is fully developed by Hirschfelder, Curtiss, and Bird; and their book contains extensive tables of these parameters. Also other complete potential-energy functions for spherical and non-spherical molecules are listed and discussed in Ref. 29 (pp. 31–35).

B. DIATOMIC MOLECULES

Discussions of chemical bonding in diatomic molecules very neatly fall into the classification of "theoretical, semiempirical, and 100-percent empirical." For diatomic hydrogen, Heitler, London, and Sugiura gave an ultrasimple, approximate, quantum-mechanical treatment (Ref. 20, pp. 340–345; Ref. 21, pp. 128–134, 420–422; Ref. 22, pp. 212–216). This treatment is simple enough for the full derivation and algebraic form of the results to be presented in elementary texts on quantum chemistry; however, it is well known that the bond energy, the wave functions, and the distribution of energy between kinetic and potential form are seriously in error. James and Coolidge (Ref. 20, pp. 349–351; Ref. 22, pp. 136–139.) solved the problem of the hydrogen molecule by a convergent approximation method. From the band spectra of diatomic molecules, the potential energy V as a function of internuclear distance R can be deduced on a purely empirical basis,[31] and a detailed table for the hydrogen molecule is given by Ref. 29 (p. 1060). Polanyi, Eyring, and Sato have shown how integrals in the Heitler-London theory can be evaluated empirically from spectroscopic data. These procedures, with references, are given in some detail below.

The simplest theoretical treatment of the hydrogen molecule is that of Heitler, London, and Sugiura. Two hydrogen atoms infinitely far apart have no effect on each other, and this state may be taken as the origin of energy. As the two atoms are brought together with parallel spins, a triplet state, they repel each other. As they are brought together with opposed electron spins, a singlet state, they attract each other to form a chemical bond. Heitler and London expressed the energy of the system as

$$E_S = \frac{Q + \alpha}{1 + \Delta} \qquad E_T = \frac{Q - \alpha}{1 - \Delta} \qquad (4\text{-}14)$$

where Q, α, and Δ are definite integrals and functions of internuclear distance R. A clear definition of these definite integrals and their algebraic evaluation is given by Ref. 21 (pp. 420–422). Numerical values for these integrals can be obtained from a table in Ref. 29 (pp. 1105–1107). In terms of this table,

$$\Delta = I_{00}^2$$

$$Q = \frac{\varepsilon^2}{a_0}\left(\frac{1}{D} - 2G_{00} + K_{00,00}\right)$$

$$\alpha = \frac{\varepsilon^2}{a_0}\left(\frac{\Delta}{D} - 2\Delta^{1/2}J_{00} + L_{00,00}\right)$$

$$(4\text{-}15)$$

where $D = R/a_0$ and I, G, K, J, and L are columns in the table. The value of ε^2/a_0 is 627.06 kcal/mole. Heitler-London theory gives a minimum potential energy of 72.6 kcal/mole at about 0.85 Å; the value observed from band spectra is 109.4 kcal/mole at 0.741 Å.

By means of a major quantum-mechanical computation, James and Coolidge accurately determined the bond energy, bond length, vibration frequency, and other properties of H_2. Similarly, James, Coolidge, and Present accurately evaluated three points on the potential energy curve for triplet, unstable H_2.[29] Recent refinements of these calculations do not change this discussion; these older calculations are emphasized here because the numerical values are all conveniently tabulated in one place, Ref. 29.

The potential-energy function for the H_2 molecule has been found from spectroscopic observations. Many simple analytical expressions have been proposed to represent experimental data such as these. One of the oldest and simplest is the Morse function[32,33,34]

$$V = D_e[\exp(-2\beta r) - 2\exp(-\beta r)] \tag{4-16}$$

where $r = R - R_e$ and β is an empirical constant, evaluated below. The Morse function may be developed as a Taylor series in r about the minimum in potential energy at R_e, where $r = 0$:

$$V = V_0 + \left(\frac{dV}{dr}\right)_0 r + \frac{1}{2}\left(\frac{d^2V}{dr^2}\right)_0 r^2 + \frac{1}{6}\left(\frac{d^3V}{dr^3}\right)_0 r^3 + \cdots \tag{4-17}$$

The constant term is $-D_e$ from choice of origin of energy, and the first derivative is zero by virtue of the minimum in V. The terms in r^3, r^4 and higher powers are negligible compared to r^2 if the displacement r is sufficiently small. Thus for small displacements (about $R = R_e$), the Morse function is adequately approximated by the quadratic expression

$$V - V_0 = \tfrac{1}{2}Fr^2 \tag{4-18}$$

where F is defined as d^2V/dr^2 at $r = 0$, and it is found to be

$$F = 2\beta^2 D_e \tag{4-19}$$

Figure 1 shows a Morse function and a parabola based on extension of the quadratic function, Eq. 18, to large values of r. The Morse function rises more steeply to the left and less steeply to the right than the parabola. There are two extrema in the plot of V against R as in Fig. 1, a minimum at R_e and a flat zone at infinity. The two extrema on the potential-energy diagram correspond to the chemically important species, the diatomic molecule and the two atoms.

The Morse curve is simple and qualitatively correct for many features of any diatomic molecule, although it fails when subjected to a fine quantitative test.   A similar expression, the Sato-Morse function,[34] has been proposed for repulsive triplet states of molecules:

$$V_{\text{tr}} = \frac{D_e}{2}\left[\exp{(-2\beta r)} + 2\exp{(-\beta r)}\right] \tag{4-20}$$

This function cannot be compared directly with experiment, since the exact values of the triplet repulsive curve have not been measured.   However,

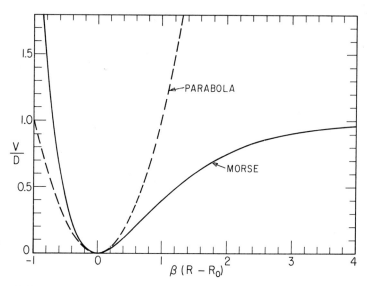

Fig. 4–I. Morse curve with inscribed parabola, continuation of quadratic potential based on curvature at origin.

this proposed relation can be compared with the values calculated quantum mechanically.   Figure 2 shows the theoretical line, and Sato's triplet function.   Also plotted is a modified Sato triplet function, that is, V_{tr} of Eq. 20 divided by 2:

$$V_{\text{tr}} = \frac{D_e}{4}\left[\exp{(-2\beta r)} + 2\exp{(-\beta r)}\right] \tag{4-21}$$

Sato's function does not parallel the theoretical curve.   Equation 20 agrees fairly well with the theoretical curve at short distances and high repulsive energies.   However, as can be seen from Fig. 2, Eq. 21 is a better approximation at intermediate distances, 1 to 2 Å.

Spectroscopic experimental data may be expressed in terms of the parameters R_e, β, and D of the Morse function.   Subject to certain severe approximations, the functions Q, α, and Δ of the Heitler-London theory may be evaluated from the Morse function at any interatomic distance R by a "semiempirical" approach. As an approximation, Polanyi and Eyring[33] proposed that Δ be zero and assumed that Q and α are proportional to each other at all distances R, that is,

$$Q = fV \qquad \alpha = (1 - f)V \tag{4-22}$$

where f is a constant and V is given by Eq. 16. The ratio $f = Q/V$ is approximately constant for large values of R, but it changes very rapidly

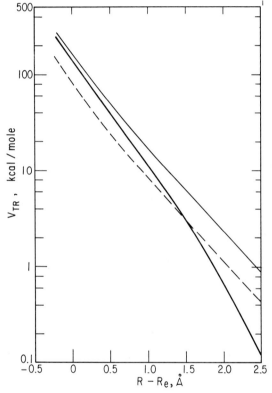

Fig. 4–2. Comparison of accurately calculated value of energy of HH triplet repulsion (heavy curve) with Sato's semiempirical method (solid curve, Eq. 21a; dashed curve, Eq. 21b).

near R_e. An alternate semiempirical method has been offered by Sato,[34] who evaluated functions Q and α from the simultaneous equations

$$D_e[\exp(-2\beta r) - 2\exp(-\beta r)] = (Q + \alpha)/(1 + \Delta) \tag{4-23}$$

$$\frac{D_e}{2}[\exp(-2\beta r) + 2\exp(-\beta r)] = (Q - \alpha)/(1 - \Delta) \tag{4-24}$$

upon the assumption that Δ is constant. Upon solving for Q and α, one obtains

$$Q = (D/4)[(3 + \Delta) \exp(-2\beta r) - 2(1 + 3\Delta) \exp(-\beta r)] \quad (4\text{--}25)$$

$$\alpha = (D/4)[(1 + 3\Delta) \exp(-2\beta r) - 2(3 + \Delta) \exp(-\beta r)] \quad (4\text{--}26)$$

C. LINEAR TRIATOMIC MOLECULES

The potential energy of a linear triatomic molecule is changed upon bending angles Φ or Φ' or upon stretching bonds R_1 or R_2. The force resisting stretching of a bond is much greater than that resisting the bending

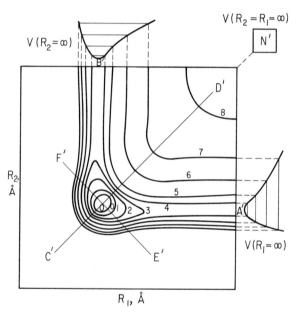

Fig. 4–3. Stable triatomic molecule with special reference to diatomic molecular decomposition products.

of a molecule. It is convenient to discuss separately the potential energy associated with bond extension and bond bending. For constant values of the angles, the potential energy with respect to change of bond length may be expressed by a third dimension above an R_1–R_2 diagram such as Fig. 3–2. Alternatively, contour lines of equal potential energy may be projected onto the R_1–R_2 plane. So far, quantum-mechanical calculations of energies of three-atom systems are not refined enough to be quantitatively useful; however, these treatments for the H_3 complex are discussed in Chapter 10. Various semiempirical methods have been used in which approximate quantum mechanical formulations suggest the form of the functions to be used, and parameters for these functions are fitted to spectroscopic or other experimental data.

The qualitative nature of the potential-energy surface for a stable symmetric triatomic molecule is given by Fig. 3. The four extrema are of especial chemical interest, that is, the chemist sums over a large number of states near each of these points and recognizes this more or less arbitrary sum as a "species." These four points are: O', the stable triatomic molecule; A', a stable diatomic molecule with one atom far removed; B', the other stable diatomic molecule and separated atom; and N', the three separated atoms. A Taylor series expansion can be made about each of the extrema of potential energy, O', A', B', and N'. The four constant terms give:

1. An origin of energy, say at O'.
2. The energy of reaction (aside from zero-point energy) to form diatomic molecule A'.
3. The energy of reaction to form the diatomic molecule B'.
4. The energy of reaction (aside from zero-point energy) to form three separated atoms at N'.

The four linear terms in the Taylor series expansions are all zero by virtue of each basis point being an extremum. The quadratic terms and all higher terms are zero in the flat region near N'. Each point, A' and B', gives a quadratic term, the force constant F of the diatomic molecule.

About the point O', there are three quadratic terms:

$$F_{11} = \partial^2 V/\partial R_1^2 \qquad F_{22} = \partial^2 V/\partial R_2^2 \qquad F_{12} = \partial^2 V/\partial R_1 \partial R_2 \qquad (4\text{--}27)$$

and for small departures from O', the potential energy is the quadratic form

$$V - V_0 = \tfrac{1}{2}(F_{11}r_1^2 + F_{22}r_2^2 + 2F_{12}r_1r_2) \qquad (4\text{--}28)$$

where $r_1 = R_1 - R_{10}$ and $r_2 = R_2 - R_{20}$. When one considers both potential energy and kinetic energy at any one of the four extrema, one can derive a $3N$-dimensional or 9-dimensional set of normal-mode coordinates, as will be demonstrated in Chapter 5. The mechanics of the system is particularly simple in terms of these coordinates in a region close to the basis point.

D. CHEMICAL REACTIONS VISUALIZED IN TERMS OF POTENTIAL-ENERGY SURFACES

A simple, hypothetical chemical reaction is the isomerization of a linear triatomic molecule

$$\text{A}{=}\text{B}{-}\text{C} \rightarrow \text{A}{-}\text{B}{=}\text{C} \qquad (4\text{--}29)$$

Both reactants and product are stable with respect to small perturbations, and these stable structures are represented by basins in the potential-energy surface (Fig. 4). Other chemical states of ABC are the molecule AB and atom C, molecule BC and atom A, and the three separated atoms; all five

chemical states are represented by Fig. 4. Suppose one started with pure
A=B——C and no A——B=C. At low temperature virtually all systems
would lie in the bottom of the A=B——C basin, and no reaction would occur.
At a somewhat higher temperature, an occasional molecule of A=B——C
would be excited from —8 up to —6, and at later time it would be deactivated by collision to some lower state. Between the acts of excitation

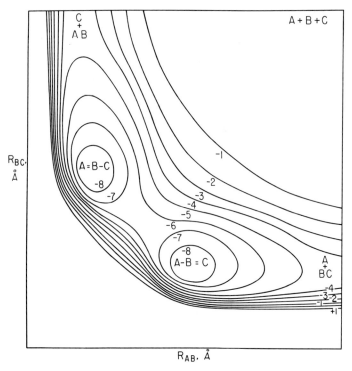

Fig. 4–4. Unimolecular isomerization.

and de-excitation, the molecule will move on a plane of constant total
energy. One way to visualize the course of the molecule is to imagine the
potential-energy basin to be a frozen lake with level surface at —6. The
molecule moves with constant total energy (the ice surface); the distance
from the surface of constant energy to the potential-energy surface (lake
depth) gives the kinetic energy; the effective mass for any direction of
motion is given by Eq. 3–23. The "skater on the surface" may move only
a short distance before being deactivated, and thus he may usually return
to the bulk of reactants; this situation corresponds to "high-pressure"
conditions; activation and deactivation are fast compared to the natural
time for reaction to occur. Alternatively, at "low-pressure" activation and
deactivation may become very slow compared to the natural time for excited

molecules to react. In the analogy of the skater, he may travel up and down region A=B— C, pass over to explore region A— B=C, and perhaps go back and forth several times. Even rarer than excitation to −6 is excitation of a reactant to −5. In this case the frozen lake must be imagined to fill the basin up to −5. At any given place on the potential-energy surface, a system at −5 has greater kinetic energy and thus moves faster than a system on −6. What constitutes "high" and "low" pressure will be

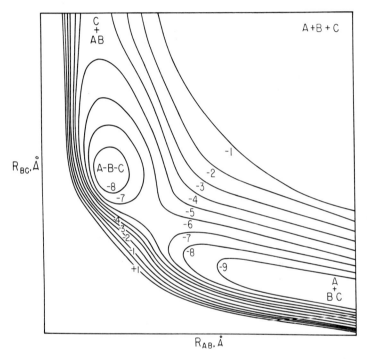

Fig. 4–5. Unimolecular decomposition.

different for systems on −5 and for those on −6. To summarize, chemical isomerization can be visualized in terms of Fig. 4 with the additional consideration of these possibilities:

1. Activation of reactant.
2. Deactivation of excited reactant.
3. Transition of excited reactant to excited product.
4. Deactivation of excited product.

The reverse reaction can be similarly expressed.

Rather similar considerations apply to the simple unimolecular decomposition of a linear triatomic molecule. This process can be visualized either from Fig. 5 or from Fig. 3 :

$$A—B—C \rightarrow A + B—C \qquad (4–30)$$

Once again one must realize that collisional activation must occur in the region A—B—C, and collisional deactivation also occurs there. The analogy of the ice-skater is good to use for this case, also. As opposed to isomerization, however, once the product is reached, a return to reactant is relatively unlikely. In Fig. 3 the "skater" excited to level 4 would move very fast near O, but slow down almost to zero as he approached A' or B'. Similarly an unexcited molecule A' plus an atom associate to form an excited triatomic molecule at O'. In terms of Eq. 30 and Fig. 5, one can say reaction has essentially occurred when a reactant has passed from the basin region A—B—C over the saddlepoint to the open valley A + BC; the saddlepoint of the potential-energy surface gives a reasonable boundary surface between reactant and products. For the dissociation of a stable molecule, Fig. 3, there is no clear-cut, easily recognized boundary between reactant and products, since the potential-energy curve is monotonic and asymptotically approaches the product state. In terms to be defined in later chapters, the former case (Fig. 5 or 4) is spoken of as a "tight activated complex," and the latter case (Fig. 3) as a "loose activated complex."

A bimolecular, atom-transfer reaction for a co-linear three-atom system

$$A—B + C = A + B—C \qquad (4–31)$$

can be visualized from Fig. 6. For the unimolecular decomposition (Fig. 5), and the unimolecular isomerization (Fig. 4), the reaction process is preceded by translational-vibrational energy transfer; the reactant must be excited from a low vibrational energy to a high vibrational energy. For the bimolecular reaction of Fig. 6, the reactants must come together with excess energy to reach the product state. This excitation of reactants resides in either R_{AB}, vibrations of the diatomic reactant, or R_{BC}, the relative translational motion of reactants toward each other. The ice-skater analogy may be used for bimolecular reactions; the surface of the frozen lake on the potential-energy landscape is given by the total energy of reactants excluding translational energy of the center of mass. If the excitation energy of reactants is all relative translational, the "skater" is to be pictured as coming straight down the A—B + C valley. If the excitation energy of reactants is vibrational energy of A—B and relative translational energy, the "skater" comes down the valley in a zig-zag course, going from one side of the narrow lake to the other as he approaches the region of the pass. It is well established that translational-translational energy transfer[35] is very fast compared to translational-vibrational energy transfer. This difference in ease of providing excitation energy for reactants is a major qualitative difference between bimolecular and unimolecular reactions. The kinetic energy of approach of reactants toward each other constitutes internal energy of the system. The magnitude of this energy is determined when reactants are still far apart. If this total energy is -8, for example, the "skater" is blocked off from the product "lake" by a "mountain pass" of height −5.5; the reactant molecules will collide but eventually revert to reactants. If the total internal energy of reactants is −5, for example, then the "frozen lake" lies higher than the "mountain pass" at −5.5, and a continuous ice path connects reactants and products. Upon such a collision the reactants could go to products, or they could interact

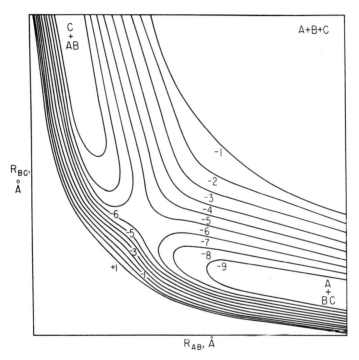

Fig. 4–6. Bimolecular atom-transfer reaction.

with the side-walls of the reactant "canyon" in such a way as to revert to reactants. If the total energy of reactants is −4, the width of the connection between reactants and products is wider than the case of total energy of −5.

Figure 7 provides a potential-energy surface for the visualization of the processes involved in the recombination of atoms with aid of an energy-transfer catalyst M:

$$A + A + M \rightarrow A_2 + M \qquad (4–32)$$

The reactants in this case are in the upper right-hand corner of the figure. The upper left-hand corner represents the free atom A and the weakly bound A-M complex. The lower right-hand corner corresponds to the products of reaction, the associated molecule A_2 and the catalyst M far removed. The basin in the lower central part of the figure corresponds to the weakly bound $A_2 \cdot M$ complex. (The "ice-skater" analogy is of only limited use here and will not be used.) Consider a series of simple paths from reactants. The extreme right-hand border of the figure represents two A atoms approaching each other with M far away (R_{MA} is large). The atoms will collide with the repulsive wall at the bottom of the figure and retrace the path back to

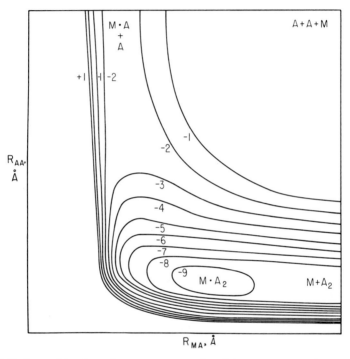

Fig. 4–7. Recombination of two atoms, catalyzed by energy-transfer agent M.

$A + A + M$. Similarly, the upper border of the figure corresponds to association of A and M with the other A atom far away. This collision path also leads to a return to reactants. A more or less diagonal path from the upper right-hand corner toward the lower left-hand corner is more interesting. All three atoms move toward each other and before the repulsive side-wall of the potential energy surface is reached a compact three-atom cluster is obtained. If this cluster breaks up with a path straight down the $M \cdot A + A$ canyon, the non-vibrating MA complex is flying apart from the A atom. If the three-atom cluster breaks up with a zig-zag path down the $M \cdot A + A$ canyon, then the MA complex is vibrating and translating away from the atom A. The stable MA complex so formed is capable of being decomposed to reactants either by collision with M or with A. However, upon another collision with A, the reaction

$$M \cdot A + A \rightarrow M + A_2 \qquad (4\text{--}33)$$

can be regarded as a bimolecular atom-transfer reaction, requiring no activation energy, and with a very broad product zone. Also, the three-atom cluster could break up in the direction of the products $M + A_2$. A straight path down this canyon corresponds to non-vibrating A_2 flying apart from M. The recombination of A_2 is also accomplished if the three-atom cluster breaks up with a zig-zag path down the $M + A_2$ canyon; the vibrating A_2 molecule is moving away from the catalyst M. The effective recombination of A_2 can occur along many paths from $A + A + M$, not just along the diagonal, $c = 1$. For example, consider a line from $A + A + M$ toward the canyon $M \cdot A + A$ with a slope of $dR_{AA}/dR_{MA} = 1/10$. All three atoms are coming together, but M and A are approaching each other much faster than A approaches A. This collision with the repulsive wall on the left-hand side of the $M \cdot A + A$ canyon could result in a zig-zag motion across the $M \cdot A + A$ canyon with a component of motion down toward the $M \cdot A_2$ cluster and with a possible escape down the $M + A_2$ canyon to products. Since the effective mass of the group changes with direction, these discussions are qualitative only. If one had a potential-energy surface for a real example, then one should skew and contract the coordinates (Appendix C) to find the collision trajectories that lead finally to products. Even so, the discussion above illustrates that atom recombination will occur by very many paths over the potential-energy surface, as opposed to the reactions illustrated by Figs. 4 to 6. The previous examples all had a pass in the potential-energy surface, and the reaction path was channeled between steep canyon walls. For atom recombination there is no activation energy, and a large variety of paths lead from reactants to products.

For all this discussion of Fig. 7, there is yet another very important path leading from reactants to products. The complex $M \cdot A$ can be formed from another three-body interaction,

$$M + M + A \rightarrow M + M \cdot A \qquad (4\text{--}34)$$

Such a process calls for a potential-energy surface analogous to Fig. 7. If A is an iodine atom and M a noble gas atom, the depth of the MA valley would be lower than that of MM. After formation of $M \cdot A$ by means of Eq. 34, the formation of A_2 could occur with fairly high probability by means of Eq. 33.

From these qualitative discussions, one sees that each elementary chemical process can be visualized in terms of a potential-energy surface for three co-linear atoms. Real chemical reactions of three atoms call for additional coordinates to represent nonlinear orientation of the atoms, but the multi-dimensional potential-energy surfaces cannot be visualized. Real chemical reactions involving more than three atoms require even higher-dimensional potential-energy surfaces, but some of the essential features can still be visualized in terms of Figs. 3 to 7.

The evaluation of potential-energy surfaces for particular chemical reactions will be deferred to Chapters 10 to 14, where specific cases are considered.

E.   FORCE CONSTANTS

Extrema in the potential-energy surfaces (such as shown in Figs. 3 to 7) are maxima, minima, saddlepoints, or flat regions.   The value of the potential energy at any extremum, V_0, may be taken as the zero of energy. The potential-energy function about any extremum may be expanded in a Taylor series:

$$V = V_0 + \left(\frac{\partial V}{\partial R_1}\right)_0 r_1 + \left(\frac{\partial V}{\partial R_2}\right)_0 r_2 + \left(\frac{\partial^2 V}{\partial R_1^2}\right)_0 \frac{r_1^2}{2} + \left(\frac{\partial^2 V}{\partial R_2^2}\right)_0 \frac{r_2^2}{2}$$
$$+ \left(\frac{\partial^2 V}{\partial R_1\, \partial R_2}\right)_0 r_1 r_2 + \text{higher derivatives} \tag{4-35}$$

where $r = R - R_0$.   The constant term may be taken as zero;   the first derivatives are zero by virtue of the reference point being an extremum; and for *sufficiently small displacements* from the reference point, cubic and higher terms in the r's are negligible compared to quadratic terms.   "Force constants" are defined as second derivatives evaluated at an extremum point:

$$F_{11} = \left(\frac{\partial^2 V}{\partial R_1^2}\right)_0 \qquad F_{22} = \left(\frac{\partial^2 V}{\partial R_2^2}\right)_0 \qquad F_{12} = \left(\frac{\partial^2 V}{\partial R_1\, \partial R_2}\right)_0 \tag{4-36}$$

If the linear structure is stable, then the potential energy is a minimum with respect to two perpendicular angles of bending, Φ and Φ', and bending force constants are defined as

$$F_\Phi = F_\Phi{}' = \left(\frac{\partial^2 V}{\partial \Phi^2}\right)_{R_{10} \cdot R_{20}} \tag{4-37}$$

For a bent triatomic molecule or complex, there is only one bending force constant of the same form as Eq. 37.   The convenient "valence bond" coordinates are R_1, R_2, Φ, and Φ' for a linear molecule, and R_1, R_2, and Φ for a bent molecule.   The method of evaluating force constants from a potential-energy multidimensional "surface" is given in Appendix B.

For small displacements from an extremum on a potential-energy surface for a linear structure, the potential energy may be approximated as

$$V - V_0 = \tfrac{1}{2}(F_{11}r_1^2 + F_{22}r_2^2 + 2F_{12}r_1 r_2 + F_\Phi \phi^2 + F_\Phi \phi'^2) \tag{4-38}$$

The quadratic potential-energy function $2(V - V_0)$ may be expressed as a matrix of the force constants in terms of the valence bonds and angles (the F-matrix of E. B. Wilson, Jr.[28]):

$$\mathbf{F} = \begin{pmatrix} F_{11} & F_{12} & 0 & 0 \\ F_{12} & F_{22} & 0 & 0 \\ 0 & 0 & F_{\Phi} & 0 \\ 0 & 0 & 0 & F_{\Phi} \end{pmatrix} \tag{4-39}$$

In valence-bond-and-angle coordinates, a force-constant matrix containing only diagonal elements is referred to as the "valence-bond force field," and it represents a simplified special case of the general quadratic potential-energy function. The off-diagonal elements, such as F_{12} in Eq. 39, are "interaction" terms; F_{12} gives the effect of distorting one bond on the effective force constant of the other bond. In general, one expects non-zero interaction constants between all bonds and angles, and Eq. 38 or 28 is an approximation (less severe than the valence-bond force field) to the general quadratic function. Neglecting bending, however, one has the general quadratic, small-displacement, potential-energy function for three-atom linear systems, Figs. 4 to 8, in terms of the force constant matrix

$$\mathbf{F} = \begin{pmatrix} F_{11} & F_{12} \\ F_{12} & F_{22} \end{pmatrix} \tag{4-40}$$

The determinant with the same elements as this matrix can be written in several forms:

$$|F| = \begin{vmatrix} F_{11} & F_{12} \\ F_{12} & F_{22} \end{vmatrix} = F_{11}F_{22} - F_{12}^2$$
$$= F_{11}F_{22}\left(1 - \frac{F_{12}^2}{F_{11}F_{22}}\right) = F_{11}F_{22}w^2 \tag{4-41}$$

The sign of this determinant gives the nature of the extremum point: for a stable triatomic molecule, $F_{11}F_{22} - F_{12}^2$ is positive; for a uniform straight parabolic channel, it is zero; and for a saddlepoint, it is negative. To the valence-bond approximation, the term

$$w^2 = 1 - F_{12}^2/F_{11}F_{22} \tag{4-42}$$

is unity; the magnitude of w^2 gives the measure of departure of the general quadratic expression from the valence-bond approximation. Thus the nature of the extremum for three-atom interactions is characterized by the valence-bond force constants F_{11} and F_{22} and by the sign and magnitude of the interaction function w^2.

F. EMPIRICAL RELATIONS BETWEEN BOND LENGTHS, BOND ENERGIES, AND FORCE CONSTANTS

There are a number of striking empirical correlations between bond lengths, force constants, and bond dissociation energies. In this field, one must be very careful to avoid confusing cause-and-effect with mere correlation. At least thirty different empirical relations have been proposed to connect force constants with other molecular parameters.[36] One of the

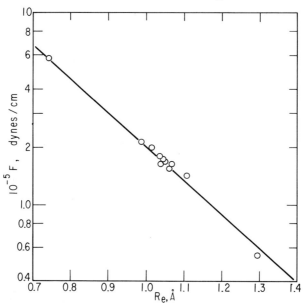

Fig. 4–8. Empirical correlation: force constants of stable and excited H_2 vs. corresponding bond length.

simplest and earliest is the correlation of force constant and bond length proposed by R. M. Badger; this correlation is often referred to as "Badger's rule," whether or not one uses his correlation function. Figure 8 shows the correlation between stretching-force constant and bond length for all well-characterized excited states of H_2, as given by Ref. 31 (pp. 531–532). A plot of the logarithm of the force constant against equilibrium bond length gives a good linear correlation. Figure 9 gives the force constants for all diatomic hydrides for the first row of the periodic table; the points are almost linear on a semilogarithmic plot, with slight positive curvature. Badger's rule is also applied to polyatomic molecules. The points for H_2O, NH_3, and CH_4 are very close to the correlation curve of Fig. 9. The family of carbon-carbon bonds is plotted on Fig. 10. Here again the correlation curve is linear on a semilogarithmic scale. The empirical rule for all these cases is

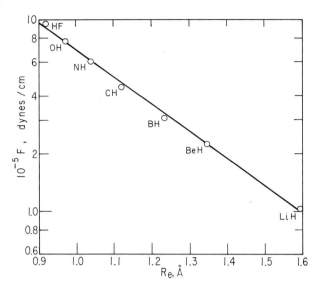

Fig. 4–9. Empirical correlation: force constant vs. bond length for stable diatomic molecules and radicals.

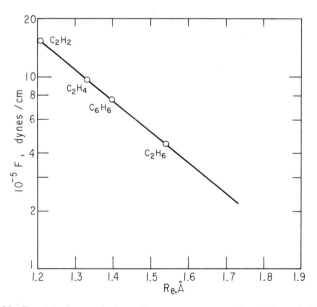

Fig. 4–10. Empirical correlation: force constant vs. bond length for carbon-carbon bonds in polyatomic molecules.

simply

$$R_e = a - b \log_{10} F \qquad (4\text{-}43)$$

where a and b are constant for a related series of bonds. In fact, a and b depend only on the rows of the periodic table for the two atoms being bonded, with the transition elements being regarded as a separate row. If one atom is in row i and the other in row j, the universal empirical relation between force constant and bond length is

$$R_e = a_{ij} - b_{ij} \log_{10} F \qquad (4\text{-}44)$$

A striking illustration of continuity of bonding between the loose, Lennard-Jones, noble-gas, two-atom cluster and the usual strong chemical bonds is given by extending the empirical correlation function (Eq. 44) to noble-gas clusters. The Lennard-Jones potential-energy function is given by Eq. 13, the value of R at minimum potential energy is

$$R_e = 2^{1/6} \sigma \qquad (4\text{-}45)$$

and ε is the depth of the potential-energy well. The stretching force constant is the second derivative of V with respect to R, evaluated at $R = R_e$, and

TABLE 4–I

Classical Dissociation Energy, Bond Length, and Stretching-Force Constant for Noble-Gas Two-Atom Clusters (Lennard-Jones Function)

Cluster	ε/k[a] (°K)	σ[a]	ε (cal/mole)	R_e	F_e (dynes/cm)
He-He	10.22	2.556	20.3	2.87	124
Ne-Ne	35.6	2.749	70.7	3.19	372
Ar-Ar	119.8	3.405	238.0	3.83	793
Kr-Kr	171	3.607	339.8	4.04	1039
Xe-Xe	221	4.100	439.1	4.60	1039
He-Ne	19.08[b]	2.652[c]	37.9	2.98	214
He-Ar	35.0	2.980	69.5	3.35	312
He-Kr	41.8	3.081	83.1	3.46	348
He-Xe	47.5	3.328	94.4	3.74	339
Ne-Ar	65.3	3.077	129.8	3.46	545
Ne-Kr	78.0	3.178	155.0	3.57	611
Ne-Xe	88.7	3.425	176.2	3.85	598
Ar-Kr	143.1	3.506	284.3	3.94	921
Ar-Xe	162.6	3.752	323.1	4.22	913
Kr-Xe	194.5	3.853	386.5	4.33	1036

[a] Ref. 29, p. 1110.
[b] $\varepsilon_{ij} = (\varepsilon_{ii}\varepsilon_{jj})^{1/2}$.
[c] $\sigma_{ij} = \frac{1}{2}(\sigma_{ii} + \sigma_{jj})$.

for this cluster it is simply

$$F_e = 72\varepsilon/2^{1/3}\sigma^2$$
$$= \frac{79.06(\varepsilon/k)}{\sigma^2} \text{ dynes/cm} \qquad (4\text{--}46)$$

where (ε/k) and σ are the quantities tabulated in Ref. 29 (pp. 1110–1112). The classical potential energy of dissociation, ε, of these clusters, the "bond length" R_e of Eq. 45, and the stretching-force constant F_e of Eq. 46 are given in Table 1 for the various noble-gas clusters. For homonuclear clusters, He-He, etc., the values of these parameters are found directly from ε/k and σ. For heteronuclear clusters, He-Ne, etc., the usual combination rules apply:

$$\varepsilon_{ij} = (\varepsilon_{ii}\varepsilon_{jj})^{1/2}$$
$$\sigma_{ij} = \tfrac{1}{2}(\sigma_{ii} + \sigma_{jj}) \qquad (4\text{--}47)$$

These points for Lennard-Jones molecules are combined with those for other molecules of the same rows of the periodic table (including excited states of molecules, ionic gaseous molecules such as NaCl as well as covalent molecules such as N_2, but omitting charged species such as HCl^+, and omitting diatomic molecules of alkali metals, Li_2, Na_2, K_2, Rb_2, Cs_2). The noble-gas clusters in all cases lie on the same curve (Eq. 44) as the corresponding family of regular molecules,[37] as can be seen from Fig. 11. The parameters a_{ij} and b_{ij} from Eq. 44 are given by Table 2; these parameters vary slowly and smoothly over the periodic table.

TABLE 4-2

Parameters a_{ij} and b_{ij} from Eq. 44, Including Noble-Gas Clusters by Omitting Homonuclear Alkali Metal Molecules[a]

	H	1	2	3	4	3T	4T
			a_{ij}				
H	1.18	1.46	1.74	1.82	1.96	1.71	1.81
1		1.85	2.06	2.15	2.28	2.12	2.22
2			2.36	2.45	2.62		
3				2.57	2.71		
4					2.87		
			b_{ij}				
H	0.58	0.56	0.64	0.66	0.72	0.71	0.78
1		0.55	0.63	0.64	0.70	0.72	0.73
2			0.70	0.73	0.79		
3				0.74	0.81		
4					0.87		

[a] Numbers refer to row of periodic table.

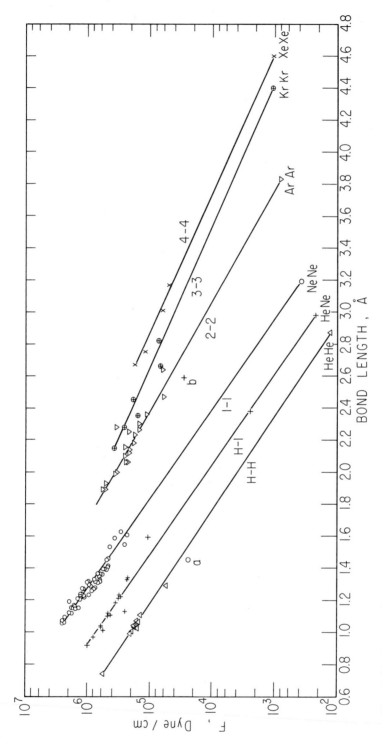

Fig. 4-11. Empirical correlations: force constant vs. bond length for entire periodic table (including ionic molecules, excited molecules, and noble gas clusters; but excluding molecule-ions and diatomic alkali metals).

A qualitative discussion for the striking empirical correlation shown by Fig. 11 is as follows: For a given row of the periodic table (beyond the alkali diatomic molecules) the repulsive potential is more or less constant for all pairs of atoms; the interactions (covalent, ionic; with singlet, doublet, triplet, or higher spin functions) that lead to bonding lower the energy, shorten the bond length, and sharpen the curvature. The fact that the bond length R_e is related to the curvature at the minimum F_e (or as seen later, D_e) is not an explanation of either quantity. (When the sun rises, the temperature goes up, the wind speed usually increases, the relative humidity goes down, etc. The correlation between wind speed and relative humidity, for example, is certainly no explanation for why the sun rises. Even without an explanation, one can *with due caution* make some predictions based on such correlations.)

G. BOND ENERGY

For diatomic molecules, one needs to distinguish between

D_e, potential energy of dissociation.
D_0, dissociation energy at absolute zero.
D_T, dissociation energy at temperature T.

These different quantities are demonstrated by the arrows in Fig. 12. D_0 is the difference between dissociated atoms at rest far apart and the zero-point vibrational energy of the molecular oscillator. D_T is the difference

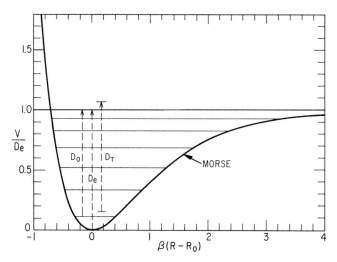

Fig. 4–12. Comparison of different dissociation energies of diatomic molecules.

between dissociated atoms with average thermal energy of *relative* translation and the molecule with average thermal energy of rotation and vibration.

For polyatomic molecules the distinction between dissociation energy D and bond energy E is so great that distinctions between D_e, D_0, and D_T are relatively unimportant. The difference will be illustrated by means of carbon dioxide:

$$D + O{=}C{=}O \to O + C{\equiv}O$$
$$2E + O{=}C{=}O \to O + C + O \tag{4-48}$$

TABLE 4–3
Bond Energies, Bond Lengths, and Chemist's Bond Orders

Bond	Bond Energy (kcal/mole)	Bond Length (Å)	Chemist's Bond Order	Molecule
CC	198	1.203	3	C_2H_2
CC	145	1.353	2	C_2H_4
CC	80	1.543	1	C_2H_6
NN	226	1.0976	3	N_2
NN	100	1.25	2	N_2F_2, $N_2(CH_3)_2$
NN	38	1.46	1	N_2H_4
OO	149	1.123	2.5	O_2^+
OO	118	1.207	2	O_2
OO	72	1.278	1.5	O_3
OO	34	1.47	1	H_2O_2
CN	207	1.153	3	HCN
CN	73	1.47	1	CH_3NH_2
CO	256	1.128	3	CO
CO	192	1.162	2	CO_2
CO	80	1.434	1	CH_3OH
NO	151	1.154	2.5	NO
NO	112	1.20	1.5	NO_2
NO	91		1.33	NO_3
NO	48		1	NH_2OH
PP	117	1.894	3	P_2
PP	48	2.21	1	P_4
SS	84	1.889	2	S_2
SS	54	2.08	1	S_8

The CO *bond energy* E in carbon dioxide is one-half the energy required to convert the molecule to three atoms. The CO *dissociation energy* D in carbon dioxide is modified by the "reorganization energy" of the residual diatomic molecule, which goes from C=O to C≡O in the process.

There are two senses in which bond energy may be related to bond length. On the one hand, one has the potential-energy function V for a given diatomic molecule as a function of internuclear separation R, for example, as in Fig. 1. On the other hand, one can consider a series of similar compounds such as acetylene, ethylene, and ethane. Each of these molecules has equilibrium internuclear carbon-carbon distance R_e and bond energy E_e. Cottrell[38] gives an extensive table of bond energies, dissociation energies, bond lengths, and force constants. For a given row of the periodic table, one finds a strong correlation between bond distance and bond energies, but there is a considerable spread in the points. It seems desirable to consider each pair of atoms separately. Examples of bond energies and bond lengths are given in Table 3. An empirical correlation of log E versus R for a family of nitrogen-nitrogen and a family of carbon-carbon bonds is given by Fig. 13.

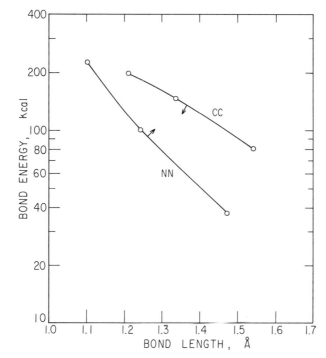

Fig. 4–13. Empirical correlation: bond energy vs. bond length for stable molecules.

These data give a line that is almost straight, but there is still some positive curvature for the N-N bonds and some negative curvature for the C-C bonds. On the basis of the correlation of bond length and force constant between ordinary molecules and Lennard-Jones clusters, one attempts the same correlation between bond energy and bond length in Fig. 14, where the CC and NN points of Fig. 13 are extended to the NeNe cluster (see Table 1). This long-range correlation is not as satisfying as that given by Fig. 11 but even so it is seen that the NeNe molecule may be regarded as a reasonable end point for either the CC or the NN curve. The very good correlations of Fig. 11 are taken as partial justification for postulating that Fig. 14 represents a significant correlation. It is proposed that if one had a perturbed N-N bond such that the equilibrium bond length came out to be 2 Å, for example, then one could make an estimate of its dissociation energy from Fig. 14. This postulate is extended to bonds such as C-H by assuming that there is continuity between the C-H bond in methane and the cluster Ne-He and that a linear plot of log E vs. R_e between these two points gives a suitable interpolation plot. The Lennard-Jones parameters for the mixed noble gas

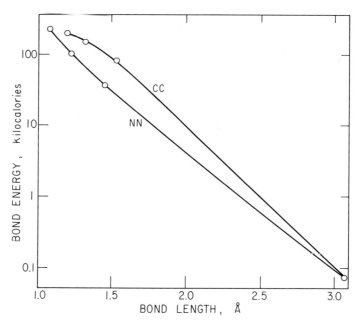

Fig. 4–14. Empirical correlation: bond energy vs. bond length, extended to include NeNe noble gas cluster.

molecules are obtained from the parameters for the pure species by Eq. 47, and they are given in Table 1.

H.　BOND ORDER

To a chemist the concept of "bond order" is an intuitive one, with a fairly wide breadth of meaning: the carbon-carbon bond has order 3 in acetylene, 2 in ethylene, 1 in ethane, etc. An extension of the chemist's intuitive, qualitative viewpoint to include fractional orders was proposed by Linnett.[39] The bond energies listed in Table 3 are classified as to "chemist's order," including Linnett's[39] view of fractional bond orders. In molecular orbital theory of molecular structure, the term "bond order" has a specific technical meaning; and in valence-bond theory of molecular structure there is another, somewhat different, specific technical meaning to the term.   In these theories orders such as 0.873 might appear, as well as fractional orders such as 4/3.

Pauling[40] proposed an ultrasimple, universal rule for defining the order n of any bond between two given atoms.   The chemist must first make up his mind as to which molecule represents the single bond between the two atoms. This single-order bond has bond length R_s.   Any other bond between the

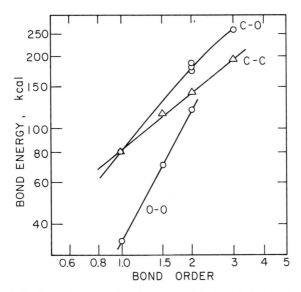

Fig. 4–15. Correlation of bond energy with chemist's bond order.

two atoms has bond length R (observable by X-ray diffraction or other techniques).   Pauling defines the order n from the relation

$$R = R_s - 0.6 \log_{10} n = R_s - 0.26 \ln n \qquad (4\text{--}49)$$

The bond energies for some of the molecules listed in Table 3 are plotted against chemist's bond order in Fig. 15 on a log-log scale.   This correlation is expressed as

$$E = E_s n^p \qquad (4\text{--}50)$$

where E_s is the bond energy of the single bond and p is the empirical slope of a curve in Fig. 15.   The assumed linear relation (Fig. 14), between single-order bonds and Lennard-Jones molecules is given by

$$\ln E/E_s = C(R_s - R) \qquad (4\text{--}51)$$

By use of Pauling's relation, Eq. 49, one notes that C of Eq. 51 is $p/0.26$ of Eq. 50.   Thus if R_x is the equilibrium internuclear distance in a noble-gas diatomic cluster or "molecule" and if ε_x is the depth of its Lennard-Jones potential, one can calculate the index p for any pair of atoms for which the single-bond parameters are known (again excluding alkali metal molecules)[41]:

$$p = \frac{0.26 \ln (E_s/\varepsilon_x)}{R_x - R_s} \tag{4-52}$$

Values of p evaluated in this way are given in Table 4.

TABLE 4–4

Evaluation of the Index p from Bond Energies and Bond Lengths

Bond	D_0° (kcal)	ω (cm^{-1})	D_{es} (kcal)	R_s (Å)	Noble Gas Analogue Bond	ε_x (cal)	R_x (Å)	p
H—H	103.2	4395	109.4	0.74	He—He	20.4	2.89	1.041
H$_3$C—H	101.3[a]	2914	105.5	1.09	Ne—He	38.0	2.99	1.087
H$_2$N—H	92.2[a]	3336	97.0	1.01	Ne—He	38.0	2.99	1.032
HO—H	109.4[a]	3735	114.7	0.96	Ne—He	38.0	2.99	1.028
F—H	134.6	4138	140.5	0.92	Ne—He	38.0	2.99	1.036
Cl—H	102.1	2989	106.4	1.27	Ar—He	69.6	3.36	0.914
Br—H	86.7	2649	90.5	1.42	Kr—He	83.2	3.46	0.892
I—H	70.6	2309	73.9	1.61	Xe—He	94.6	3.75	0.811

[a] These are bond energies E.

The empirical force constant of Eq. 44 can be rewritten as

$$R - R_s = b_{ij} \log_{10} (F_s/F) \tag{4-53}$$

but from Eq. 49 the bond lengths can be replaced by Pauling's bond order

$$b_{ij} \log_{10} (F/F_s) = 0.6 \log n \tag{4-54}$$

The values of b_{ij} are listed in Table 2, and they vary between 0.55 and 0.88. For the very important cases, H-H, H-1, H-2, and 1-1, these constants are 0.60 ± 0.05. To the approximation that these constants b_{ij} for these groups are 0.6, one sees that Eq. 54 gives the simple relation

$$F = F_s n \tag{4-55}$$

There is no relation analogous to Badger's rule for bending-force constants. To some extent, the value from spectroscopy depends on the number of off-diagonal elements of the **F**-matrix one assumes to be zero. The origin of the angular restoring force is partly from change of hybridization about the central atom, and partly it is from non-bonding interactions between end atoms. The following extension of Eq. 55 to cover bending-force constants is to be regarded simply as a postulate: if the bending-force constant $F_{\Phi s}$

for single-bonded A—B—C or B—C—A or C—A—B is known empirically, the bending force constant for the fractional-order complexes A $\cdots$ B $\cdots$ C is

$$F_\Phi = F_{\Phi s} n_1 n_2 \qquad (4\text{--}56)$$

The straightforward empirical relations between force constants or bond energy and bond length are given by Figs. 11 and 14. The artificial concept "bond order" is introduced by means of Eq. 49 for two reasons: certain further assumptions are readily expressed in terms of the concept; and the relations of bond energies and force constants to bond length take the very simple forms of Eqs. 50 and 55 for a large list of important cases.

PROBLEMS

(1) To three significant figures, evaluate Pauling's bond order for the double and triple bonds of CC, NN, and CO from the data of Table 3.

(2) Make a freehand, qualitative drawing of a potential-energy surface for a stable triatomic molecule, for which the dissociation energy of one bond is 50 kcal/mole and the dissociation energy of the other bond is 100 kcal/mole.

5

Normal Coordinates

A. NORMAL MODES OF VIBRATION

In the chapter on effective mass, it was convenient to define a progress variable ρ and a generalized motion of the entire molecule in which all internal coordinates change in a prescribed manner proportional to the variable ρ. If in the immediate vicinity of any extremum (maximum, minimum, saddlepoint, or flat surface of a potential-energy surface) both kinetic energy and potential energy are considered simultaneously, it is found that each molecule has a set of natural coordinates, each of which is a special case of the progress variable ρ as used in Chapter 3. The natural progress variables are called "normal modes." The normal modes are found from considerations of infinitesimal deviations from the extremum of potential energy; hence they are based on classical mechanics. Excellent discussions of normal modes are found in books by Herzberg[42] and by Wilson, Decius, and Cross.[28]

(i) Diatomic Molecules

It is instructive to carry through a detailed algebraic analysis of the normal modes of a very simple case to illustrate the mathematical and physical structure of the problem. A simple case is a diatomic molecule, a-b, with the atoms constrained to move in one dimension, x. The atoms have equilibrium separation, $x_{a0} - x_{b0}$. For small displacements, the potential energy is

$$V = \tfrac{1}{2}F[(x_b - x_{b0}) - (x_a - x_{a0})]^2 \tag{5–1}$$

and the kinetic energy is

$$T = \tfrac{1}{2}m_a \dot{x}_a^2 + \tfrac{1}{2}m_b \dot{x}_b^2 \tag{5–2}$$

Newton's equations are given by

$$\frac{d}{dt}\left(\frac{\partial T}{\partial \dot{x}_a}\right) = -\frac{\partial V}{\partial x_a} \qquad \frac{d}{dt}\left(\frac{\partial T}{\partial \dot{x}_b}\right) = -\frac{\partial V}{\partial x_b} \tag{5–3}$$

so that

$$\ddot{x}_a = (F/m_a)[(x_b - x_{b0}) - (x_a - x_{a0})]$$
$$\ddot{x}_b = -(F/m_b)[(x_b - x_{b0}) - (x_a - x_{a0})]$$

(5-4)

The natural modes of motion are assumed to be periodic, and the solution of the problem is to discover what periodic functions satisfy Newton's equation for the system of interest. A trial solution is assumed:

$$x_a - x_{a0} = L_a \sin (2\pi\nu t + \delta)$$
$$x_b - x_{b0} = L_b \sin (2\pi\nu t + \delta)$$

(5-5)

where L_a, L_b, and δ are constants, and ν is the unknown vibration frequency of the normal mode. Equations 5 are differentiated twice with respect to time:

$$\ddot{x}_a = -4\pi^2\nu^2 L_a \sin (2\pi\nu t + \delta) = -\lambda(x_a - x_{a0})$$
$$\ddot{x}_b = -4\pi^2\nu^2 L_b \sin (2\pi\nu t + \delta) = -\lambda(x_b - x_{b0})$$

(5-6)

where λ is defined as $4\pi^2\nu^2$. Equations 6 are substituted in Eq. 4 and terms are regrouped:

$$(F/m_a - \lambda)(x_a - x_{a0}) - (F/m_a)(x_b - x_{b0}) = 0$$
$$-(F/m_b)(x_a - x_{a0}) + (F/m_b - \lambda)(x_b - x_{b0}) = 0$$

(5-7)

Equation 5 was simply assumed; from Eq. 7 one sees that the assumption is valid only for such values of λ as satisfy the equation

$$\begin{vmatrix} (F/m_a - \lambda) & -(F/m_a) \\ -(F/m_b) & (F/m_b - \lambda) \end{vmatrix} = 0$$

(5-8)

The determinant gives a polynomial in λ:

$$\lambda^2 - \lambda(F/m_a + F/m_b) = 0$$

(5-9)

or in terms of reduced mass (Eq. 3–11):

$$\lambda(\lambda - F/\mu) = 0$$

(5-10)

The two solutions of Eq. 10 are

$$\lambda = 0 \qquad \lambda = F/\mu$$

(5-11)

The physical interpretation of each of these values of λ is found by substituting it in Eq. 7. The zero value of λ gives

$$x_a - x_{a0} = x_b - x_{b0}$$

(5-12)

from each of the two Eqs. 7.   The motion has zero frequency, and it represents equal increments in x_a and x_b.   Clearly, this normal mode is the translation of the molecule as a whole.   The second λ in Eq. 11, when inserted in either of the two Eqs. 7, gives

$$\frac{m_a x_a + m_b x_b}{m_a + m_b} = \frac{m_a x_{a0} + m_b x_{b0}}{m_a + m_b} \tag{5-13}$$

that is, this normal mode is one that conserves the center of mass.   This normal mode is the vibration of the nuclei with frequency

$$\nu = (1/2\ \pi)\lambda^{1/2} = (1/2\ \pi)(F/\mu)^{1/2} \tag{5-14}$$

and with relative amplitudes

$$L_a/L_b = -m_b/m_a \tag{5-15}$$

One reason for carrying through this rather trivial example in great detail is to show that the method picks out "zero-frequency" normal modes, translations or rotations, as well as the normal modes of vibration with positive eigenvalues λ.   Also, λ can be negative as well as zero or positive. A positive λ is associated with small displacements from a potential-energy minimum, a zero λ is associated with a flat potential-energy region, and a negative λ is associated with a potential-energy maximum.   When a "frequency" is evaluated from Eq. 14 for a negative λ, one formally obtains an "imaginary frequency."   A real frequency in Eq. 5 gives a real sinusoidal vibration, a zero frequency in Eq. 5 gives free unrestricted translation or rotation, and an imaginary frequency gives the exponentially divergent hyperbolic sine function (unstable system).

(ii) Molecules in General

The method used above for the diatomic molecule involves an overwhelming amount of computation if extended to more complicated molecules, even a nonlinear triatomic molecule.   The method of vibrational analysis of complex molecules is worked out in detail by Wilson, Decius, and Cross, and in particular they show how very large molecules can be simply treated if they are sufficiently symmetrical.   The "zero-frequency" translations and rotations are separated and one considers the motions of internal coordinates relative to a fixed center of mass.   For the linear triatomic complex, including bends, the $\mathbf{G}$-matrix in internal coordinates is given by Eq. 3-32, the $\mathbf{F}$-matrix by Eq. 4-39, and equations for the frequencies are given in Appendix D.   In general, the normal modes are found by solution of the secular equation

$$|\mathbf{FG} - \mathbf{E}\lambda| = 0 \tag{5-16}$$

The expansion of the secular Eq. 16 gives a polynomial in λ, the roots of which are the eigenvalues $\lambda_1, \lambda_2 \cdots \lambda_i \cdots \lambda_n$. From simple properties of determinants one gets the following general, useful relations:

$$\sum_1^n \lambda_i = \text{trace } \mathbf{FG} \qquad (5\text{--}17)$$

$$\prod^n \lambda_i = |F|\,|G| \qquad (5\text{--}18)$$

B. SETS OF NORMAL COORDINATES

For further discussion it is not necessary to evaluate normal coordinates for special cases, but a few of their general properties are important. Near the point of extremum, the energy of the molecule is separable in normal coordinates

$$2V = \sum_i \lambda_i m_i Q_i^2 \qquad (5\text{--}19)$$

$$2T = \sum_i P_i^2/m_i \qquad (5\text{--}20)$$

where Q_i is one of the set of normal-mode coordinates, P_i is the conjugate momentum, and m_i is found from Eq. 3-29. With separable energies as in Eqs. 19 and 20, Newton's equations of motion are separable, and according to classical mechanics each normal mode moves independently of all others. Any infinitesimal motion of the molecule or complex can be expressed as a linear combination of normal-mode motions. For motions of large amplitude the higher-order terms in the potential-energy function (compare Eq. 4-35) may not be negligible compared to quadratic terms. In the dynamics of molecules, the first effect of this "anharmonicity" is that the motions of the normal modes are no longer independent, and energy is exchanged between the normal modes. In this case the normal-mode *coordinates* are still very convenient for describing the motions of the system. For quite large deviations from a point of extremum, the motions of the system are in general non-separable and are not conveniently expressed in normal-mode coordinates. Even so, each *set* of normal-mode coordinates, the four from Fig. 4–3 for example, is a complete coordinate system, and any trajectory in Fig. 4–3 could be described by any one of the four normal coordinate systems. Description of a trajectory in terms of normal coordinates is possible anywhere, but it is natural and simple only if the trajectory is in the general vicinity of the point of extremum on which it is based.

Normal coordinates are discussed from another point of view in Appendix C.

PROBLEM

For the linear three-atom system constrained to remain in one dimension,

$$a \underset{R_1}{\rule{3cm}{0.4pt}} x \underset{R_2}{\rule{3cm}{0.4pt}} b$$

the potential energy in internal coordinates is

$$V = \tfrac{1}{2}(F_{11}r_1^2 + 2F_{12}r_1r_2 + F_{22}r_2^2)$$

where r_1 is the displacement of R_1 from its equilibrium value, and the kinetic energy is

$$T = \frac{1}{2M}[m_a(m_x + m_b)\dot{r}_1^2 + 2m_a m_b \dot{r}_1 \dot{r}_2 + m_b(m_x + m_a)\dot{r}_2^2]$$

where $M = m_a + m_x + m_b$.

(1) Derive algebraic expressions for the frequencies of the two normal modes. (The answer can be found in Appendix D.)

(2) Evaluate the frequency in units of cm^{-1} for each of the following models:

Molecule	m_a	m_x	m_b	F_{11}	F_{22}	F_{12}
O—C—O	16	12	16	15.5	15.5	1.30
N—N—O	14	14	16	17.88	11.39	1.36
H—C—N	1	12	14	5.70	18.6	−0.22
H $\cdots$ H $\cdots$ H	1	1	1	0.94	0.94	1.31
Cl $\cdots$ H $\cdots$ H	35	1	1	0.572	1.559	1.499

where masses are in atomic mass units and force constants are in units of 10^5 dynes/cm.

(3) For these models evaluate the slopes c (Chapter 3) of the normal coordinates in the R_1–R_2 plane.

(4) What is the effective mass for each normal mode of vibration?

(5) In "Molecular Vibrations" by Wilson, Decius, and Cross, look up the bending force constant and bond lengths for HCN and evaluate the bending frequency.

6
Chemical Equilibrium[43,44,45,46]

A. PARTITION FUNCTIONS IN NORMAL COORDINATES

For independent atoms or molecules X, at equilibrium the relative number per unit volume in one quantum state i to another quantum state j is the well-known Boltzmann relation:

$$\frac{[X_i]}{[X_j]} = \frac{\exp\,(-\varepsilon_i/kT)}{\exp\,(-\varepsilon_j/kT)} \tag{6–1}$$

If ω_i quantum states have the same energy ε_i and if ω_j quantum states have the same energy ε_j, the ratio of concentration of species in energy level i to energy level j is

$$\frac{[X_i]}{[X_j]} = \frac{\omega_i \exp\,(-\varepsilon_i/kT)}{\omega_j \exp\,(-\varepsilon_j/kT)} \tag{6–2}$$

The fraction of all species in energy level i is found by summing the denominator of Eq. 2 over all states:

$$\frac{[X_i]}{[X]} = \frac{\omega_i \exp\,(-\varepsilon_i/kT)}{f_X} \tag{6–3}$$

The denominator in Eq. 3 is the "partition function"

$$f_X = \sum_{j=0}^{\infty} \omega_j \exp\,(-\varepsilon_j/kT) \tag{6–4}$$

The Boltzmann factor $e^{-\varepsilon_i/kT}$ varies in value from zero to one; from Eq. 1 or 3 one sees that it may be interpreted as the "availability of state i at the temperature T." The partition function is a number, equal to or greater than one; the partition function may be interpreted as the "number of quantum states available to the molecule at the temperature T."

The fraction of species in a restricted range of quantum numbers, between M_1 and M_2, is found by summing the numerator of Eq. 3 over the range of interest:

$$\frac{[X_M]}{[X]} = \sum_{i=M_1}^{i=M_2} \omega_i \exp\,(-\varepsilon_i/kT)/f_X \tag{6–5}$$

If a discrete variable G_i over a set of states $i = 1, 2, 3 \cdots$ is associated with a population whose relative distribution over the states i is given by ρ_i, the general definition of its average value is

$$\langle G \rangle = \sum_i G_i \rho_i / \sum_i \rho_i \tag{6-6}$$

The general chemical reaction at equilibrium may be written as

$$x\text{A} + y\text{B} = z\text{C} + w\text{D} \tag{6-7}$$

$$K_c = \frac{f_\text{C}^z f_\text{D}^w}{f_\text{A}^x f_\text{B}^y} (n_\text{A}V)^{-\Delta N} \tag{6-8}$$

where $\Delta N = (z + w) - (x + y)$, the change in mole-number for the reaction. The equilibrium constant is in units of molecules per unit volume if Avogadro's number n_A is omitted from Eq. 8. The equilibrium constant is expressed in units of atmospheres by use of $PV = RT$ per mole:

$$K_p = K_c (RT)^{\Delta N} \tag{6-9}$$

$$= \frac{f_\text{C}^z f_\text{D}^w}{f_\text{A}^x f_\text{B}^y} \left(\frac{RT}{n_\text{A}V} \right)^{\Delta N} \tag{6-10}$$

The symmetry and simplicity of Eq. 8 or 10 depend on choosing the *same origin of energy* for both reactants and products. It is usually more convenient to choose the lowest energy level of each molecule as the zero point of energy for the partition function f of that molecule. If the difference in these lowest energies (relative, say, to atoms at rest an infinite distance apart) is factored out:

$$\Delta_r \varepsilon_0 = z\varepsilon_{0\text{C}} + w\varepsilon_{0\text{D}} - x\varepsilon_{0\text{A}} - y\varepsilon_{0\text{B}} \tag{6-11}$$

where ε_0 is the energy required to break the molecule down to its atoms, then partition functions may be evaluated relative to the natural origin of energy for each molecule, and Eq. 8 becomes

$$K_c = \frac{f_\text{C}^z f_\text{D}^w}{f_\text{A}^x f_\text{B}^y} \frac{\exp\left(-\Delta_r \varepsilon_0 / kT\right)}{(Vn_\text{A})^{\Delta N}} \tag{6-12}$$

with similar relations for Eq. 10. The exponential term, of course, can be expressed in molal form, $\exp\left(-\Delta_r E_0^\circ / RT\right)$.

If, and only if, the energy of a molecule can be expressed as the sum of independent types of energy:

$$\varepsilon = \varepsilon_\alpha + \varepsilon_\beta + \varepsilon_\gamma + \varepsilon_\delta + \cdots \tag{6-13}$$

the partition function of the molecule may be expressed as the product of partition functions for different energy types:

$$f = f_\alpha f_\beta f_\gamma f_\delta \cdots \tag{6-14}$$

To the perfect-gas approximation one can always separate translational energy from internal (electronic, vibrational, rotational, etc.) energy, so that

$$f = f_t f_{\text{int}} \tag{6–15}$$

Separability of energy is most nearly accomplished in terms of electronic energy and the $3N$ normal modes of the molecule: 3 translations, 3 rotations or 2 rotations if linear, $3N - 6$ or $3N - 5$ vibrations including internal rotations (nuclear spin modes are omitted for chemical reactions at ordinary temperatures). The notation often used to show each coordinate in the partition-function product is

$$f = f_t^3 f_r^3 f_v^{3N-6} f_e \qquad \text{nonlinear} \tag{6–16}$$

$$f = f_t^3 f_r^2 f_v^{3N-5} f_e \qquad \text{linear} \tag{6–17}$$

The algebraic and numerical values associated with partition functions in normal coordinates will be reviewed. These partition functions are simply related to the "Boltzmann-average" de Broglie wavelength (Eq. 2-3). The classical translational partition function for a molecule of mass m and temperature T, and in physical volume V, is

$$f_t^3 = V/\Lambda_t^3$$
$$\Lambda_t = h/(2\pi m k T)^{1/2} \tag{6–18}$$

In units of gram-molar mass M, $T°K$, and per cubic centimeter, the translational partition function is

$$f_t^3 = 1.88 \times 10^{20} (MT)^{3/2} \tag{6–19}$$

The classical rotational partition functions are

$$f_r^2 = (4\pi/\sigma)/\Lambda_\Phi^2 \qquad \text{linear}$$
$$\Lambda_\Phi = h/(2\pi I k T)^{1/2} \tag{6–20}$$

where the generalized de Broglie wavelength is really a "de Broglie angle" in this case. If the moment of inertia is expressed in units of gram-atomic mass and angstrom units, the numerical values are $f^2 = 0.0412 I T/\sigma$. For nonlinear molecules, the corresponding expressions are

$$f_r^3 = (8\pi^2/\sigma)/(\Lambda_1 \Lambda_2 \Lambda_3)$$
$$\Lambda_1 = h/(2\pi I_1 k T)^{1/2} \qquad \text{etc.} \tag{6–21}$$
$$f_r^3 = 0.0148 (I_1 I_2 I_3)^{1/2} T^{3/2}/\sigma \qquad \text{nonlinear}$$

The quantum form of the vibrational partition function with lowest quantum state as origin of energy is

$$f_v = (1 - e^{-u})^{-1}$$
$$u = (h\nu/kT) = 1.4387\omega/T \tag{6–22}$$

where ω is the vibration frequency in cm^{-1}. In classical mechanics, the "Boltzmann average" of the vibrational amplitude is

$$l = \int_{-\infty}^{\infty} \exp\left(-FQ^2/2kT\right) dQ = (2\pi kT/F)^{1/2}$$
$$= 0.009312(T/F)^{1/2} \qquad (6\text{--}23)$$

where F is in units of 10^5 dynes/cm. The de Broglie wavelength for a normal mode of vibration is $h/(2\pi mkT)^{1/2}$ where m is the effective mass of the normal coordinate. The vibration frequency is related to the normal-mode force constant and mass by

$$2\pi\nu = \lambda^{1/2} = (F/m)^{1/2} \qquad (6\text{--}24)$$

The high-temperature, classical-mechanical limit of the vibrational partition function is

$$f = u^{-1} = kT/h\nu = l/\Lambda \qquad (6\text{--}25)$$

Thus, for vibrations, as for translations (Eq. 18) and rotations (Eqs. 20 and 21), the classical partition function per degree of freedom has the form of the ratio of maximum available generalized "length" to the de Broglie wavelength, formally expressed as the product of "free length per de Broglie wavelength":

$$f_{cl} = \prod^{3N} L_i/\Lambda_i \qquad (6\text{--}26)$$

The low-temperature, quantum-mechanical form of the vibrational partition function is given by Eq. 22 where origin of energy is the lowest quantum level. For many purposes it is more convenient to locate the origin of energy at the minimum point of the potential-energy curve, and this is done by multiplying each vibrational partition function by a Boltzmann factor in terms of the zero-point energy $h\nu/2$:

$$f_{qu} = \frac{e^{-u/2}}{1 - e^{-u}} = \frac{1/2}{\sinh u/2} \qquad (6\text{--}27)$$

For vibrational degrees of freedom the ratio, Γ, of quantum to classical partition functions is Eq. 27 divided by Eq. 25:

$$\Gamma = \left(\frac{f_{qu}}{f_{cl}}\right)_v = \frac{ue^{-u/2}}{1 - e^{-u}} = \frac{u/2}{\sinh u/2} \qquad (6\text{--}28)$$

For small values of u (low frequency, high temperature) the reciprocal of the quantum correction factor becomes

$$\Gamma^{-1} = 1 + \frac{u^2}{24} + \frac{u^4}{1920} + \frac{u^6}{7!\,2^6} \cdots \qquad (6\text{--}29)$$

and Γ approaches unity. For large values of u (high frequency, low temperature) the quantum-to-classical ratio approaches

$$\Gamma = ue^{-u/2} \tag{6-30}$$

Low frequencies, bends, wags, ring distortion, torsion, etc., which usually are difficult to know accurately, contribute a factor of one to $(f_{qu}/f_{cl})_v$. High frequencies, above 700 cm^{-1}, which are easy to measure and to associate with features of molecular structure contribute an important factor, between 0 and 1, Eq. 28. In the quantum-mechanical partition function itself, Eq. 22, the reverse situation applies: high-frequency, easily observed vibrations contribute a factor of one; the difficultly measured, hard-to-know, low-frequency vibrations contribute large factors to the partition function. In section C (below), there will be reviewed the method that uses Eq. 28, not 27 or 22, in the complete partition function.[47]

B. CLASSICAL-MECHANICAL PHASE INTEGRAL BASED ON CARTESIAN COORDINATES

In classical mechanics the state of a molecular system is given in terms of "phase space." The position of an atom, for example, is given by a set of coordinates q, and the motion is given by the conjugate momenta p. For a molecule of N atoms in three-dimensional laboratory space, the phase hyperspace consists of $6N$ mutually orthogonal axes, and a single point in this space gives the position and momentum of each atom in the molecule. For a large number, n, of molecules, phase space has $6Nn$ dimensions; and one point specifies the position and motion of every atom in every molecule.

The simultaneous specification of the exact location and momentum of a particle is in conflict with the uncertainty principle of quantum mechanics. However, there is no conflict with quantum mechanics so long as phase space in each dimension is subdivided no finer than into units of area h, Planck's constant. If the molecular phase space for each q and p is subdivided into a net in which each cell $dq\,dp$ is equal to h, then each $6N$-dimensional cell may be treated as a unit i, and Eq. 1 follows. If a small element of phase space of energy ε_i has dimensions $dq\,dp$ and if the area is greater than Planck's constant, the ratio $dq\,dp/h$ has properties similar to ω_i in Eqs. 2, 3, or 4.

It is convenient to abbreviate the energy of a particular cell of multidimensional phase space as

$$\varepsilon_i = \varepsilon(q_1, p_1, q_2 \cdots p_{3N}) \tag{6-31}$$

and the volume element associated with this energy as

$$d\tau_i = dq_1\,dp_1\,dq_2 \cdots dp_{3N} \tag{6-32}$$

The partition function of Eq. 4 is replaced by the classical phase integral

$$f_X = 1/h^{3N} \int \cdots \int e^{-\varepsilon/kT}\,d\tau \tag{6-33}$$

The fraction of species in the cell i is

$$\frac{]X_i]}{]X]} = \frac{(1/h^{3N}) \exp{(-\varepsilon_i/kT)} \, d\tau_i}{f_X} \qquad (6\text{–}34)$$

The fraction of species in a restricted range of phase space is the integral of the numerator of Eq. 34 over the restricted range of interest (compare Eq. 5). If $G(q_1 \cdots p_{3N})$ is associated with a population whose relative distribution over phase space is $\rho(q_1 \cdots p_{3N}) \, d\tau$, the general definition of its average value is

$$\langle G \rangle = \frac{\int \cdots \int G\rho \, d\tau}{\int \cdots \int \rho \, d\tau} \qquad (6\text{–}35)$$

For chemical equilibrium, Eq. 12 (with f given by Eq. 33) follows directly.

In cartesian coordinates, the total energy is expressed as

$$\varepsilon = \sum_{\alpha=1}^{N} \frac{1}{2m_\alpha} (p_x^2 + p_y^2 + p_z^2) + V(x_1 \cdots z_N) \qquad (6\text{–}36)$$

where α refers to the atoms. The phase integral (Eq. 33) can immediately be evaluated for the momenta

$$f_{\text{cl}} = \prod_{\alpha=1}^{N} \frac{(2\pi m_\alpha kT)^{3/2}}{h^3} Z \qquad (6\text{–}37)$$

where the "configurational integral " Z is

$$Z = \int \cdots \int_{3N} \exp{[-V(x_1 \cdots z_N)/kT]} \, dx_1 \cdots dz_N \qquad (6\text{–}38)$$

Equation 37 has a simple interpretation:

$$f_{\text{cl}} = Z \bigg/ \prod_{\alpha}^{N} \Lambda_\alpha^3 \qquad (6\text{–}39)$$

The configurational integral has dimensions of volume raised to the power N, and it can be interpreted as "free volume" in N-dimensional space. The denominator of Eq. 39 is a product of volumes, one for each atom, and each volume is a cubic de Broglie wavelength. In N-dimensional space, the partition function is the volume accessible to the molecule divided by the volume of a "cubic" de Broglie wavelength. The "number of accessible quantum states" (Eq. 4) is equal to the accessible volume of configuration space in units of "cubic" de Broglie wavelengths (Eq. 39).

C.   PHASE INTEGRAL BASED ON VALENCE-BOND COORDINATES

The phase integral, f_{cl} of Eq. 37, is the classical-mechanical limit of the quantum-mechanical partition function, Eq. 4. The Hamiltonian function can be based on any desired coordinate system, for example, cartesian coordinates, normal-mode coordinates, or valence-bond coordinates. There are advantages and disadvantages, conveniences and inconveniences associated with each of these coordinate systems, as indicated by this comparison:

	Cartesian	Normal mode	Valence bond
Form of V	Hard	Easy, Eq. 5-19	Easy, Eq. 4-39
Form of T	Easy	Easy, Eq. 5-20	Hard, Eq. 3-26
To find coordinate	Easy	Hard, Eq. 5-16	Easy, Fig. 3-1
Phase integral	Hard	Easy	Hard

Actually, the difficulty in expressing kinetic energy in valence-bond coordinates has been largely removed by E. B. Wilson's table of **G**-matrix elements.[28] A similar development[47] leads to a table of Jacobian functions J that makes it extremely easy to evaluate the classical-mechanical phase integral in valence-bond coordinates; a review of this derivation is the subject matter of this section.

The physical nature of the partition function in local, valence-bond coordinates will be reviewed for a nonlinear triatomic molecule. As in other coordinate systems, the dimensionless partition function may be interpreted as the free volume divided by the volume of a generalized "cubic" de Broglie wavelength. A molecule of interest has N atoms in the volume V. If there were no forces between the atoms, each of them could move independently throughout the container, so that V_α for each atom is V and Z is V^N. In the molecule, one atom may be still regarded as "free to wander about the whole system, dragging the molecule with it."[43] Overall rotations of the molecule give the second atom relative to the first a spherical shell of area $4\pi R_{12}^2$, and vibration of amplitude l_{12} along the bond gives a "free volume" of $4\pi R_{12}^2 l_{12}$. The third atom is described by the third Euler angle, rotation about which gives a circle of perimeter $2\pi R_{23} \sin \Phi$; vibration along the bond R_{23} gives a vibrational amplitude l_{23}; and angular vibration l_Φ gives atom 3 a vibration amplitude $l_\Phi R_{23}$. Thus atom 3 has a "doughnut"-shaped volume, $2\pi R_{23} \sin \Phi \, l_{23} l_\Phi R_{23}$. The classical-mechanical partition function is thus

$$f_{\text{cl}} = \frac{V}{\Lambda_1} \frac{4\pi R_{12}^2 l_{12}}{\Lambda^2} \frac{2\pi R_{23}^2 \sin \Phi \, l_{23} l_\Phi}{\Lambda_3} \tag{6–40}$$

where the de Broglie wavelengths are those of the atoms.

There is no potential energy (aside from gas imperfections) associated with translation or rotation of a molecule; thus for any linear molecule the partition function will contain a factor $V4\pi$; and for any nonlinear molecule the partition function has a factor $V8\pi^2$. In fact, it is readily shown that the partition function is proportional to a product of functions, one for each atom, that depend only on geometry and not on mass or potential-energy function.

The complete classical-mechanical partition function has the same value, regardless of the coordinate system used for its evaluation. In normal-mode coordinates, f_{cl} for a given electronic state of a nonlinear molecule is given by Eqs. 16, 18, 21, and 25; in cartesian coordinates, f_{cl} is given by Eqs. 37, 38, and 39. Thus one has the relation

$$f_{cl} = (Z/h^{3N})(2\pi kT)^{3N/2} \prod_{\alpha}^{N} m_{\alpha}^{3/2} \qquad (6\text{--}41)$$

$$= V8\pi^2 (2\pi kT/h^2)^3 M^{3/2} |I|^{1/2} \prod_{i}^{3N-6} u_i^{-1} \qquad (6\text{--}42)$$

The vibration frequencies in $u = h\nu/kT$ are the only quantities in these equations that depend on both mass and force constants. However, by use of Eqs. 6–22, 6–23, 5–14, and 5–18, one can separate these variables:

$$\prod^{3N-6} u_i^{-1} = \frac{(2\pi kT/h)^{3N-6}}{|F|^{1/2} |G|^{1/2}} \qquad (6\text{--}43)$$

Upon eliminating the product of u between Eqs. 42 and 43, one can rearrange terms to obtain a considerable separation of variables and two definitions of a new function J:

$$J = |F|^{1/2} Z/(2\pi kT)^{(3N-6)/2} \qquad (6\text{--}44)$$

$$= \frac{V8\pi^2 M^{3/2} |I|^{1/2}}{|G|^{1/2} \prod^{N} m_{\alpha}^{3/2}} \qquad (6\text{--}45)$$

The function J as defined by Eq. 44 seems to depend on force constants, temperature, and structure; but it does not depend on any kind of mass. The function J as defined by Eq. 45 seems to depend on mass and structure, but it does not depend on temperature or force constant. Therefore, the function J is not a function of force constants nor of temperature nor of mass. The determinant of the **F**-matrix in Eq. 44 must identically cancel from terms implicit in Z. Similarly, for any molecule there are systematic cancellations such that the complicated function of masses in Eq. 45, $|I|^{1/2} M^{3/2}/|G|^{1/2} \prod m_{\alpha}^{3/2}$, is independent of mass. Therefore, J is a function of geometrical structure alone. As shown in the reference,[47] the function J is a product of terms, one for each atom:

$$J = \prod_{\alpha=1}^{N} J_{\alpha} \qquad (6\text{--}46)$$

For the first atom, J_1 is the volume of the container. For each successive atom, the term is the "box product"

$$J_{\alpha} = (\mathbf{s}_{i\alpha} \times \mathbf{s}_{j\alpha} \cdot \mathbf{s}_{k\alpha})^{-1} \qquad (6\text{--}47)$$

where the vectors $\mathbf{s}$ are defined by E. B. Wilson, Jr.

In valence-bond coordinates, bond lengths, and bond angles, the first few J functions are listed in Table 1. For additional atoms added linearly the factor is R^2, for additional atoms added nonlinearly the factor is $R^2 \sin \Phi$, etc.

From Eqs. 44 and 45, one sees that the configuration integral has the simple, easily evaluated form

$$Z = \frac{(2\pi kT)^{(3N-6)/2}}{|F|^{1/2}} \prod^{N} J_\alpha \qquad (6\text{--}48)$$

TABLE 6–I

Jacobian Factors for Simple Molecular Structures

Atom	Configuration	Coordinates	J
1	•	x, y, z	V
2	•——•	$R_{12}, \Theta_{ex}, \Phi_{ex}$	$4\pi R_{12}^2$
3	•—•—•	$R_{23}, \Phi_{123}, \Phi'_{123}$	R_{23}^2
		R_{23}, Φ_{123}, Φ	$2\pi R_{23}^2 \sin \Phi_{123}$
		R_{23}, R_{13}, Φ	$2\pi (R_{23} R_{13}/R_{12})$
4	•—•—•—•	$R_{34}, \Phi_{234}, \Phi'_{234}$	R_{34}^2
		R_{34}, Φ_{234}, τ	$R_{34}^2 \sin \Phi_{234}$
		$R_{24}, \Phi_{124}, \Phi_{234}$	$R_{24}^2/\sin \Phi_{341}$

If the force field for the molecule is given by the simple valence-bond model, that is, diagonal force constant matrix, then each force constant $F^{1/2}$ can be associated with one factor of $(2\pi kT)^{1/2}$ to give a vibrational amplitude l, (Eq. 23). In any case, the force constant matrix can be diagonalized, but in the determinant may appear a factor

$$|F| = w^2 \prod^{3N-6} F_{ss} \qquad (6\text{--}49)$$

Thus, in general, the complete classical-mechanical partition function is

$$f_{cl} = w^{-1} \prod_{s=1}^{3N-6} l_s \prod_{\alpha=1}^{N} J_\alpha/\Lambda_\alpha^3 \qquad (6\text{--}50)$$

Aside from the factor w, which is of the order of magnitude of unity, the classical partition function is a product over local properties, atom by atom.

This development is closely related to the Teller-Redlich product rule.[48] The rule states that for a molecule X and its isotopically substituted species X', the product of all vibration frequencies of X and X' are related as

$$\frac{\prod\limits^{3N-6} \nu_i}{\prod\limits^{3N-6} \nu_i'} = \left(\frac{M}{M'}\right)^{3/2} \left(\frac{|I|}{|I'|}\right)^{1/2} \prod\limits^{N} \left(\frac{m'}{m}\right)_\alpha^{3/2} \qquad (6\text{--}51)$$

The present derivation gives the factor cancelled between numerator and denominator on the right-hand side of Eq. 51, and thus it gives the absolute value of the product rule.

$$\prod\limits^{3N-6} \nu_i = \left\{\frac{8\pi^2 V \, |F|^{1/2}}{(2\pi)^{3N-6} J}\right\} \frac{M^{3/2} \, |I|^{1/2}}{\prod\limits^{N} m_\alpha^{3/2}} \qquad (6\text{--}52)$$

D. COMPLETE PARTITION FUNCTION IN TERMS OF LOCAL PROPERTIES

The complete partition function in quantum-mechanical form is abbreviated as f_{qu}, and the complete partition function in classical mechanical form is written as f_{cl}. The following identity is obvious:

$$f_{qu} = f_{cl}(f_{qu}/f_{cl}) \qquad (6\text{--}53)$$

If the partition function is expressed in $3N$ normal-mode coordinates, the ratio in Eq. 53 is

$$\frac{f_{qu}}{f_{cl}} = \left(\frac{f_{qu}}{f_{cl}}\right)_t \left(\frac{f_{qu}}{f_{cl}}\right)_r \left(\frac{f_{qu}}{f_{cl}}\right)_v \frac{f_e}{\sigma} \qquad (6\text{--}54)$$

For ordinary molecules at ordinary temperatures the quantum and classical partition functions for translations and rotations are the same, and the ratio of vibrational expressions is given by Γ (Eqs. 28, 29, or 30). The term σ gives the effect of symmetry on the number of distinguishable quantum states. For example, σ is: 1 for HCl or HD; 2 for H_2, Cl_2, H_2O, HC≡CH, OCOCO, $ClNO_2$; 3 for NH_3; 6 for symmetrical NO_3; 12 for CH_4. It is "the number of indistinguishable positions into which the molecule can be turned by simple rigid rotations."[49] The definition of the electronic partition function is

$$f_e = \omega_0 + \omega_1 \exp\left(-\varepsilon_1/kT\right) + \omega_2 \exp\left(-\varepsilon_2/kT\right) + \cdots \qquad (6\text{--}55)$$

Use of this partition function in Eq. 54 or 17 or 16 is valid only if all the vibration frequencies and moments of inertia of the excited electronic states are the same as those of the ground state (compare Eq. 13). For most excited electronic states, the force constants and bond distances differ from the ground state. The preferred procedure is to regard each electronic state as a separate species with different vibrational and geometric properties. (Of course, one uses the same zero point of energy for each state so that a factor of $e^{-\varepsilon_1/kT}$ appears in front of the partition function for the independent excited-state species). For the present discussion, the electronic partition function is regarded as the multiplicity of the ground state, ω_0, although the case for excited electronic states can be handled.

The complete quantum-mechanical partition function for a nonlinear molecule in its ground electronic state is thus

$$f_{\text{qu}} = \left(\frac{\omega_0}{\sigma w}\right) \underbrace{\prod_{}^{N} J_\alpha \Lambda_\alpha^{-3}}_{\substack{\text{atoms}}} \underbrace{\prod_{}^{3N-6} l_s}_{\substack{\text{bonds} \\ \text{and} \\ \text{angles}}} \underbrace{\prod_{}^{3N-6} \Gamma_Q}_{\substack{\text{normal} \\ \text{modes}}} \qquad (6\text{–}56)$$

where ω_0 is the multiplicity of the ground electronic state, σ is the complete rotational symmetry number, w (Eq. 49) is the factor that may be required to diagonalize the force constant determinant, J_α (Eq. 47 or Table 6-1) depends only on molecular structure, Λ_α (Eq. 2-3) is the atomic "Boltzmann-average" de Broglie wavelength, l_s (Eq. 23) is the "Boltzmann-average" classical-mechanical vibrational amplitude, and Γ_Q (Eq. 28) is the quantum correction factor for vibrations, which differs from unity only for high-frequency vibrations or rather for high values of ν/T. For a linear molecule, replace $3N - 6$ by $3N - 5$.

Some internal degrees of freedom may be internal rotations instead of vibrations. For free internal rotations, one factor l in Eq. 56 is omitted and $(2\pi/\sigma_i)$ appears in its place, where σ_i is the symmetry number of the internal rotations. For highly restricted internal rotations, the motion is a torsional vibration with a vibrational amplitude of the same form as Eq. 23. For the difficult intermediate cases, see Chapter 12 and references cited there.

The practical advantage of the partition function as a product of local properties is brought out by considering an example of chemical equilibrium:

$$A + B \rightleftharpoons X \qquad (6\text{–}57)$$

The equilibrium constant is given by Eq. 13. Since reactants and products have an identical set of atoms, the atomic de Broglie wavelengths in Eq. 56 all cancel. Defining W as $(f_e/\sigma w)_X/(f_e/\sigma w)_A(f_e/\sigma w)_B$, one obtains for the equilibrium constant

$$K = W \frac{\overbrace{\prod^{3N_X-6} l_s}}{\underbrace{\prod^{3N_A-6} l_s \prod^{3N_B-6} l_s}_{\text{bonds and angles}}} \frac{\overbrace{\prod^{3N_X-6} \Gamma_Q}}{\underbrace{\prod^{3N_A-6} \Gamma_Q \prod^{3N_B-6} \Gamma_Q}_{\text{normal modes}}} \frac{\overbrace{\prod^{N_X} J_\alpha} \exp^{(-\Delta\varepsilon_e/kT)}}{\underbrace{\prod^{N_A} J_\alpha \prod^{N_B} J_\alpha}_{\text{atoms}}} \qquad (6\text{–}58)$$

If, for example, A and thus X are large complicated molecules, there will be many local degrees of freedom (bonds and angles) that are essentially the same in reactant and product; some bonds and angles near the reaction site will be strongly changed; and, in the product, some new bonds and angles may appear. Similarly, but less definitely, the vibrational frequencies may be classified as unchanged, changed, or new. The product terms in Eq. 58 may be regrouped as

$$\Pi \left(\frac{l'}{l}\right)_{***} \left(\frac{l'}{l}\right)_{**} l_* \Pi \left(\frac{J'}{J}\right)_{***} \left(\frac{J'}{J}\right)_{**} \Pi \left(\frac{\Gamma'}{\Gamma}\right)_{***} \left(\frac{\Gamma'}{\Gamma}\right)_{**} \Gamma'_* \qquad (6\text{--}59)$$

where prime denotes "product," *** denotes "unchanged," ** denotes "that change," and * stands for "new." The unchanged vibrational amplitudes cancel identically without ever having to be evaluated; the force constants that change contribute easily evaluated ratios; and the new bonds and angles contribute important new terms. The unchanged geometrical groups give identical J factors in numerator and denominator, and the bonds and angles that change give easily evaluated ratios. Since normal coordinates in principle embrace the entire molecule, purely local analysis applicable to the other product of terms does not apply. However, as an approximation, groups of unchanging geometry and force constants can be blocked off and regarded as rigid bodies in an approximate analysis of normal coordinates that change. After an analysis of "degrees of freedom that change" in a chemical reaction, it is instructive to symbolize the equilibrium constant as

$$K = W \left(\Pi \frac{l'}{l} \frac{\Gamma'}{\Gamma} \frac{J'}{J}\right)_{**} \underset{\text{new}}{(\Pi \, l\Gamma)_*} e^{-\Delta \varepsilon_e / kT} \qquad (6\text{--}60)$$

that change   new

This expression clearly shows the factors responsible for the magnitude of an equilibrium constant in terms of structures and force fields of reactants and products at the site of reaction. It avoids the computational complication of the usual formulation in terms of moments of inertia for the entire molecule that identically cancel a series of terms in the vibration frequencies.

PROBLEM

For the chemical reaction

$$H_2 + I_2 = 2HI$$

evaluate the equilibrium constant at 400°K by (1) partition functions in terms of normal coordinates and (2) in terms of local properties with quantum correction factors. Molecular data useful for this problem are:

	H_2	I_2	HI
R_e, Å	0.7417	2.667	1.604
D_e, e.v.	4.476	1.5417	3.056
ω, cm^{-1}	4395.2	214.6	2309.5
M, a.m.u.	2.016	254	128
f_e	1	1	1

7

Bimolecular Collision Dynamics[29,35,50]

A. ELEMENTARY KINETIC THEORY OF GASES

To the extent needed for this discussion, the elementary kinetic theory of gases is presented in textbooks of physical chemistry.[46]   The derivations will not be repeated here; but a few standard, simple equations will be set down for convenient reference.   The model is that of n "hard-sphere" molecules in volume V, each of mass m and diameter d.   The concentration is $[n] = n/V$. Collisions are perfectly elastic between molecules and with the walls of the container.   The molecules at thermal equilibrium have a distribution of components of momentum: p_x, p_y, and p_z. The distribution of momenta in one dimension (for example, x) is

$$\frac{dn_x}{n} = \frac{1}{(2\pi mkT)^{1/2}} \exp\left(-p_x^2/2mkT\right) dp_x \tag{7-1}$$

The distribution of momenta in three dimensions is

$$\frac{dn_{xyz}}{n} = \frac{1}{(2\pi mkT)^{3/2}} \exp\left(-\frac{p_x^2 + p_y^2 + p_z^2}{2kT}\right) dp_x\, dp_y\, dp_z \tag{7-2}$$

The distribution of speed c, regardless of direction, can be found by changing from cartesian orientations of p_x, p_y, p_z to a spherical polar representation, mc, θ, Φ:

$$m^2c^2 = p_x^2 + p_y^2 + p_z^2 \tag{7-3}$$

$$\frac{dn_{c\theta\Phi}}{n} = \frac{m^3}{(2\pi mkT)^{3/2}} \exp\left(-mc^2/2kT\right)c^2 \sin\theta\, dc\, d\theta\, d\Phi \tag{7-4}$$

Equations 2 and 4 are the same; they give the probability for a particular speed c and a particular direction, given either as components of momentum or as specified angles. The probability for a given range of speeds c to $c + dc$ regardless of direction is found by integrating Eq. 4 over all angles, to give the Maxwell-Boltzmann distribution of molecular speeds

$$\frac{dn_c}{n} = 4\pi\left(\frac{m}{2\pi kT}\right)^{3/2} \exp\left(-mc^2/2kT\right)c^2\,dc \tag{7–5}$$

The average speed and average squared speed are

$$\langle c \rangle = \bar{c} = (8kT/\pi m)^{1/2}$$
$$\langle c^2 \rangle = \overline{c^2} = 3kT/m \tag{7–6}$$

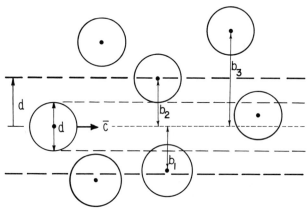

Fig. 7–1. Hard-sphere model for computing the frequency of collisions.

A trajectory of a representative molecule of average speed $\bar{c}$ is given by Fig. 1, upon the temporary assumption that only one molecule moves and no interactions occur. The closest distance of approach of the centers of two molecules to each other (on the assumption of no interaction) is defined as the impact parameter:

b: impact parameter, minimum distance between centers of
            hypothetical, no-interaction trajectory (Fig. 1)   (7–7)

If the impact parameter is greater than a molecular diameter d, no collision occurs. The representative molecule "sweeps out" a cylinder of cross-sectional area πd^2 and length $\bar{c}$ per second. Every molecule whose center lies in this cylinder will be struck:

collision frequency
    = (collision cross-section)(relative velocity)(particle density)   (7–8)

Equation 8 calls for the relative velocity of the two particles averaged over angle of approach and distribution of speeds. The relative velocity of approach $\bar{g}$ is given by Eq. 6 with the mass m replaced by reduced mass

μ. For unlike particles A and B the collision diameter is

$$d_{AB} = \tfrac{1}{2}(d_A + d_B) \tag{7-9}$$

The collision frequency of a given molecule A with molecules of type B is

$$Z_1 = (\pi d_{AB}^2)(8kT/\pi\mu)^{1/2}[n_B] \tag{7-10}$$

TABLE 7-I

Molecular Diameters in Angstrom Units from Gas Viscosity

Molecule	Diameter	Molecule	Diameter
He	2.6	I_2	5.0
Ne	2.8	HCl	3.3
Ar	3.4	CO_2	4.0
Kr	3.6	N_2O	3.9
Xe	4.0	CH_4	3.8
Hg	2.9	CF_4	4.7
H_2	2.9	CCl_4	5.8
N_2	3.7	C_2H_6	4.4
O_2	3.4	CH_3OH	3.6
F_2	3.6	CH_3Cl	3.4
CO	3.6	CH_2Cl_2	4.8
NO	3.5	$CHCl_3$	5.4
Cl_2	4.1	C_3H_8	5.1
Br_2	4.3		

The bimolecular collision rate is

$$Z_{12} = \frac{1}{\sigma_{AB}}(\pi d_{AB}^2)\left(\frac{8kT}{\pi\mu}\right)^{1/2}[n_A][n_B] \tag{7-11}$$

where σ is 1 if A and B are different and 2 if A and B are the same (since each collision then involves two A molecules). Molecular diameters are derived from measurement of gas viscosity; representative values are given in Table 1; more extensive tables and full derivations are given by Hirschfelder, Curtiss, and Bird.[29]

B. COLLISION DYNAMICS

Some bimolecular reactions occur at a rate *faster* than the collision rate deduced for the hard-sphere model. The explanation for this apparent discrepancy is that atoms and molecules attract each other over large distances, and for some molecular encounters these attractions pull the reactants together, whereas hard spheres would not have collided.

A pure gas is regarded as n point particles each of mass m, and each particle is the origin of a field of force with respect to other particles. The gas is sufficiently dilute that one need consider only single particles and interacting pairs of particles. The positions of each of a pair of particles is conveniently represented by cartesian coordinates—x_1, y_1, z_1; x_2, y_2, z_2—but the potential energy of interaction is most conveniently given by the distance between the particles, R. Appropriate coordinate systems and the dynamics of two body encounters in classical mechanics are given below.

(i) Classical-Mechanical Treatment

The positions of two point particles of mass m_1 and m_2 are given by cartesian coordinates x_1, y_1, z_1, x_2, y_2, z_2 and the components of velocity by $\dot{x}_1$, $\dot{y}_1$, $\dot{z}_1$, $\dot{x}_2$, $\dot{y}_2$, $\dot{z}_2$. The potential energy depends only on the difference in coordinates $x_2 - x_1$, $y_2 - y_1$, $z_2 - z_1$. The Lagrangian function is thus

$$L_T = \tfrac{1}{2}m_1(\dot{x}_1^2 + \dot{y}_1^2 + \dot{z}_1^2) + \tfrac{1}{2}m_2(\dot{x}_2^2 + \dot{y}_2^2 + \dot{z}_2^2) - V(x_1 \cdots z_2) \quad (7\text{–}12)$$

The Lagrangian function is put in a particularly simple form if the 6 cartesian coordinates are replaced by 3 cartesian center-of-mass coordinates and 3 spherical polar coordinates with one particle as origin. The center of mass coordinates are related to the cartesian coordinates by

$$X = (m_1 x_1 + m_2 x_2)/(m_1 + m_2)$$
$$Y = (m_1 y_1 + m_2 y_2)/(m_1 + m_2) \quad (7\text{–}13)$$
$$Z = (m_1 z_1 + m_2 z_2)/(m_1 + m_2)$$

and the spherical polar coordinates are given by

$$x_2 - x_1 = R \sin \theta \cos \Phi$$
$$y_2 - y_1 = R \sin \theta \sin \Phi \quad (7\text{–}14)$$
$$z_2 - z_1 = R \cos \theta$$

In these coordinates the Lagrangian function is

$$L_T = \tfrac{1}{2}M(\dot{X}^2 + \dot{Y}^2 + \dot{Z}^2)$$
$$+ \tfrac{1}{2}\mu(\dot{R}^2 + R^2\dot{\theta}^2 + R^2 \sin^2 \theta \dot{\Phi}^2) - V(R) \quad (7\text{–}15)$$

where M is $m_1 + m_2$ and μ is the reduced mass. If the potential energy depends only on distance of separation R, the entire collision trajectory of a given pair of atoms lies in one plane, but the orientation of the plane is random over the population of all collisions. This feature of two-body interactions makes it worthwhile to transform angular velocities from $\dot{\theta}$ and $\dot{\Phi}$ to new variables $\dot{\phi}$ and η:

$$\dot{\phi}^2 = (\dot{\theta}^2 + \sin^2 \theta \dot{\Phi}^2)$$
$$\tan \eta = \frac{\dot{\theta}}{\sin \theta \, \dot{\Phi}} \quad (7\text{–}16)$$

where the inverse transformations are

$$\dot{\theta} = \dot{\phi} \sin \eta$$
$$\dot{\Phi} = \dot{\phi} \cos \eta / \sin \theta \qquad (7\text{–}17)$$

The Lagrangian function is

$$L = \tfrac{1}{2}M(\dot{X}^2 + \dot{Y}^2 + \dot{Z}^2) + \tfrac{1}{2}\mu(\dot{R}^2 + R^2\dot{\phi}^2) - V(R) \qquad (7\text{–}18)$$

For each coordinate, Newton's equation is

$$\frac{d}{dt}\left(\frac{\partial L}{\partial \dot{q}}\right) - \frac{\partial L}{\partial q} = 0 \qquad (7\text{–}19)$$

Since the Lagrangian does not depend on four coordinates (X, Y, Z, ϕ), there are four constant momenta:

$$M\dot{X} = p_x,\ M\dot{Y} = p_y,\ M\dot{Z} = p_z \qquad \text{translational momenta} \quad (7\text{–}20)$$

$$\mu R^2 \dot{\phi} = p \qquad \text{angular momentum} \qquad (7\text{–}21)$$

Thus the center of mass moves as if of a single particle of mass M with constant velocity, and the translational problem is separable from the internal motions.

The internal Lagrangian function is thus simply

$$L = \tfrac{1}{2}\mu(\dot{R}^2 + R^2\dot{\phi}^2) - V(R) \qquad (7\text{–}22)$$

The Hamiltonian function (for this problem) is the constant total energy expressed in terms of radial and angular momenta $(p_R = \mu\dot{R},\ p = \mu R^2\dot{\phi})$:

$$H(p_R, p) = p_R^2/2\mu + p^2/2\mu R^2 + V(R) = E \qquad (7\text{–}23)$$

The two constants of the internal motion, E and p, can be evaluated from the initial state of the collision where R is so large that $V(R)$ is negligible. The kinetic energy is the sum of that for the two particles:

$$T = \tfrac{1}{2}m_1\dot{x}_1^2 + \tfrac{1}{2}m_2\dot{x}_2^2 \qquad (7\text{–}24)$$

Eliminating motion of the center of mass, one finds the internal kinetic energy to be $\tfrac{1}{2}\mu\dot{R}^2$. For two particles in the xy plane, the general definition of angular momentum is

$$p = m_1(x_1\dot{y}_1 - y_1\dot{x}_1) + m_2(x_2\dot{y}_2 - y_2\dot{x}_2) \qquad (7\text{–}25)$$

For fixed center of mass and for impact parameter (Eq. 8) b, the angular momentum is

$$p = \mu b\dot{R} = \mu bg \qquad (7\text{–}26)$$

where g is the radial velocity at large separations. Thus the constants of motion for the collision, energy and angular momentum, E and p, can be expressed in terms of the initial radial velocity g and impact parameter b:

$$E = \tfrac{1}{2}\mu g^2 \tag{7–27}$$

$$p = \mu b g \tag{7–28}$$

All aspects of the collision can be derived from the two simultaneous equations

$$\mu b g = \mu R^2 \dot{\phi} \tag{7–29}$$

$$\tfrac{1}{2}\mu g^2 = \tfrac{1}{2}\mu \dot{R}^2 + \tfrac{1}{2}\mu g^2 \left(\frac{b}{R}\right)^2 + V(R) \tag{7–30}$$

Time may be eliminated from these two equations to give the complete *trajectory* of the collision, that is, the simultaneous values of R and ϕ over the entire collision. For many purposes a less complete description is adequate, in particular the total *angle of deflection* is the property needed for the evaluation of viscosity, thermal conductivity, diffusion coefficients, and chemical-physical reactions in molecular beams. In discussing chemical reactions, the *distance of closest approach* is the quantity of primary interest. The general method of evaluating these three items will be given here, and illustrated for special cases of potential-energy functions in a subsequent section.

The angular velocity is found from Eq. 29:

$$\dot{\phi} = \frac{d\phi}{dt} = \frac{bg}{R^2} \tag{7–31}$$

The radial velocity is similarly found from Eq. 30:

$$\dot{R} = \frac{dR}{dt} = g\left[1 - \left(\frac{b}{R}\right)^2 - \frac{V(R)}{\tfrac{1}{2}\mu g^2}\right]^{1/2} \tag{7–32}$$

The ratio of these equations gives the differential equation for the trajectory

$$\frac{d\phi}{dR} = -\frac{b}{R^2}\left[1 - \left(\frac{b}{R}\right)^2 - \frac{V(R)}{\tfrac{1}{2}\mu g^2}\right]^{-1/2} \tag{7–33}$$

It is more convenient to take $1/R$ as the independent variable, instead of R, so that the differential equation is

$$\frac{d\phi}{d(1/R)} = b\left[1 - \left(\frac{b}{R}\right)^2 - \frac{V(R)}{\tfrac{1}{2}\mu g^2}\right]^{-1/2} \tag{7–34}$$

The value of the angle is zero when $R = \infty$ or $1/R = 0$. The value of the angle for any radius is then

$$\phi = \int_0^\phi d\phi = \int_0^{b/R} \frac{d(b/R)}{\left[1 - \left(\dfrac{b}{R}\right)^2 - \dfrac{V(R)}{\tfrac{1}{2}\mu g^2}\right]^{1/2}} \tag{7–35}$$

The integral may require numerical or graphical evaluation.

The turning point of the collision, R_m, occurs where the radial velocity is zero, and from Eq. 30 this is seen to be

$$\left(\frac{b}{R_m}\right)^2 = 1 - \frac{V(R_m)}{\frac{1}{2}\mu g^2} \qquad (7\text{--}36)$$

The value of the polar angle at the turning point, ϕ_m, is given by the integral (Eq. 35), evaluated from 0 to b/R_m:

$$\phi_m = \int_0^{b/R_m} \frac{d(b/R)}{\left[1 - \left(\frac{b}{R}\right)^2 - \frac{V(R)}{\frac{1}{2}\mu g^2}\right]^{1/2}} \qquad (7\text{--}37)$$

As can be seen from Eq. 30, the trajectory is symmetrical about ϕ_m. Thus the total angle of deflection χ is

$$\chi = \pi - 2\phi_m \qquad (7\text{--}38)$$

This angle of deflection is the important quantity for transport properties. The Hamiltonian function (Eq. 23), may be cast in another form:

$$H = \frac{p_R^2}{2\mu} + V_{\text{eff}} \qquad (7\text{--}39)$$

where the "effective potential energy," V_{eff}, is defined as

$$V_{\text{eff}} = V(R) + \frac{p^2}{2\mu R^2} = V(R) + \frac{1}{2}\mu g^2\left(\frac{b}{R}\right)^2 \qquad (7\text{--}40)$$

From this point of view, the centrifugal energy $p^2/2\mu R^2$ is combined with the potential energy $V(R)$ to give an effective potential-energy function. Equation 39 is equivalent to the case of one particle of mass μ in one dimension and subject to the potential energy V_{eff}.

(ii) Collisions of Molecules (6-12 Lennard-Jones Potential)

General features of a two-particle collision were expressed by algebraic equations in the sections above. For one specific form of the potential-energy function, namely the Lennard-Jones 6-12 potential (Eq. 4–13), the various features of collisions will be reviewed with an emphasis on graphical representation of a few cases.

The "effective potential-energy function" in a dimensionless form is

$$\frac{V_{\text{eff}}}{\varepsilon} = 4\left[\left(\frac{\sigma}{R}\right)^{12} - \left(\frac{\sigma}{R}\right)^6\right] + \frac{\frac{1}{2}\mu g^2}{\varepsilon}\left(\frac{b}{\sigma}\right)^2\left(\frac{\sigma}{R}\right)^2 \qquad (7\text{--}41)$$

The initial state of the collision is given by the ratio of the initial kinetic energy to the magnitude of the depth of the potential function,

$$G = (\tfrac{1}{2}\mu g^2)/\varepsilon \qquad (7\text{–}42)$$

and the impact parameter in multiples of the "diameter" is

$$B = (b/\sigma) \qquad (7\text{–}43)$$

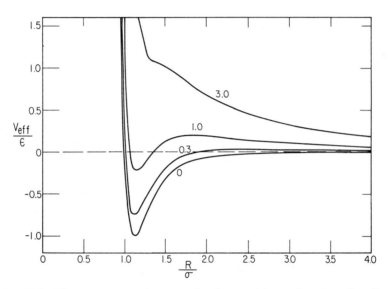

Fig. 7–2. Effective potential energy for Lennard-Jones function, Eq. 4I, for various values of the parameter GB^2 (Eqs. 42–43).

Thus the effective potential-energy function does not depend separately on the initial kinetic energy and impact parameter but on the product GB^2, and has the form

$$\frac{V_{\text{eff}}}{\varepsilon} = 4(y^{12} - y^6) + GB^2 y^2 \qquad (7\text{–}44)$$

where y is σ/R. The dimensionless Lennard-Jones 6-12 function is shown in Fig. 2 for $GB^2 = 0$, that is, the effective potential-energy function with zero impact parameter is the same as the simpler potential-energy function, Eq. 4–13. In Fig. 2, three other effective potential-energy curves are shown with values of GB^2 equal to 0.3, 1.0, and 3.0. The curves with GB^2 of 0.3 or 1.0 show a maximum around $R/\sigma = 2.5$ and 1.8. This maximum is often referred to as the "rotational barrier." If the product GB^2 is greater than 2.46, the maximum is absent, as is illustrated in Fig. 2 by the curve with $GB^2 = 3$. The maximum is a resultant between the positive centrifugal energy varying as $1/R^2$ and the negative London energy of attraction varying as $1/R^6$. For the curve with $GB^2 = 3$, the sharply rising repulsion varying as $1/R^{12}$ dominates the other two terms before the maximum has been realized.

Since there is one effective potential-energy curve for each value of the product GB^2, such a curve represents an infinite number of possible collisions, some with large values of G (kinetic energy) and small values of B^2 (impact

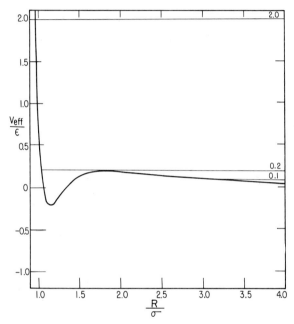

Fig. 7-3. Same as Fig. I with $GB^2 = $ I, showing three values of total energy, $G = 2.0, 0.1, 0.2$.

parameter), some with comparable values of G and B^2, and some with small values of initial kinetic energy and large impact parameters. The effective potential energy with $GB^2 = 1$ is shown again in Fig. 3, with three different values of the total energy, $G = 0.1$, 0.2, and 2.0. The low value of the total energy (or low kinetic energy at infinity) is lower than the height of the rotational barrier, the intermediate value is just slightly higher than the rotational barrier, and the high-energy case is far above the top of the rotational barrier. The low total energy corresponds to a large impact parameter, $b = 3.16\sigma$; the high energy corresponds to a small impact parameter, $b = 0.707\sigma$; and for $G = 0.2$ the impact parameter is 2.24σ. A collision may be visualized as a particle moving on a line of constant total energy: the distance from the line to the effective potential-energy curve is the kinetic energy $\frac{1}{2}\mu\dot{R}^2$, and the turning point of the collision, R_{m},

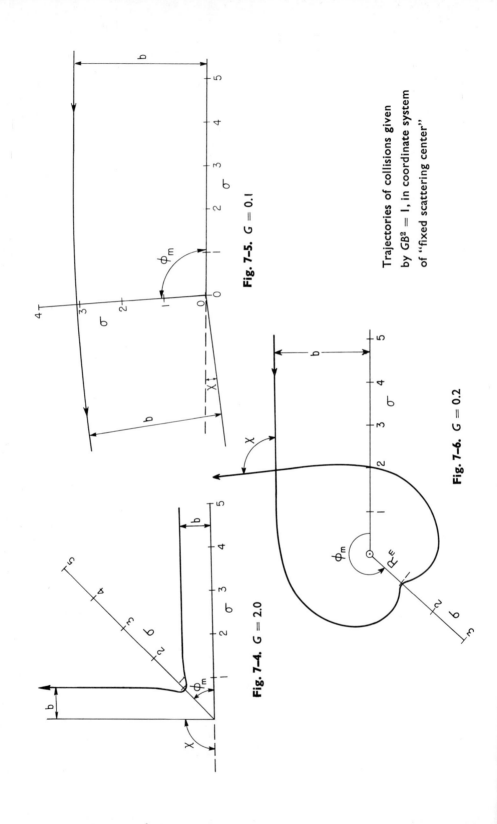

Fig. 7-5. $G = 0.1$

Fig. 7-6. $G = 0.2$

Fig. 7-4. $G = 2.0$

Trajectories of collisions given
by $GB^2 = 1$, in coordinate system
of "fixed scattering center"

is given by the point of contact of the total-energy line and the effective potential-energy curve. For the cases chosen, the low-energy line corresponds to deflection from the rotational barrier without close contact, the intermediate energy line represents a close-contact collision, and the high-energy collision is also one of close contact.

By graphical integration of Eq. 37, one evaluates the trajectory of the three collisions indicated by Fig. 3; these trajectories are given by Figs. 4 to 6. (These trajectories are as if one had one particle, of mass μ, of distance R from the origin of the effective potential-energy function, and at the angle ϕ relative to infinite separation.) Figure 4 shows the collision of high energy and low impact parameter. The impact parameter, b, the same before and after the collision as $R \to \infty$, is shown on the figure. One can also see that the distance of closest approach, R_m, is less than σ; the polar angle at the distance of closest approach is ϕ_m, and the angle of deflection is χ (Eq. 38). The collision of low energy and large impact parameter is shown by Fig. 5. Here too, one can see R_m, ϕ_m, χ, and b from the figure. The angle of deflection in this case is very small, and it corresponds to a slight downward deflection. The collision of $G = 0.2$ and $B^2 = 5$ corresponds to the total-energy line lying just above the maximum of the rotational barrier, and the trajectory is given by Fig. 6. As the point (representing motion of two particles, of course) slowly passes over the rotational barrier, a large angular deflection occurs (at slightly lower total energy it would have spiraled several times around the origin). The turning point occurs at a radius slightly longer than σ, at a large angle ϕ_m, but the angle of deflection χ is only slightly different from that for the high energy collision.

The representation of a collision by Fig. 3 is highly abstract, and Figs. 4 to 6 are also highly abstract. All quantities are given in a reduced or dimensionless form, and each curve could represent a large family of cases depending on relative masses of the particles (not to mention the infinite variety possible when translation of the center of mass is superimposed on these trajectories of fixed center of mass). The hard collision or the high-energy, low-impact-parameter collision is shown as the motion of two particles in two dimensions by Fig. 7. The special case is taken of $m_1 = 3m_2$. The center of mass is the origin of Fig. 7, particle 1 approaches with positive velocity parallel to the x-axis, particle 2 approaches with negative velocity parallel to the x-axis, and the impact parameter is the sum of the absolute values of the initial y-coordinates. The distance of closest approach R_m and the angle at this distance ϕ_m can be seen in this figure. It is to be noted that each particle is deflected by the "angle of deflection" χ. The real three-dimensional trajectories of collisions are to be found by superimposing the translation of center of mass (uniform in speed but capable of any direction) upon the trajectory of the internal motions as shown by Fig. 7. A very clear representation of such a three-dimensional collision and its relation to abstractions such as Figs. 3, 4, and 7 are given by Hirschfelder, Curtiss, and Bird[29] (pp. 47–50).

The trajectories discussed above are very interesting and in some cases of a fairly elegant form. To get a qualitative idea about the nature of collisions, one should analyze several such trajectories in full detail. However, observable transport properties do not depend on the entire trajectory

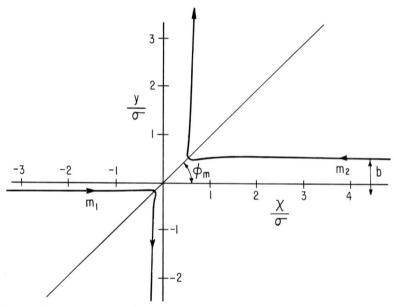

Fig. 7–7. Actual trajectory (in fixed center of mass system) of the collision given by $GB^2 = 2$ and $G = 2$ in Fig. 3 and for $m_1 = 3m_2$.

but only on the angle of deflection. Also, chemical reaction rates probably depend largely on the distance of closest approach, and not on the entire trajectory. For the Lennard-Jones potential, the distance of closest approach R_m (compare Eq. 36) is

$$1 = \left(\frac{b}{R_m}\right)^2 + \frac{4\varepsilon\left[\left(\frac{\sigma}{R_m}\right)^{12} - \left(\frac{\sigma}{R_m}\right)^6\right]}{\frac{1}{2}\mu g^2} \qquad (7\text{-}45)$$

In a dimensionless form, the relation of distance of closest approach, R_m/σ, to impact parameter b/σ, for various values of initial kinetic energy, G, is given by Fig. 8.

The dashed line in Fig. 8 gives, incidentally, the distance of closest approach between centers for collisions of hard spheres: if the impact parameter b is less than the diameter σ, the distance of closest approach is the diameter σ; if the impact parameter b is greater than the diameter σ, the distance of closest approach is simply the impact parameter or

$$R_m = \sigma \quad \text{if} \quad b \leq \sigma \qquad\qquad\qquad \text{(7–46a)}$$

$$R_m = b \quad \text{if} \quad b > \sigma \qquad \text{hard spheres} \qquad \text{(7–46b)}$$

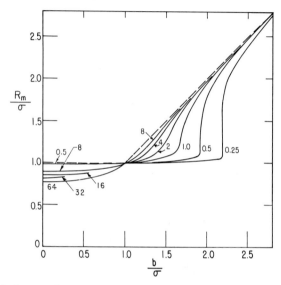

Fig. 7–8. Relation of impact parameter b to the distance of closest approach R_m for Lennard-Jones collisions for various ratios, 0.25 to 64, of the initial kinetic energy to well depth ε.

From Fig. 8 one sees that for large energies, Lennard-Jones collisions resemble hard-sphere collisions for impact parameters greater than the diameter σ, that is, behavior approaches Eq. 46b. Also, for low energies, Lennard-Jones particles approach the behavior of hard-sphere particles at impact parameters less than the diameter σ, that is, Eq. 46a is approached. For low energies and large impact parameters, the distance of closest approach greatly exceeds the diameter σ. For high energies and more or less "head-on" collisions, the distance of closest approach may be slightly less than the diameter σ. For a 25 percent reduction of R_m below σ, it requires an initial kinetic energy with the extremely high value of 64ε.

C.   CHEMICAL REACTIONS AND BIMOLECULAR COLLISION RATES

For the hard-sphere model, a pair of molecules approaching each other either collide or not. For potential-energy functions that extend over all space, even if approaching zero as $1/R^6$, such definiteness is not possible, and "the rate of collision" without further restrictions or definitions is meaningless.   In classical mechanics every encounter, no matter what the value of the impact parameters, has some angle of deflection other than zero (compare Fig. 5).   For a device that can measure infinitely fine angles of deflection, the collision cross-section is infinite, in classical mechanics.

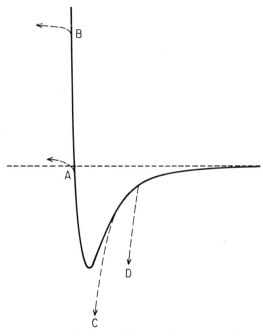

Fig. 7–9. Various points of onset of chemical reaction, relative to position on Lennard-Jones potential function.

Clearly the slight deflections, such as is illustrated by Fig. 5, do not contribute to the reaction rate.   Such small deflections with very large distances of closest approach correspond to collisions with the "rotational barrier" of Figs. 2 or 3.   It seems safe to assume that such collisions can be ignored so far as chemical reactions are concerned.

What are the criteria for occurrence of chemical reaction ?   The answer must involve other degrees of freedom not yet specified or discussed.   Two atoms cannot combine unless some third atom or molecule collides with the atomic pair to remove energy.   Two polyatomic radicals cannot combine unless other bonds in the molecule accept the energy of the newly formed bond, thus diluting the energy until a subsequent collision removes some of the energy.   Two molecules cannot carry out a metathetical reaction until the transfer atom or atoms undergo changes in bonding. All these changes occur in coordinates other than the six that are associated with the two-body collision problem. It is the uncomfortable fact that the problem of chemical reactions must now be grafted onto the simple separable problem of two-body collision theory. It is assumed, as an illustrative model, that the Lennard-Jones 6-12 potential is valid up to a given distance, and then the other degrees of freedom intrude and reaction can occur. The system falls into the "chemical trap." Of course, there can be restrictions as to the phase or as to the energy in these other coordinates, so that the collision rate with the required distance of closest approach is not necessarily to be identified with the rate of reaction.

In terms of the Lennard-Jones potential-energy function (not the effective-potential-energy curve), four models for the locus of the onset of other degrees of freedom are illustrated by Fig. 9. These models are:

A. The Lennard-Jones function applies until the distance of closest approach equals the parameter σ, at which point chemical reaction occurs in coordinates not shown. For this case the reaction rate is well approximated by the hard-sphere collision rate, where the diameter is σ.

B. The Lennard-Jones function applies until the distance of closest approach is deep inside the repulsive portion of the potential-energy function. For this case there will be a factor $\exp(-E/RT)$ in the rate (Eq. 36 appears inside the integral between Eqs. 8 and 10), and the equivalent hard-sphere diameter is slightly less than σ.[50]

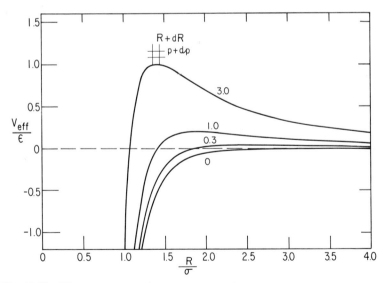

Fig. 7–10. Effective potential-energy curves based only on attractive term in Lennard-Jones potential for various values of GB^2. Compare Fig. 3.

C. The potential energy is attractive as $-a/R^6$ at all distances that matter; at close distances the reaction zone is encountered instead of the repulsive potential. The criterion for a reactive collision is that the "rotational barrier" (Fig. 10) is cleared. A simple equation for this collision rate is derived in Chapter 9.

D. Although long-range attractions vary as $-a/R^6$, the "chemical trap" extends out to significant distances, far beyond the minimum R_e of the Lennard-Jones function. The rotational barrier of Fig. 10 (based on centrifugal energy and $-a/R^6$) is seriously undermined by the chemical forces. For this situation, the rate may be substantially faster than that calculated for models *A*, *B*, or *C* above.

8

Derivation of Reaction-Rate Expressions

A. INTRODUCTION

One wants, of course, a quantum-mechanical expression for the rate of the chemical reaction. A fundamental quantum-mechanical treatment considers all nuclei and electrons of reactants and products in terms of Schroedinger's equation, including the time. At high energies (where the Born approximation is applicable) a reaction such as

$$e^- + H(1s) \rightarrow e^- + H(2p) \tag{8-1}$$

can be treated in a fundamental manner (Ref. 23, Chap. VIII, section 30). At low energies (a few electron volts) the rate of the charge exchange reaction

$$H^+ + D \rightarrow H + D^+ \tag{8-2}$$

can be treated theoretically, but the problem is a difficult one, calling for use of a fast computer to evaluate a large number of phase shifts.[6] In general, chemical reaction rates cannot be calculated in this manner. There are a number of general theoretical approaches that set up the general rate problem, and in some cases limited deductions can be made relative to experimental data. Usually, however, these general quantum-mechanical treatments cannot be carried through for chemical reaction rates. It is the purpose of this book to consider theories that can be carried through and that can be compared with experiment. Thus a substantial sacrifice in rigor is called for.

The rate of a chemical reaction will be expressed as the classical-mechanical rate multiplied by a quantum correction factor

$$\mathbf{R} = \mathbf{R}_{cl}(\mathbf{R}_{qu}/\mathbf{R}_{cl}) \tag{8-3}$$

The classical rate expression $\mathbf{R}_{cl}$ will be analyzed in terms of phase space; care will be taken not to violate Heisenberg's uncertainty principle by normalization with the proper power of Planck's constant h; and approximate quantum-mechanical corrections $(\mathbf{R}_{qu}/\mathbf{R}_{cl})$ will be discussed in a later section. The rate expressions so obtained are not fundamental quantum-mechanical theories, but they are appropriate approximations for chemical reactions.

B.   RATE EXPRESSIONS

(i) Linear Three-Atom Models

In Chapter 4, four simple chemical reactions were represented by a linear model and a simple potential-energy surface. One should restudy these figures to get a general view of chemical reactions in terms of potential-energy surfaces for those simple examples; more complicated reactants require potential-energy surfaces that are not readily plotted or visualized.

If one plotted effective potential energy, that is, potential energy plus rotational energy, the potential-energy surface would be raised as one goes from the upper right-hand corner to the lower left-hand corner. However, the effective potential energy is relatively unaffected as one moves from the upper left-hand corner to the lower right-hand corner. The reason for this statement is brought out by an examination of Fig. 3–2.

At low temperatures, the depressions, such as those in Figs. 4–4 or 4–5, are heavily populated with systems, and the high upper-right-hand plateau of dissociated atoms is very lightly populated. The saddle points and hillsides are also lightly populated. For stable molecules, at low temperatures the vibrational partition functions are close to unity, that is, almost all systems are in the lowest vibrational energy level. At very high temperatures, all volume of phase space tends to become populated; the depressions in the potential-energy surface are scarcely more heavily populated than an equal area in the plateau of dissociated atoms. It is only at low temperature that one can locate "reactants" and "products" on a potential-energy surface, or devise experiments to distinguish between the two. At low temperatures, a chemist can usually make a meaningful classification of "reactants" and "products," and on a potential-energy surface these are clearly separated by extensive areas that are virtually unpopulated. *Anywhere* in this unpopulated area separating reactants from products (Figs. 4–4 to 4–7), one can draw a line in the R_1–R_2 plane, and the rate of reaction can be discussed in terms of the flux over the line. Above any point on the line one must consider the full range of momenta. During a single collision, some reactants cross such a line once and then again to revert to reactants with zero contribution to the reaction rate. Some reactants cross the line once, twice, three times; such a trajectory gives no reaction for the first two crossings, but the third crossing counts as a reaction. Some reactants cross the line once and go to products; these crossings count toward the rate. The rate of reaction is given by the frequency with which crossings occur from left to right, multiplied by the suitable averaged probability factor that these systems go on to form products (compare Eqs. 2–25 to 2–30). This qualitative discussion is applied to more general molecules in the next section.

(ii) General Chemical Reactions

Elementary chemical reactions in the gas phase are conveniently classified as follows (where the letters stand for molecules, not atoms):

Group 1

$$M + A \rightleftharpoons D + M \qquad \text{unimolecular isomerization} \qquad (8\text{–}4)$$
$$M + A \rightarrow D + E + M \qquad \text{unimolecular decomposition} \qquad (8\text{–}5)$$
$$M + A + B \rightarrow D + M \qquad \text{bimolecular association} \qquad (8\text{–}6)$$

Group 2

$$A + B \rightleftharpoons D + E \qquad \text{bimolecular reaction} \qquad (8\text{–}7)$$
$$A + B \rightarrow D + E + F \qquad \text{bimolecular reaction} \qquad (8\text{–}8)$$
$$A + B + C \rightarrow D + E \qquad \text{termolecular reaction} \qquad (8\text{–}9)$$

The reactions of group 1 involve only one molecule as a reactant or as a product; and for reaction to occur, internal energy must be supplied or removed by "foreign gas" molecules M. The 6 (or 9) degrees of translational freedom of the reactants in group 2 include the translation of center of mass of the collision complex, and the other 3 (or 6) translations of the reactants are internal energy of the collision complex. Thus these two groups differ in an important respect: group 1 requires vibrational-translational energy transfer, but in group 2 any required activation energy may be largely or entirely supplied directly as translational energy of mutual approach of reactants. All reactions above may be written in a more abstract form as

$$\alpha A + \beta B + \gamma C \rightarrow X \rightarrow \text{products}$$

where α, β, γ are 0, 1, or 2. The number of atoms in each reactant is given by N_A, N_B, and N_C, and the total number of atoms in the reactants is

$$N = \alpha N_A + \beta N_B + \gamma N_C$$

The number is also the total number of atoms in the products and in any stoichiometric "collision complex" or "transition state" between reactants and products. The structure of all N atoms, whether reactant or product or intermediate, is given by one point in $3N$-dimensional configuration space, and the dynamics of all atoms is given by further specifying the $3N$ conjugate momenta p. The full classical mechanics of the problem is given by $6N$-dimensional phase space, $q_1 \cdots q_{3N}, p_1 \cdots p_{3N}$. A volume element in phase space is

$$d\tau = dq_1 \, dq_2 \cdots dq_{3N} \, dp_1 \, dp_2 \cdots dp_{3N} \qquad (8\text{–}10)$$

If the reaction is adiabatic (in the quantum-mechanical sense of the word), then reactants and products can all be represented by a multi-dimensional potential-energy "volume." The criterion for reaction is readily expressed in terms of a multidimensional "surface"; the flux through the surface is multiplied by the probability that products are to be formed. The location, orientation, shape, etc., of the transition surface is arbitrarily at the disposal of the investigator. The criterion for reaction as based on a potential-energy surface is transcribed to phase space. The microscopic rate is stated in terms of a differential volume $d\tau$ in phase space, and the macroscopic rate is found by integrating over all phase space corresponding to the surface of separation. The basic volume element $d\tau$ must be small enough to be treated by methods of the calculus and yet be larger than h^{3N}; also, each product $dq_i \, dp_i$ must be equal to or greater than h. The time scale of this discussion is long compared to the duration of a collision (10^{-13} to 10^{-12} sec., typically) and shorter than the time between collisions (about 10^{-9} sec at standard temperature and pressure).

The concentration (in particles per cm³, for example) of systems in the given volume element $d\tau$ is represented by $[X(q_1 \cdots p_{3N})]$; this concentration may depend on all coordinates and momenta. Under actual conditions of chemical reaction this concentration will not necessarily have the equilibrium value. However, the distribution function of complexes on the dividing surface is defined as

$$P(q_1 \cdots p_{3N}) \, d\tau = \frac{[X(q_1 \cdots p_{3N})]}{[A]^\alpha [B]^\beta [C]^\gamma} \qquad (8\text{-}11)$$

If one particle is placed on the reactant side of a volume element $d\tau$, the time to pass through the volume element to reach the product side is $1/\nu$; in other words, ν is the frequency with which particles pass from the reactant side to the product side of the volume element. In general, this frequency depends on the location of the volume element on the dividing surface:

$$\nu = \nu(q_1 \cdots q_{3N} \, p_1 \cdots p_{3N}) \qquad (8\text{-}12)$$

although a careful choice of coordinate system can greatly reduce the dimensionality of ν. Once a particle has crossed the dividing surface, it may go on to products or return to reactants. One defines κ as the probability that the particle go to products without again crossing the surface of separation. In $6N$-dimensional phase space, classical mechanics is fully deterministic: κ is either zero or one for any given point in phase space. If a trajectory crosses the dividing surface two or more times, κ is zero for the given volume element, even though the same trajectory may give unit κ at another volume element.

With these definitions, one sees that a given volume element $d\tau$ on the dividing surface contributes a factor of $\mathbf{R}(q_1 \cdots p_{3N})$ to the rate:

$$\mathbf{R}(q_1 \cdots p_{3N}) = \kappa(q_1 \cdots p_{3N})\nu(q_1 \cdots p_{3N})[X(q_1 \cdots p_{3N})] \qquad (8\text{-}13)$$

The total rate of reaction is the integral of this contribution over the entire dividing surface:

$$\mathbf{R}_{cl} = [A]^\alpha[B]^\beta[C]^\gamma \int \cdots \int_{6N} \kappa \nu P \, d\tau \qquad (8\text{--}14)$$

The rate constant **k** is defined as

$$\mathbf{k} = \frac{\mathbf{R}}{[A]^\alpha[B]^\beta[C]^\gamma}$$

and it is given by

$$\mathbf{k} = \int \cdots \int \kappa \nu P \, d\tau \qquad (8\text{--}15)$$

where κ, ν, P, and $d\tau$ may each be as much as $6N$-dimensional.

The coordinates used to describe the system and the location of the dividing surface are arbitrary. Naturally, one seeks to find a system of coordinates and a location of the surface to make the integral Eq. 15 as simple as possible. To simplify the function κ, one is tempted to select the normal-mode coordinates of the products and to locate the surface of separation as close to products as possible. In this way κ will be one, almost every time. However, the probability distribution function P is extremely hard to evaluate; the details of the potential-energy function will have cut off certain energies of reactants (visualize C + AB as reactants and A + BC as products in Fig. 4–6; no product can have energy less than -5.5). On the other hand, one may choose the normal-mode coordinates of the reactants, and one may place the dividing surface very close to reactants. This choice guarantees that the probability function P is that of the reactants (presumably known or knowable). Unfortunately, this choice may make κ a very complicated function, since it may depend on all the potential-energy surface between reactants and products. For some problems, one or the other of the extreme choices given above may be the best solution. For many problems treated by this approach, one tends to compromise: one uses as coordinates the normal-mode coordinates of the lowest saddlepoint between reactants and products, and the dividing surface is located through or near the saddlepoint and parallel to as many normal coordinates as possible. There is no requirement, however, that this choice be made. There are perfectly reasonable theories where coordinates are defined and dividing surface is located with no reference to saddlepoints. To repeat, in this approach one usually accepts a moderate uncertainty in κ and a moderate uncertainty in P by use of some "half-way" dividing surface in preference to a large uncertainty in one quantity or the other.

When the dividing surface is placed fully on the side of reactants, the custom has been to call the method the "collision theory." When the dividing surface is placed through or near the saddlepoint, the method is called "activated-complex" theory, or "transition-state" theory, or "absolute rate" theory.

In some cases the rate expression of Eq. 15 may be simplified by symmetry considerations. There may be two or more identical reaction paths. For example, in the abstraction of a chlorine atom from CCl_4 by gaseous sodium atoms, any chlorine atom may be attacked by a sodium atom, and in $6N$-dimensional phase space these four reaction paths are identical and widely spearated. If σ_{ch} is defined as the number of identical reaction paths, the range of integration in Eq. 15 may be restricted to the surface of separation over one such path, and the corresponding result multiplied by the "chemical multiplicity" σ_{ch}. The rate constant is then

$$\mathbf{k} = \sigma_{ch} \int \cdots \int_{\substack{\text{one reaction} \\ \text{path}, 6N}} \kappa \nu P \, d\tau \qquad (8\text{--}16)$$

In the further expressions of this section σ_{ch} will not be factored out, but it is understood that for symmetrical reactants it may be so factored.

C.   REACTION RATES AT TOTAL CHEMICAL EQUILIBRIUM

Temporarily, it is assumed that reactants and products (and thus all intermediates) are at total chemical equilibrium. By some relaxation technique such as nuclear magnetic resonance or by isotopic substitution, the rate is assumed to be measurable. The distribution function $P \, d\tau$ becomes the Boltzmann factor:

$$P \, d\tau = \frac{[X(q \cdots p)]_{eq}}{[A]^\alpha [B]^\beta [C]^\gamma} = \frac{\exp\left(-\varepsilon/kT\right)(d\tau/h^{3N})}{f_A^\alpha f_B^\beta f_C^\gamma} \qquad (8\text{--}17)$$

(compare Eq. 6–34, where f_A is the partition function per unit volume of the reactant A.)   The classical rate-constant expression for a Boltzmann distribution of all states is

$$\mathbf{k} = \frac{1}{f_A^\alpha f_B^\beta f_C^\gamma} \frac{1}{h^{3N}} \int \cdots \int_{6N} \kappa \nu \exp\left(-\varepsilon/kT\right) d\tau \qquad (8\text{--}18)$$

Suppose, just for the sake of analysis of the consequences, that (1) the frequency ν of crossing the surface of separation does *not* depend on some coordinate q_i and its momentum p_i, (2) the probability κ of reaction does *not* depend on any and all values of q_i and p_i, and (3) the energy of the entire complex is separable into energy in q_i and p_i and all the rest of the energy. These assumptions are:

$$\nu = \nu(q_1 \cdots q_{3N-1} p_1 \cdots p_{3N-1})$$
$$\kappa = \kappa(q_1 \cdots q_{3N-1} p_1 \cdots p_{3N-1}) \qquad (8\text{--}19)$$
$$\varepsilon = \varepsilon(q_i, p_i) + \varepsilon'$$

These assumptions may be expressed in the more condensed form

$$\nu_{6N} = \nu_{6N-2}$$
$$\kappa_{6N} = \kappa_{6N-2} \qquad (8\text{-}20)$$
$$\varepsilon_{6N} = \varepsilon_i + \varepsilon'$$

The volume element in phase space is, of course, separable:

$$d\tau = d\tau_i \, d\tau' = dq_i \, dp_i \, d\tau' \qquad (8\text{-}21)$$

The rate constant integral (Eq. 18) may then be factored as

$$\mathbf{k} = \frac{1}{f_A^\alpha f_B^\beta f_C^\gamma} \left\{ \frac{1}{h} \iint_{\text{all values}} \exp\left(-\varepsilon_i/kT\right) dq_i \, dp_i \right\}$$
$$\times \left\{ \frac{1}{h^{3N-1}} \int \cdots \int_{6N-2} \kappa\nu \exp\left(-\varepsilon'/kT\right) d\tau' \right\} \qquad (8\text{-}22)$$

Thus if the microscopic, molecular rate constant does *not* depend on some coordinate and its conjugate momentum, there appears an integral in the rate expression that has the same *form* as the partition function:

$$\frac{1}{h} \iint \exp\left(-\varepsilon_i/kT\right) dq_i \, dp_i = f_{i\ddagger} \qquad (8\text{-}23)$$

The symbol $\ddagger$ is used to identify any or all of the coordinates used to define the surface of separation. To repeat, for emphasis, *non-dependence of molecular rate on a particular separable degree of freedom formally leads to the appearance of the partition function for this degree of freedom in the expression for the macroscopic rate.*

There is one set of coordinates and momenta on which the molecular rate does not depend so that conditions of Eqs. 19 or 20 are surely met: the three translations of the center of mass (the theory of special relativity may be consulted here). Thus the rate expression is

$$\mathbf{k} = \frac{1}{f_A^\alpha f_B^\beta f_C^\gamma} \left\{ \frac{1}{h^3} \int \cdots \int_6 \exp\left(-\varepsilon_{cM}/kT\right) dX \, dY \, dZ \, dp_x \, dp_y \, dp_z \right\}$$
$$\times \left\{ \frac{1}{h^{3N-3}} \int \cdots \int_{6N-6} \kappa\nu \exp\left(-\varepsilon'/kT\right) d\tau' \right\}$$
$$= \frac{(f_t^3)_{\ddagger}}{f_A^\alpha f_B^\beta f_C^\gamma} \frac{1}{h^{3N-3}} \int \cdots \int_{6N-6} \kappa\nu \exp\left(-\varepsilon'/kT\right) d\tau' \qquad (8\text{-}24)$$

Equation 24 is almost as general and valid as Eq. 18.

In general rate expressions, Eq. 18 for example, the coordinate system and the location of the dividing surface are arbitrary. Clearly it is desirable, for the sake of computational simplicity, to pick coordinates and locate the surface so that as many coordinates as possible are parallel to the surface, so that the probability of forming products depends on as few coordinates as possible, and such that the energy is separable in all coordinates. There is certainly no reason to believe that all of these simplifying features can be realized at once. However, for sake of further analysis, an ultrasimple theory will be considered, subject to these assumptions: (1) The frequency of crossing a surface of separation depends on one and only one coordinate and momentum, q^*, p^*. (2) Once this surface is crossed, the probability of the trajectory leading to products is independent of all values of all coordinates and momenta except for q^* and p^*. (3) The energy is separable between the variables q^* and p^* and the other variables. These assumptions may be put in the form of equations:

$$\nu(q_1 \cdots p_{3N}) = \nu(q^*, p^*), \text{ only}$$
$$\kappa(q_1 \cdots p_{3N}) = \kappa(q^*, p^*), \text{ only}$$
$$\varepsilon = \varepsilon^* + \varepsilon' \tag{8-25}$$
$$d\tau = d\tau' \, dq^* \, dp^*$$

The rate expression (Eq. 18) becomes

$$\mathbf{k} = \left\{ \frac{1}{h^{3N-1}} \int \cdots \int_{6N-2} \exp\left(-\varepsilon'/kT\right) d\tau' \right\} \left\{ \frac{1}{h} \iint \kappa\nu \exp\left(-\varepsilon^*/kT\right) dq^* \, dp^* \right\}$$

$$= \frac{(f^{3N-1})_{\ddagger} \exp\left(-\varepsilon^\circ/kT\right)}{f_A^\alpha f_B^\beta f_C^\gamma} \left\{ \frac{1}{h} \iint \kappa\nu \exp\left(-\varepsilon^*/kT\right) dq^* \, dp^* \right\} \tag{8-26}$$

This expression has its simplest form if the surface of separation is through a "saddlepoint" in a potential-energy surface or at a flat region. The origin of energy ε° for the complex $\ddagger$ may be chosen to be the value of the potential energy at this flat region, and the only energy ε^* is kinetic, $p^{*2}/2m^*$. The width δ of this flat region along the coordinate q^* may be chosen as small as desired, so long as it is not less than one de Broglie wavelength Λ^*, $h/(2\pi m^* kT)^{1/2}$. The frequency to cross a strip of width δ (compare Eq. 2-25) is

$$\nu = p^*/m^*\delta \tag{8-27}$$

The transmission coefficient is assumed to be unity for all positive momenta p^*, and zero for all other values. The integral in Eq. 26 takes the simple form

$$\frac{1}{h} \int_{q^*}^{q^*+\delta} \frac{dq^*}{\delta} \int_0^\infty \exp\left(-p^2/2mkT\right) \frac{p^* \, dp^*}{m} = \frac{kT}{h} \tag{8-28}$$

As shown in connection with Eq. 2-25, the same expression is derived if the dividing surface is placed on a flat region far from the maximum in the potential energy along q^*; in this case, κ is zero if the energy ε^* is less than the barrier height and unity if ε^* is greater than the barrier height. With these (Eq. 25) very drastic assumptions, one obtains the rate expression

$$k = \frac{f'_\ddagger}{f^\alpha_A f^\beta_B f^\gamma_C} \frac{kT}{h} \exp(-\varepsilon_0/kT) \qquad (8\text{–}29)$$

If, and only if, the internal energies of the collision complex and of the reactants are separable,

$$\varepsilon = \varepsilon_t + \varepsilon_r + \varepsilon_v + \cdots \qquad (8\text{–}30)$$

then the partition functions are factorable:

$$f = f_t^3 f_r^3 f_v^{3N-6} \qquad \text{non-linear}$$
$$f = f_t^3 f_r^2 f_v^{3N-5} \qquad \text{linear} \qquad (8\text{–}31)$$

The final ultrasimple rate expression (for nonlinear reactants, for example) is

$$k = \frac{(f_t^3 f_r^3 f_v^{3N-7})_\ddagger \dfrac{kT}{h} \exp(-\varepsilon_0/kT)}{(f_t^3 f_r^3 f_v^{3N_A-6})_A^{3\alpha}(f_t^3 f_r^3 f_v^{N_B-6})_B^\beta (f_t^3 f_r^3 f_v^{3N_C-6})_C^\gamma} \qquad (8\text{–}32)$$

Students sometimes ask: "Why is one partition function omitted?" This is the wrong question. The appropriate question is, "Why are so many partition functions of the transition surface in the rate expression!" The partition function for a degree of freedom of the transition complex appears in the rate expression because it is assumed that that degree of freedom has no effect on the molecular rate functions, ν and κ. A particular example will make this assumption more clearly understood. Consider a bimolecular, three-atom, atom-transfer reaction

$$A - B + C \rightarrow A - B - C \rightarrow A + B - C$$

The potential energy of linear structures is indicated by Fig. 4–6. A reasonable surface of separation is that of $c = 1$ of Fig. 3–2. The "reaction coordinate" is then the antisymmetric stretch, $c = -1$ of Fig. 3–2, that is,

$$q^* = (R_1 - R_{1\ddagger}) - (R_2 - R_{2\ddagger}) = r_1 - r_2$$

where $R_{1\ddagger}$ and $R_{2\ddagger}$ are bond lengths at the saddlepoint. Other coordinates are

$$q_2 = (R_1 - R_{1\ddagger}) + (R_2 - R_{2\ddagger}) = r_1 + r_2, \text{ symmetric stretch}$$
$$q_3 = \phi, \text{ bend}$$
$$q_4 = \phi', \text{ bend}$$
$$q_5 = \text{rotation angle } \theta$$
$$q_6 = \text{rotation angle } \theta'$$
$$q_7 = X, \text{ center of mass}$$
$$q_8 = Y, \text{ center of mass}$$
$$q_9 = Z, \text{ center of mass}$$

It is agreed that the molecular rate will not depend on position in the container, that is, the center-of-mass coordinates, nor the corresponding momenta. For a particular value of the "reaction coordinate," $q^* = 0.4$ Å (where the equilibrium value of R_1 is 1.0 Å), various structures including various values of the other coordinates are shown in Fig. 8-1. Large values of the symmetric-stretch coordinate q_2 are shown; also large distortions of

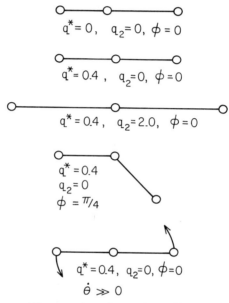

Fig. 8–1. Undistorted linear activated complex. Four models of same complex with same degree of excitation of the antisymmetric-stretch mode: other normal modes undistorted; symmetric stretch greatly excited; bending mode highly excited; very fast rotation.

the bending angle and high rotational velocities are shown. The assumptions behind Eqs. 29 and 32 are that the molecular rates ν and κ are determined by the values of the "reaction coordinate" regardless of the values of the other degrees of freedom. Every accessible state of the other coordinates is given equal weight toward the rate expression; each is regarded as an equally good parallel path for the reaction. Highly excited states, to be sure, are given a reduced weight because of the small value of the Boltzmann factor. A simple inspection of Fig. 1 shows that it is very unreasonable to expect the assumptions behind Eq. 25 to be valid. The distorted structures of Fig. 1 surely have a strong effect on ν and κ; the theory discounts these structures by means of the Boltzmann factor, perhaps in the right direction but for the wrong reason.

In the derivation given above, many assumptions were made all at once. In principle, one can have a rate equation more nearly correct than Eq. 29 or 32 and yet more specific than Eq. 24. In Section D below, the assumptions so rapidly presented in Eq. 25 will be examined one by one. First, however, the rate expression will be put in the "thermodynamic form."

Equation 29, which carried the burden of the offensive assumptions given by Eq. 25, is very close in form to an equation that is equally valid as Eq. 18, and in fact is completely equivalent to Eq. 18. Both numerator and denominator of Eq. 18 are multiplied by the $6N$-fold phase integral of the Boltzmann factor, $\exp(-\varepsilon/kT)$:

$$\mathbf{k} = \frac{\dfrac{1}{h^{3N}} \displaystyle\int \cdots \int_{6N} \exp(-\varepsilon/kT)\, d\tau \displaystyle\int \cdots \int_{6N} \kappa \nu \exp(-\varepsilon/kT)\, d\tau}{f^{\alpha}_{A} f^{\beta}_{B} f^{\gamma}_{C} \displaystyle\int \cdots \int_{6N} \exp(-\varepsilon/kT)\, d\tau} \tag{8-33}$$

From the general definition of an average value (Eq. 6–35), one sees that the second fraction on the right-hand side of Eq. 33 is the average value of the product $\kappa \nu$ (in $6N$ dimensions) over the Boltzmann distribution of energies over all of the dividing strip $\ddagger$:

$$\langle \kappa \nu \rangle^{B}_{6N\ddagger} = \frac{\displaystyle\int \cdots \int_{6N} \kappa \nu \exp(-\varepsilon/kT)\, d\tau}{\displaystyle\int \cdots \int_{6N} \exp(-\varepsilon/kT)\, d\tau} \tag{8-34}$$

Also, the numerator of the first fraction on the right-hand side of Eq. 33 is just the complete phase integral $f_{\ddagger}$ of the collision complex X on the dividing strip $\ddagger$ (Eq. 6–37, 38). By factoring out the difference in zero-point energy for the complex $\ddagger$ and the reactants, one has an expression that is completely equivalent to Eq. 18:

$$\mathbf{k} = \frac{f_{\ddagger} \exp(-\varepsilon_0/kT)}{f^{\alpha}_{A} f^{\beta}_{B} f^{\gamma}_{C}} \langle \kappa \nu \rangle^{B}_{6N\ddagger} \tag{8-35}$$

The truly general Eq. 35 has almost the same form as the drastically simplified Eq. 29. The general equation has the molecular reaction frequency averaged over *all* molecular coordinates; the approximate equation has the flat-barrier frequency kT/h. The general equation has the complete phase integral or partition function of the collision complex; the approximate equation eliminates one, f^*.

In form, a portion of Eq. 35 is an equilibrium constant

$$\frac{f_{\ddagger} \exp(-\varepsilon_0/kT)}{f^{\alpha}_{A} f^{\beta}_{B} f^{\gamma}_{C}} = K \tag{8-36}$$

In thermodynamics an equilibrium constant is related to the change of molal Gibbs free enthalpy G between reactants and products in their standard state by

$$K = \exp\left(-\Delta G^\circ / RT\right) \tag{8-37}$$

$$\Delta G^\circ = G_{\ddagger}^\circ - \alpha G_A^\circ - \beta G_B^\circ - \gamma G_C^\circ. \tag{8-38}$$

At one temperature T the Gibbs free enthalpy G is related to enthalpy H and entropy S by

$$\Delta G = \Delta H - T\Delta S \tag{8-39}$$

Thus the general rate constant (Eq. 35) is expressed in thermodynamic form as

$$\mathbf{k} = \langle \kappa\nu \rangle_{\ddagger}^{B} \exp\left(-\Delta G_{\ddagger}^\circ / RT\right) \tag{8-40}$$

$$= \langle \kappa\nu \rangle_{\ddagger}^{B} \exp\left(\Delta S_{\ddagger}^\circ / R\right) \exp\left(-\Delta H_{\ddagger}^\circ / RT\right) \tag{8-41}$$

The ultrasimplified rate constant (Eq. 29) can be expressed in a closely similar form:

$$\mathbf{k} = \frac{kT}{hf^*} \exp\left(-\Delta G_{\ddagger}^\circ / RT\right) \tag{8-42}$$

$$= \frac{kT}{hf^*} \exp\left(\Delta S_{\ddagger}^\circ / R\right) \exp\left(-\Delta H_{\ddagger}^\circ / RT\right) \tag{8-43}$$

The frequency of molecular vibrations is 10^{13} to 10^{14} sec^{-1}. The reciprocal duration of a bimolecular collision is about 10^{12} to 10^{13} sec^{-1}. The average value of the barrier-crossing frequency ν is probably within this range, and the average value of $\kappa\nu$ is probably not much lower than this. Thus the average value $\langle \kappa\nu \rangle_{\ddagger}^{B}$ is probably within the range 10^{12} to 10^{14} sec^{-1} for bimolecular chemical reactions. The value of kT/h is 6.2×10^{12} sec^{-1} at 298°K. (The value of the partition function of the reaction coordinate is its arbitrarily selected thickness δ divided by the de Broglie wavelength Λ^*. Since the thickness δ is arbitrary, it may be selected as equal to Λ, or f^* is unity if the flat-top region is wide enough. As can be seen from Table 2–1, this requirement is difficult to attain.) Thus the ultrasimple theory of Eq. 29 with the falsely universal frequency kT/h is remarkably similar, numerically, to the more general theory of Eq. 35, when both are expressed in the "thermodynamic" form.

Experimental data are often interpreted by means of Eq. 43 as follows: experimental rate constants are divided by T and plotted as log $\mathbf{k}/T$ against $1/T$. The slope is $-\Delta H_{\ddagger}^\circ / R$. The rate constant $\mathbf{k}_1$ at the mid-temperature $\bar{T}$ of the data is inserted in Eq. 43 and the "entropy of activation" evaluated as

$$\exp\left(\Delta S_{\ddagger}^\circ / R\right) = \mathbf{k}_1 (h/k\bar{T}) \exp\left(\Delta H_{\ddagger}^\circ / R\bar{T}\right) \tag{8-44}$$

To evaluate "entropy of activation" one must use all of the data. However, one can compare changes of entropy, as evaluated by this formula, with changes in entropy for chemical reactions with similar structural features (see Chapter 16). It is not known at this time how much observed "entropies of activation" are distorted by use of the "flat-top" frequency kT/h instead of the properly averaged (but generally unknown) frequency $\langle \kappa \nu \rangle^B_{\ddagger}$.

D.   REACTION RATES IN SITUATIONS WHERE INTERNAL DEGREES OF FREEDOM MAY NOT BE IN EQUILIBRIUM

In this section, it is assumed that the translation of center of mass of the reactants and collision complex is at equilibrium, thus defining a temperature T. The internal degrees of freedom of the complex may or may not have the equilibrium distribution. For a differential volume in phase space $d\tau(q_1 \cdots p_{3N})$, the actual concentrations of species in three-dimensional laboratory space may be greater than or less than the equilibrium concentration; this ratio is represented as

$$\frac{[X(q_1 \cdots p_{3N})]_{\text{actual}}}{[X(q_1 \cdots p_{3N})]_{\text{eq}}} = 1 + \phi(q_1 \cdots p_{3N}) \qquad (8\text{-}45)$$

The equilibrium concentration of a given volume element in phase space has been defined by Eq. 17. Thus the general rate expression (Eq. 15) becomes (compare Eq. 24)

$$k = \frac{(f^3_t)_{\ddagger}}{f^\alpha_A f^\beta_B f^\gamma_C} \frac{1}{h^{3N-3}} \int \cdots \int_{6N-6} \kappa \nu (1 + \phi) \exp(-\varepsilon/kT) \, d\tau \qquad (8\text{-}46)$$

where ε is the internal Hamiltonian function, as before. This integral may be multiplied and divided by the right-hand side of Eq. 24.

$$\frac{\displaystyle\int \cdots \int_{6N-6} (1 + \phi)\kappa\nu \exp(-\varepsilon/kT)\, d\tau}{\displaystyle\int \cdots \int_{6N-6} \kappa\nu \exp(-\varepsilon/kT)\, d\tau} \frac{\displaystyle\int \cdots \int_{6N-6} \kappa\nu \exp(-\varepsilon/kT)\, d\tau}{h^{3N-3}}$$
$$= \langle 1 + \phi \rangle^T_{6N-6} \frac{1}{h^{3N-3}} \int \cdots \int \kappa\nu \exp(-\varepsilon/kT)\, d\tau \qquad (8\text{-}47)$$

where $\langle 1 + \phi \rangle^T_{6N-6}$ is the function $(1 + \phi)$ averaged over Tolman's distribution function, "the complexes that react":

$$\rho_{\text{Tolman}} = \kappa\nu \exp(-\varepsilon/kT)$$

The rate expression becomes

$$k = \frac{(f^3_t)_{\ddagger}}{f^\alpha_A f^\beta_B f^\gamma_C} \langle 1 + \phi \rangle^T_{6N-6} \frac{1}{h^{3N-3}} \int \cdots \int_{6N-6} \kappa\nu \exp(-\varepsilon/kT)\, d\tau \qquad (8\text{-}48)$$

This expression is the same as Eq. 24 except for the averaged correction for non-equilibrium distribution.

For chemical reactions, the configuration of reactants and products can be described in terms of $3N - 3$ internal coordinates; a surface of separation may be described in terms of one less coordinate. This surface of separation may be defined as orthogonal to some one coordinate; all other coordinates may be parallel to the surface of separation. Thus any trajectory crossing the surface may be resolved into a component along q^*, and all other components are parallel to the surface. The frequency with which one particle crosses from $-\delta/2$ to $+\delta/2$ from the surface of separation is expected to depend on only one coordinate and its conjugate momentum. Thus one assumption of Eq. 25 represents a reasonable hope, and calls for a careful selection of coordinate system and location of dividing surface:

$$\nu = \nu(q^*, p^*) \tag{8-49}$$

If the reaction coordinate (q^*, p^*) is everywhere separable from all other coordinates from the transition surface to the products, then the probability of reaching products κ depends only on q^* and p^*. For chemical reactions, in general, the coordinate system that makes Eq. 30 possible will not be separable over wide ranges of values. In general, one expects the trajectory between transition surface and products to depend on all internal degrees of freedom. The reaction probability κ may be regarded as a function of the dividing surface; but its value at any point, 0 or 1, depends on all of phase space between the dividing surface and the products. Since the reaction coordinate is assumed to be separable from the other coordinates on the dividing surface, then the transmission function may be factored:

$$\kappa_{6N-6} = \kappa^*(q^*, p^*)\kappa_{6N-8} \tag{8-50}$$

The numerator and denominator of Eq. 48 may be multiplied by the $6N - 8$-fold integral of the Boltzmann factor $\exp(-\varepsilon/kT)\, d\tau$, and from the general definition of an average, one has

$$\langle\kappa\rangle_{6N-8}^{B} = \frac{\int \cdots \int_{6N-8} \kappa \exp(-\varepsilon/kT)\, d\tau}{\int \cdots \int_{6N-8} \exp(-\varepsilon/kT)\, d\tau} \tag{8-51}$$

and from the definition of the classical-mechanical partition function one obtains

$$f_{\ddagger}^{3N-1} = f_t^3 \frac{1}{h^{3N-4}} \int \cdots \int_{6N-8} \exp(-\varepsilon/kT)\, d\tau \tag{8-52}$$

Thus the rate equation, subject to the relatively realistic assumptions of

Eqs. 45, 49, and 50, is

$$\mathbf{k} = \frac{f_{\ddagger}^{3N-1} \exp\left(-\varepsilon_0/kT\right)}{f_A^{\alpha} f_B^{\beta} f_C^{\gamma}} \langle 1 + \phi \rangle_{6N-6}^{T} \langle \kappa \rangle_{6N-8}^{B} \frac{1}{h} \iint \kappa^* \nu \exp\left(-\varepsilon^*/kT\right) dq^* \, dp^*$$

$$(8\text{-}53)$$

If the dividing surface is located at a saddlepoint, the double integral in Eq. 53 gives the value kT as before. Thus instead of Eq. 29, one has the more general relation

$$\mathbf{k} = \frac{f_{\ddagger}^{3N-1}}{f_A^{\alpha} f_B^{\beta} f_C^{\gamma}} \frac{kT}{h} \exp\left(-\varepsilon_0/kT\right) \langle 1 + \phi \rangle_{6N-6}^{T} \langle \kappa \rangle_{6N-8}^{B} \qquad (8\text{-}54)$$

It is worthwhile to recapitulate the origin and meaning of the various terms in Eq. 54. The "partition functions" for the collision complex arose as normalizing functions for the averaging of the reaction probability κ over the dividing surface. The value of the average reaction probability $\langle \kappa \rangle_{6N-8}^{B}$ is expected to depend on all of the phase space from dividing surface to products. The average correction for non-equilibrium distribution $\langle 1 + \phi \rangle_{3N-6}^{T}$ depends on the actual distribution of reactants and all of the trajectories from reactants to products; however, one expects this function to be most strongly affected by phase space between reactants and the dividing surface. The expression omitting $\langle \kappa \rangle^{B} \langle 1 + \phi \rangle^{T}$, that is, Eq. 29, is just the rate of crossing the dividing surface for an equilibrium distribution of collision complexes. Such a rate is not a rate of reaction. A general theory for reaction rate must consider all of phase space from reactants to products; Eq. 54 does this. The effect of most of this volume of phase space is expressed in terms of averages, $\langle \kappa \rangle^{B}$ and $\langle 1 + \phi \rangle^{T}$. It may be that for a narrow, but chemically very interesting, range of temperatures and reactions, these averages are not far from unity in value.

At this point, it is proposed to take Eq. 54 seriously as a general, classical-mechanical rate expression for chemical reactions. A sharp-eyed student has probably already asked, "No classical-mechanical property can depend on the value of h; what is Planck's constant h doing in a final classical equation?" The answer is that there are $3N - 1$ powers of h^{-1} implicit in $f_{\ddagger}$ and $3N$ powers of h^{-1} implicit in the partition functions of the reactants; and, of course, h is not really there.

E. AN ALTERNATE FORMULATION FOR THE CLASSICAL RATE EQUATION

The classical partition function for a stable molecule has been written in terms of the Jacobian function J (Eqs. 6-50). The classical partition functions appearing in the rate equation may be similarly re-expressed in an equivalent form. The product $f'_{\ddagger}(kT/h)$ from Eq. 54 is expanded for a nonlinear complex:

$$f'_{\ddagger} \frac{kT}{h} = \frac{(2\pi MkT)^{3/2}}{h^3} \frac{(8\pi^2)(2\pi kT)^{3/2} |I|^{1/2}}{h^3} \prod^{3N-7} \left(\frac{kT}{h\nu_i}\right) \frac{kT}{h} \qquad (8-55)$$

The last two terms may be expanded further:

$$\prod^{3N-7} \left(\frac{kT}{h\nu_i}\right) \frac{kT}{h} = \left(\frac{kT}{h}\right)^{3N-6} \prod^{3N-7} \frac{1}{\nu_i} = \left(\frac{2\pi kT}{h}\right)^{3N-6} \frac{1}{2\pi} \prod^{3N-7} \frac{1}{\lambda_i^{1/2}} \qquad (8-56)$$

where λ_i are $3N - 7$ out of $3N - 6$ solutions of Eq. 5–16. For a transition surface through a saddlepoint in a potential-energy surface, one solution of Eq. 5–16 will have a negative value of λ, written λ^*. Numerator and denominator of Eq. 56 may be multiplied by $\lambda^{*1/2}$, and then Eq. 5–18 applies.

$$\frac{1}{2\pi} \prod^{3N-7} \frac{1}{\lambda_i^{1/2}} = \frac{\lambda^{*1/2}}{2\pi} \prod^{3N-6} \frac{1}{\lambda_i^{1/2}} = \frac{\lambda^{*1/2}}{2\pi |F|^{1/2} |G|^{1/2}} = \frac{\nu^*}{|F_s|^{1/2} |G_s|^{1/2}} \qquad (8-57)$$

Numerator and denominator of Eq. 55 may be multiplied by the product of all atomic masses to 3/2 power and de Broglie wavelengths are factored out. Collecting all expansions above, one obtains

$$f'_{\ddagger} \frac{kT}{h} = \left[\frac{M^{3/2} |I|^{1/2} 8\pi^2}{|G_s|^{1/2} \prod^N m_\alpha^{3/2}}\right] \frac{\nu^*}{\prod^N \Lambda_\alpha^3} \frac{(2\pi kT)^{(3N-6)/2}}{|F_s|^{1/2}} \qquad (8-58)$$

However, the term in square brackets is just the Jacobean factor J, Eq. 6–45, which depends only on structure, not on potential energy or mass. Thus the new form for Eq. 55 is

$$f'_{\ddagger} \frac{kT}{h} = \frac{\nu^* J}{\prod \Lambda_\alpha^3} \frac{(2\pi kT)^{(3N-6)/2}}{|F_s|^{1/2}} \qquad (8-59)$$

The prescription for finding the terms in Eq. 59 will be reviewed: At a "saddlepoint" in $3N - 6$-dimensional configuration space, the potential energy is expanded in Taylor series, all linear terms are zero, and deviations from the saddlepoint are so small that only quadratic terms are retained:

$$V - V_0 = (1/2) \sum_i \sum_j \left(\frac{\partial^2 V}{\partial S_i \partial S_j}\right) s_i s_j \qquad (8-60)$$

where s is departure from reference saddlepoint. The second derivatives are the force constants

$$F_{ij} = \left(\frac{\partial^2 V}{\partial S_i \partial S_j}\right)_0 \qquad (8-61)$$

and these are the elements in the determinant in Eq. 59. The function J is a product, ΠJ_α, over the atoms, its general value is given by Eq. 6–47, and a convenient set for simple molecular coordinates is given as Table 6–1. The negative eigenvalue of secular Eq. 5–16 gives the term v^*. For the quantum corrections, discussed below, it is necessary also to have the real frequencies or positive solutions of Eq. 5–16.

It is improbable that the force constant determinant will be simply diagonal in form. Some non-diagonal elements are expected to be larger than some diagonal elements; for examples, see Chapters 10 to 13. Even so, the force constant determinant can always be expressed as

$$|F| = w^2 \prod^{3N-6} F_{ss} \tag{8–62}$$

where w^2 is a numerical constant (negative for unstable complexes) to be evaluated for individual cases. Equation 59 may be put in the form that emphasizes local properties,

$$f'_{\ddagger} \frac{kT}{h} = \frac{v^*}{w} \prod^{N} \left(\frac{J_\alpha}{\Lambda_\alpha^3}\right) \prod^{3N-6} l_s \tag{8–63}$$

In rate Eq. 54 the atomic de Broglie wavelengths all cancel:

$$k = \frac{\dfrac{v^*}{w}\left(\prod^{N} J_\alpha \prod^{3N-6} l_s\right)_{\ddagger} e^{-V^*/kT}}{\left(\prod^{N} J_\alpha \prod l_s\right)_{\text{reactants}}} \langle \kappa \rangle^{\text{B}} \langle 1 + \phi \rangle^T \tag{8–64}$$

Equation 64 is equal to Eq. 54, but it calls for different data. For simple three- or four-atom reactions, the two equations are about equally easy to apply. For very complex reactions, Eq. 64 is vastly simpler than Eq. 54.

F.   QUANTUM CORRECTIONS

The classical-mechanical partition function as used in the theory of chemical equilibrium was given as Eqs. 6–37 and 6–38. The quantum-mechanical correction to the complete partition function of ideal-gas molecules at room temperature and higher applies only to the vibrational terms, and the correction for each vibration is given by Eq. 6–28 and the high-temperature expansion by 6–29:

$$\Gamma = \frac{u/2}{\sinh u/2} \to 1 - \frac{u^2}{24} + \cdots$$
$$\text{high temperature}$$

A mathematical expression with the same *form* as a partition function appears in the rate expression of Eq. 38, for example, when it is assumed that the molecular rate does not depend on a particular coordinate and momentum. It is by no means obvious that the quantum correction for the reaction rate should resemble in any way the quantum correction on the true steady-state partition function. The equilibrium partition function is the *effective number of accessible states*, averaged over a large ensemble. The "partition function" for degrees of freedom of the "activated complex" that do not affect the molecular rate is the *effective number of parallel reaction paths* between reactants and products. These parallel paths are sought out by the colliding reactants, and available paths are finally found by a large number of reactants over a long length of time even though each trajectory requires but 10^{-12} or so seconds. The partition function is an "ensemble average" over many reacting pairs of molecules; it is not a "time average" for each collision complex. Thus the quantum correction on the rate may or may not have some features in common with the quantum corrections on chemical equilibrium.

The general problem of quantum corrections on the rate of a chemical reaction was treated in detail by Wigner[51]. For a one-dimensional barrier of arbitrary shape, Wigner derived the first approximation to the tunneling correction: the rate of reaction for a stream of incident particles with a Boltzmann distribution of velocities as calculated by quantum mechanics (first approximation) is faster than the rate calculated by classical mechanics by the factor

$$\Gamma^* = 1 + |u^*|^2/24 \qquad \text{or} \qquad 1 - u^{*2}/24 \qquad (8\text{--}65)$$

where $|u^*| = h\,|v^*|/kT$, $|v^*| = (1/2\pi)(|F^*|/m)^{1/2}$, and $|F^*| = |d^2V/dx^2|$, since F^* is negative. Wigner set up the problem of calculating this correction factor to any degree of approximation in terms of higher derivatives of V for an arbitrary one dimensional barrier. (For an Eckart barrier the problem is susceptible to an exact solution, and Wigner's series expansion in powers of h^2 is not needed; see Chapter 2.)

The general problem of quantum corrections for a chemical reaction involving many dimensions was also treated by Wigner (translated from German): "In the case of additional dimensions, we are dealing not so much with penetration of a barrier as of a *ridge* as is known from the theory of the simplest of chemical reactions. Two effects play compensating roles here: the previously considered tunnel effect, which raises the probability of ridge penetration, and the zero-point energy, which requires a greater energy to cross a narrow pass, when it corresponds to the minimum in the pass. We establish the coordinate system so that the potential in the neighborhood of the pass has the form of

$$V(x_1 \cdots x_n) = V_0 + \tfrac{1}{2}(A_1 x_1^2 + A_2 x_2^2 + \cdots + A_n x_n^2)$$

where A_1 is negative and all other coefficients are positive." Wigner showed that, to the first approximation, the correction on the rate constant has the form

$$\Gamma = (1 + |u_1|^2/24)(1 - u_2^2/24) \cdots (1 - u_n^2/24) \qquad (8\text{--}66)$$

where $u = hv/kT$, $v = (1/2\pi)(A/m)^{1/2}$, and A is Wigner's expression for force constants or second derivatives (F has been used for force constants here). As noted in the preceding paragraph, the first approximation to the quantum correction on the equilibrium vibrational partition function is the same, $1 - u^2/24 + \cdots$, as the first approximation to the quantum correction on the rate, Eq. 66.

Thus Wigner's analysis has led chemists to make the following postulate: The quantum-mechanical correction on reaction-rate pseudo-partition functions shall be taken to be the same as quantum correction on true, equilibrium partition functions for stable vibrations:

$$\Gamma = \frac{u/2}{\sinh u/2} \quad \text{for} \quad \lambda > 0 \qquad (8\text{-}67)$$

and the quantum-mechanical correction on the unstable vibration or "reaction coordinate" is given by a one-dimensional barrier-penetration function (compare Eq. 2–31)

$$\Gamma^* = \frac{\exp (V/kT)}{kT} \int_0^\infty \kappa(\varepsilon) \exp (-\varepsilon/kT) \, d\varepsilon \qquad (8\text{-}68)$$

These postulates appear to be better chemical engineering than natural philosophy; but as Wigner says, there are compensating factors.

Thus the classical rate expressions, Eqs. 54 or 64, may (by virtue of brave postulates) be converted to quantum rate expressions by multiplying each vibrational or internal partition function by its quantum correction factor Γ. Equation 54 is written as

$$\mathbf{k} = \frac{f'\Gamma^*}{f_A^\alpha f_B^\beta f_C^\gamma} \frac{kT}{h} \exp (-\varepsilon_0^0/kT)\langle\kappa\rangle^B\langle 1 + \phi\rangle^T \qquad (8\text{-}69)$$

where the partition functions f are understood to be in quantum-mechanical form. Equation 64 is expressed as

$$\mathbf{k} = \frac{Wv^*\left(\prod\limits^N J_\alpha \prod\limits^{3N-6} l_s \prod\limits^{3N-6} \Gamma_Q\right)_{\ddagger} \exp (-V^*/kT)\langle\kappa\rangle^B\langle 1 + \phi\rangle^T}{\left(\prod\limits^N J_\alpha \prod l_s \prod \Gamma_Q\right)_{\text{reactants}}} \qquad (8\text{-}70)$$

where W was defined in connection with Eq. 6–58, and it includes electronic multiplicity, identity factors σ, and the factors w of Eqs. 6–49 or 8–62. For reactions not involving structural isomerization, the factor of $\sigma_A^\alpha\sigma_B^\beta\sigma_C^\gamma/\sigma_{\ddagger}$ is usually the same as σ_{ch} of Eq. 16. One should use σ_{ch} and omit σ arising from rotational partition functions.

The quantum-mechanical vibrational partition functions appear in Eq. 69; these functions are unity for high-frequency vibrations and approach kT/hv for low frequencies. The vibrational terms in Eq. 70 are given by Eq. 67; these terms approach unity for low-frequency vibrations and approach $u \exp(-u/2)$ for high-frequency vibrations. Since it is generally easier to evaluate or guess high-frequency vibrations, Eq. 70 has great advantage over Eq. 69 in some cases.

For complicated reactions, Eq. 69 takes on extremely great complexity with very low (and unknown) frequencies of torsion, bends, wags, etc. The normal-mode coordinates usually used in Eq. 69, in principle, extend over all the collision complex. Equation 70, on the other hand, can be put in a form that allows very extensive cancellation of nonessential terms:

$$\mathbf{k} = W\nu^*\langle\kappa\rangle^{\mathrm{B}}\langle 1 + \phi\rangle^T \exp(-V^*/kT) \prod \underset{\substack{\text{that do}\\\text{not change}}}{\frac{(Jl\Gamma)''_\ddagger}{(Jl\Gamma)''}} \prod \underset{\substack{\text{that}\\\text{change}}}{\frac{(Jl\Gamma)'_\ddagger}{(Jl\Gamma)'}} \prod \underset{\text{new}}{(l\Gamma)_\ddagger} \quad (8\text{--}71)$$

By virtue of the large cancellation between local properties (bond lengths and force constants), one can carry through rate calculations for much more complicated reactions with Eq. 71 than with Eq. 69.

9

Collision Rates

A. COLLISION RATE WITH A SURFACE

(i) Collision Theory

A differential area ds is imagined to be on the surface of a container of a gas with particles of mass m and concentration $[n]$ particles per cubic centimeter. The situation in the gas phase about one mean free path from the surface is examined. For a given speed c of the molecules, the rate of approach to the surface is given by the component of velocity perpendicular to the surface and moving toward the surface. A system of spherical polar coordinates with the z-axis normal to the surface gives the magnitude of the velocity c and the direction θ and Φ. The component of velocity moving toward the surface is $c \cos \theta$, with θ restricted from 0 to $\pi/2$; values of θ from $\pi/2$ to π represent molecules that have just bounced off the surface. The contribution to the rate of collision of molecules with velocities between c and $c + dc$, Φ and $\Phi + d\Phi$, θ and $\theta + d\theta$, is

$$\mathbf{R}(c, \Phi, \theta) = c \cos \theta [dn(c, \Phi, \theta)] \, ds \qquad (9\text{--}1)$$

where $[dn(c, \Phi, \theta)]$ is the number of molecules per cubic centimeter within the designated range of variables. The total rate of collision per unit area is found by integrating ds over unit area and the other variables over the entire range:

$$\mathbf{R} = \int_0^1 ds \int_0^{2\pi} \int_0^{\pi/2} \int_0^\infty c \cos \theta [dn(c, \Phi, \theta)] \qquad (9\text{--}2)$$

If the molecules have an equilibrium distribution of velocities, then the number of molecules in a given range of variables is given by the Maxwell-Boltzmann Eq. 7–4:

$$\mathbf{R} = \int_0^{\pi/2} \int_0^{2\pi} \int_0^\infty c \cos \theta \, \frac{[n_0]m^3}{(2\pi mkT)^{3/2}} \exp\left(-mc^2/2kT\right) c^2 \sin \theta \, dc \, d\theta \, d\Phi \qquad (9\text{--}3)$$

It is interesting to rearrange this expression before integrating:

$$\mathbf{R} = \frac{[n]}{4\pi} \int_0^{\pi/2} \int_0^{2\pi} \cos\theta \sin\theta \, d\theta \, d\Phi \left[\frac{4\pi m^3}{(2\pi mkT)^{3/2}} \int_0^\infty \exp\left(-mc^2/2kT\right)c^3 \, dc \right]$$

(9-4)

The integrations over angles is simply π, and the term in the square bracket is recognized, Eq. 7–6, as the average velocity, $\bar{c}$. Thus the rate of collision with unit area of surface is

$$\mathbf{R} = \frac{[n]}{4}\bar{c} = \frac{[n]}{4}\left(\frac{8kT}{\pi m}\right)^{1/2}$$
$$= 2.67 \times 10^{25} P/(MT)^{1/2} \text{ collisions/sec}$$

(9-5)

where P is in atmospheres, M is gram-molar mass, and T is absolute temperature.

If the vessel has a hole of area ds, the same equation applies if the mean free path in the gas phase is long compared to the diameter of the hole. Otherwise, the loss of molecules through the hole creates a large perturbation of the Maxwell-Boltzmann distribution function in the neighborhood of the hole.

(ii) Transition-State Theory (Partition-Function Form)

The reactant is a free molecule in the gas phase, the product is a molecule that has just collided with the surface, and the dividing surface or transition state is placed infinitesimally close (at least within one mean free path) to the surface and parallel to it. The "reaction coordinate" is the component of translation normal to the surface. To the ideal-gas approximation the molecules are independent, and all internal degrees of freedom of the molecule near the surface are the same as in the free-gas phase. The origin of energy is zero speed, both for reactant and transition state. Every molecule that passes the transition surface hits the real surface, $\kappa = 1$, since they are no more than one mean free path apart. The rate, according to Eq. 8–69, is then

$$\mathbf{R} = k[n] = \frac{kT}{h}\frac{f'_\ddagger}{f}[n]$$

(9-6)

$$= \frac{\left[\dfrac{(2\pi mkT)^{2/2}L^2}{h^2} f_r^3 f_v^{3N-6}\right]_\ddagger \dfrac{kT}{h}[n]}{\dfrac{(2\pi mkT)^{3/2}L^3}{h^3} f_r^3 f_v^{3N-6}}$$

(9-7)

The rotational and vibrational partition functions are the same in the free-gas phase and one mean free path from the surface, so that these terms cancel, and the rate of collision with unit area of surface is

$$\mathbf{R} = \frac{[n]}{4}\left(\frac{8kT}{\pi m}\right)^{1/2} \tag{9–8}$$

in agreement with Eq. 5 as found by collision theory. Of course Planck's quantum constant h, which seems to appear in Eq. 6, cancels out in the final, classical-mechanical relation.

(iii) Jacobian-Factor Form of Transition-State Theory

The model for the reaction is the same as that given above, except that formal use is made of the concept of duration of collision $1/\nu^*$ and length of collisional interaction l^*. The rate expression is simply (Eq. 8–70)

$$\mathbf{R} = \nu^* \frac{\prod\limits^{3N} (Jl\Gamma)_{\div}^{\ddagger}}{\prod\limits^{3N} (Jl\Gamma)} [n] \tag{9–9}$$

All internal Jacobian factors J, vibrational amplitudes l, and quantum correction terms Γ are the same for reactant and complex, and the residual terms are simply

$$\mathbf{R} = \nu^* \frac{L^2 l^*}{L^3} [n] = \nu^* l^* [n] \tag{9–10}$$

where the final term is collision rate per unit area. The frequency is formally $\frac{1}{2}\pi(F^*/m)^{1/2}$ and the interaction amplitude is formally $(2\pi kT/F^*)^{1/2}$. The rate is thus

$$\mathbf{R} = \frac{[n]}{4}\left(\frac{8kT}{\pi m}\right)^{1/2} \tag{9–11}$$

and is, as expected, in agreement with the other formulations.

(iv) Comparison of the Different Derivations of the Rate Expression

In case of collision with a surface, the rate expression is more quickly and easily derived by transition-state theory than by collision theory, so long as both consider an equilibrium distribution of reactants. The vibrational amplitudes in Eq. 9 and the partition functions in Eq. 7 have already been integrated over an equilibrium distribution function. If one does not have an equilibrium distribution of velocities one could formally use transition-state theory according to Eq. 8–15, but a much simpler and more direct approach is to consider the collision theory (Eq. 2). This situation will often be found: collision theory and transition-state theory (1) give identically the same predictions if the same criterion for reaction is used in each case, (2) the computation of the rate is more easily carried out for transition state theory if reactants have an equilibrium distribution function, and (3) the extension to non-equilibrium situations is much more easily carried out in terms of collision theory. There are exceptions to points 2 and 3 above, but they do seem to be the general rule.

B.   COLLISION OF HARD-SPHERE MOLECULES

(i) Collision Theory

It has already been shown that the general two-body problem, with velocities c_A, Φ_A, θ_A and c_B, Φ_B, θ_B and masses m_A and m_B, can be reduced to a one-body scattering problem with velocity g, Φ, θ and mass $\mu = m_A m_B/(m_A + m_B)$. The equivalent one-body scattering problem is fully determined by initial relative velocity g and the impact parameter b. If the individual molecules have an equilibrium distribution of velocities, the equivalent one-body "beam" of molecules has a Maxwell-Boltzmann distribution (Eq. 7–5) with c replaced by g and m replaced by μ. For the hard-sphere model the probability of collision is unity, $\kappa = 1$, if the impact parameter b is less than $\frac{1}{2}(d_A + d_B)$, and the probability of collision is zero ($\kappa = 0$) if the impact parameter b exceeds $\frac{1}{2}(d_A + d_B)$. The frequency with which the reference molecule A undergoes collision from molecule B with a particular relative velocity between g and $g + dg$ is

$$\mathbf{R}(g) = (\pi d_{AB}^2)g[dn_B(g)] \qquad (9\text{–}12)$$

where d_{AB} is $\frac{1}{2}(d_A + d_B)$, πd^2 is the "collision cross-section," and $[dn_B(g)]$ is the number of molecules B per cubic centimeter with relative velocity g to $g + dg$. Since the collision cross-section πd_{AB}^2 does not depend on relative velocity for this model, the total rate is simply the integral

$$\mathbf{R} = \pi d_{AB}^2 \int_0^\infty g[dn_B(g)] \qquad (9\text{–}13)$$

If the molecules have an equilibrium distribution of velocities, the rate is simply

$$\mathbf{R} = (\pi d_{AB}^2)[n]4\pi \left(\frac{\mu}{2\pi kT}\right)^{3/2} \int_0^\infty \exp\left(-\mu g^2/2kT\right)g^3\, dg \qquad (9\text{–}14)$$

$$Z_A = (\pi d_{AB}^2)\bar{g}[n_B] = (\pi d_{AB}^2)\left(\frac{8kT}{\pi\mu}\right)^{1/2}[n_B] \qquad (9\text{–}15)$$

This expression gives the frequency Z_A with which a given molecule A is struck by a molecule B. In a pure gas containing only A molecules, the same expression applies; d is d_A, μ is $m_A/2$, and the concentration of interest is $[n_A]$. The total rate of bimolecular collisions between A and B molecules per cubic centimeter per second is just the collision frequency times the concentration of A molecules per cubic centimeter:

$$Z_{AB} = Z_A[n_A] = \pi d_{AB}^2 \bar{g}[n_B][n_A] \qquad (9\text{–}16)$$

In pure gas containing only A molecules, Eq. 16 overcounts the number of collisions by a factor of two if B is simply replaced by A. The rate expression is

$$Z_{AA} = \tfrac{1}{2} Z_A [n_A]^2 \tag{9-17}$$

These rate expressions are readily cast in terms of gram-molar masses M, moles per cubic centimeter concentration units $[n]$, and molar gas constant R by use of Avogadro's constant n_{Av}.

$$Z_A = \pi \left(\frac{d_A + d_B}{2} \right)^2 \left[\frac{8RT}{\pi} \left(\frac{1}{M_A} + \frac{1}{M_B} \right) \right]^{1/2} [N_A] n_{Av} \tag{9-18}$$

$$Z_{AB} = Z_A [N_B] n_{Av} \tag{9-19}$$

$$Z_{AA} = \pi d_A^2 \left[\frac{4RT}{\pi M_A} \right]^{1/2} [N_A] n_{Av} \tag{9-20}$$

Orders of magnitude are of some interest here. For helium at 0°C and 1-atmosphere pressure, the frequency of collisions is 9.71×10^9 per second. Thus for any gas the frequency of collision is

$$Z_A = 9.71 \times 10^9 \left(\frac{4.0}{M} \frac{273}{T} \right)^{1/2} \frac{P}{1} \left(\frac{d}{2.6} \right)^2 \text{ sec}^{-1} \tag{9-21}$$

The bimolecular collision rate for helium is 1.31×10^{29} collisions per cubic centimeter per second so that in general for a pure gas

$$Z_{AA} = 1.31 \times 10^{29} \left(\frac{4.0}{M} \right)^{1/2} \left(\frac{273}{T} \right)^{3/2} \left(\frac{P}{1} \right)^2 \left(\frac{d}{2.6} \right)^2 \text{ collisions/cm}^3\text{-sec} \tag{9-22}$$

The collision rate changes in this manner with temperature since $PV = NRT$ and $\bar{g}$ is proportional to $T^{1/2}$. The expression for collision rate is conveniently re-expressed in terms of second-order collision-rate constants:

$$Z_{AA} = \omega_{AA} [n_A]^2, \qquad \Omega_{AA} [N_A]^2 = \frac{Z_{AA}}{n_{Av}} \tag{9-23}$$

For helium at STP, the numerical values of these constants are

$$\omega_{AA} = 1.82 \times 10^{-10} \text{ cm}^3/\text{molecule-sec} \tag{9-24}$$

$$\Omega_{AA} = 1.10 \times 10^{14} \text{ cm}^3/\text{mole-sec} \tag{9-25}$$

The values in general are

$$\omega_{AA} = 1.82 \times 10^{-10} \left(\frac{4.0}{M} \frac{T}{273} \right)^{1/2} \left(\frac{d}{2.6} \right)^2 \tag{9-26}$$

$$\Omega_{AA} = 1.10 \times 10^{14} \left(\frac{4.0}{M} \frac{T}{273} \right)^{1/2} \left(\frac{d}{2.6} \right)^2 \tag{9-27}$$

$$\Omega_{AB} = 2.20 \times 10^{14} \left(\frac{2.0}{\mu_{AB}} \frac{T}{273} \right)^{1/2} \left(\frac{d_A + d_B}{5.2} \right)^2 \tag{9-28}$$

where $\mu_{AB} = M_A M_B / (M_A + M_B)$.

(ii) Partition-Function Form of Transition-State Theory

The reactants are two atoms A and B, of diameters d_A and d_B, masses m_A and m_B. The products are the same molecules that have just collided. The separation surface or transition state are two atoms $\frac{1}{2}(d_A + d_B)$ apart with a negative radial momentum (that is, R is getting shorter). Reactants and transition state have the same origin of energy. The rate expression (Eq. 8–32) is

$$\mathbf{R} = \frac{[n_A]}{f_A} \frac{[n_B]}{f_B} f'_{\ddagger} \frac{kT}{h} V = \frac{[n_A][n_B](f_t^3 f_r^2)_{\ddagger}}{f_{tA}^3 f_{tB}^3} \frac{kT}{h} V \tag{9–29}$$

$$= \frac{[n_A][n_B] \dfrac{[2\pi(m_A + m_B)kT]^{3/2}V}{h^3} \dfrac{8\pi^2 \mu d^2 kT}{\sigma h^2} \dfrac{kT}{h} V}{\dfrac{(2\pi m_A kT)^{3/2}V}{h^3} \dfrac{(2\pi m_B kT)^{3/2}V}{h^3}} \tag{9–30}$$

$$= \frac{\pi d^2}{\sigma} \left(\frac{8kT}{\pi\mu}\right)^{1/2} [n_A][n_B] = \frac{\pi d^2}{\sigma} \bar{g}[n_A][n_B] \tag{9–31}$$

where $\mu = m_A m_B/(m_A + m_B)$, $d = (d_A + d_B)/2$, and $\sigma = 1$ if A is different from B and $\sigma = 2$ if A is the same as B. This rate expression is the same as that found by collision theory (Eqs. 15 to 17).

(iii) Jacobian-Factor Version of Transition-State Theory

The rate expression is

$$\mathbf{R} = \frac{\nu^*}{\sigma} \frac{\prod(Jl\Gamma)_{\ddagger}}{\prod(Jl\Gamma)_{A,B}} V[n_A][n_B] \tag{9–32}$$

$$= \frac{1}{\sigma} \frac{1}{2\pi} \left(\frac{F^*}{\mu}\right)^{1/2} \frac{V(4\pi d_{AB}^2)\left(\dfrac{2\pi kT}{F^*}\right)^{1/2}}{V \, V} [n_A][n_B] \tag{9–33}$$

$$= \frac{\pi d_{AB}^2}{\sigma} \left(\frac{8kT}{\pi\mu}\right)^{1/2} [n_A][n_B] \tag{9–34}$$

in agreement with Eq. 31.

C. CLOSE-COLLISION RATE OF PARTICLES THAT ATTRACT AS $-a/R^s$

(i) Collision Theory

If two particles interact by way of a potential-energy function that depends only on the distance of separation, $V(R)$, then the dynamics can be reduced to a one-body scattering problem where scattering is from the fixed origin of $V(R)$ and the scattered particle has mass μ, initial (large separation) relative velocity g, and impact parameter b. As was shown in Chapter 7, the dynamics of the interaction is given by the two equations

$$\mu R^2 \dot{\phi} = \mu b g \tag{9-35}$$

$$\tfrac{1}{2}\mu g^2 = \tfrac{1}{2}\mu \dot{R}^2 + \tfrac{1}{2}\mu g^2 (b/R)^2 + V(R) \tag{9-36}$$

The potential-energy function of interest here is attraction according to an inverse power of the separation

$$V = -a/R^s, \qquad s > 2 \tag{9-37}$$

The "effective potential energy" is the sum of the true potential energy and the "centrifugal potential"

$$V_{\text{eff}} = \tfrac{1}{2}\mu g^2 (b/R)^2 - a/R^s \tag{9-38}$$

An effective potential-energy function for inverse R^6 is illustrated by Fig. 7–10. The effective potential-energy function is determined by the product bg and not by the individual initial conditions, impact parameter and velocity. The curve V_{eff} has a maximum at R^* and V^*. For a given curve V_{eff}, the collision is represented by a straight line, of constant total energy, parallel to the R axis. A line lower than the maximum in V_{eff} represents relatively low velocity and large impact parameter. The trajectory of the collision is a small-angle deflection occurring at large distances of separation. A total-energy line higher than the maximum in V_{eff} represents high velocities and small impact parameter. The trajectory of the collision is more or less "head-on"; the particles undergo a close collision with the repulsive core, which is not shown in Fig. 7–10 nor given by Eq. 37. A total-energy line exactly tangent to the maximum in V_{eff} would (according to classical mechanics) result in a collision in which the two particles orbit indefinitely around the center of mass.

The "rate of close collision" is thus identified as applying to collisions with total energy greater than the maximum in the effective potential-energy curve. The first problem is to find the radius R^* at this maximum, the value of the effective potential energy at this maximum V_{eff}^*, and the critical impact parameter b_c that goes with R^* and V_{eff}^*. The radius at the maximum in V_{eff}^* is found by differentiating V_{eff} with respect to R and equating to zero; and it is

$$R^* = \left(\frac{sa}{\mu g^2 b^2}\right)^{1/(s-2)} \tag{9-39}$$

Substituting Eq. 39 in Eq. 38, one finds for the maximum value of effective potential energy

$$V_{\text{eff}}^* = (\mu g^2 b^2)^{s/s-2} \left(\frac{1}{sa}\right)^{2/(s-2)} \left(\frac{1}{2} - \frac{1}{s}\right) \tag{9-40}$$

At the maximum point of V_{eff} the radial velocity $\dot{R}$ is zero, so from Eqs. 36, 37, and 39 one can evaluate the critical impact parameter b_c in terms of initial velocity g:

$$b_c^2 = \left(\frac{sa}{\mu g^2}\right)^{2/s}\left(\frac{s+2}{s}\right)^{(2-s)/s} \quad (9\text{--}41)$$

For the velocity g that gives b_c according to Eq. 41, it is clear that any impact parameter less than b_c will also lead to a close collision (even though it now corresponds to another effective-potential-energy curve). For a given velocity g, the probability of a close collision is unity ($\kappa = 1$) if the impact parameter is equal to or less than b_c, and the probability of close collision is zero ($\kappa = 0$) if the impact parameter is greater than b_c. Thus the collision rate (compare Eq. 12) for initial velocity between g and $g + dg$ is

$$\mathbf{R}(g) = \pi b_c^2(g)g[dn_{\text{B}}(g)] \quad (9\text{--}42)$$

Unlike the hard-sphere case of Eq. 12, this collision cross-section πb_c^2 is a function of the initial energy (Eq. 41). If the distribution of velocities is not at equilibrium (for a detailed examination of this interesting situation for the extremely rapid recombination of methyl radicals, see Ref. 35), the non-equilibrium distribution function for $[dn_{\text{B}}(g)]$ is inserted in Eq. 42 and integrated over velocity to give the total rate. If the distribution of velocities is the equilibrium distribution, $[dn_{\text{B}}(g)]$ is just the Maxwell-Boltzmann equation again, and the integral is

$$\mathbf{R} = [n_{\text{B}}]\left(\frac{sa}{\mu}\right)^{2/s}\left(\frac{s-2}{s}\right)^{(2-s)/2}\frac{4\pi^2\mu^{3/2}}{(2\pi kT)^{3/2}}\int_0^\infty g^{(3-4/s)}\exp\left(-\mu g^2/2kT\right)dg \quad (9\text{--}43)$$

TABLE 9–I

Rate of Close Collisions for Pairs of Particles with $-a/R^s$ as Potential-Energy Function

s	k, cc^2 sec^{-1}	
3	$\dfrac{2^{5/6}\pi^{1/2}a^{2/3}\Gamma(1/3)}{(kT)^{1/6}\mu^{1/2}}$	$= \dfrac{8.47a^{2/3}}{(kT)^{1/6}\mu^{1/2}}$
4	$\dfrac{2^{3/2}\pi^{1/2}a^{1/2}\Gamma(1/2)}{\mu^{1/2}}$	$= 8.89\left(\dfrac{a}{\mu}\right)^{1/2}$
5	$\dfrac{2^{11/10}3^{2/5}\pi^{1/2}(kT)^{0.1}a^{0.4}\Gamma(3/5)}{\mu^{1/2}}$	$= \dfrac{8.79a^{0.4}(kT)^{0.1}}{\mu^{1/2}}$
6	$\dfrac{2^{11/6}\pi^{1/2}\Gamma(2/3)a^{1/3}(kT)^{1/6}}{\mu^{1/2}}$	$= \dfrac{8.47a^{1/3}(kT)^{1/6}}{\mu^{1/2}}$
8	$\dfrac{2^{3/2}3^{1/4}\pi^{1/2}\Gamma(3/4)(akT)^{1/4}}{\mu^{1/2}}$	$= \dfrac{8.10(akT)^{1/4}}{\mu^{1/2}}$
10	$\dfrac{2^{1.9}\pi^{1/2}\Gamma(4/5)a^{0.2}(kT)^{0.3}}{\mu^{1/2}}$	$= \dfrac{7.67a^{0.2}(kT)^{0.3}}{\mu^{1/2}}$

This integral is readily evaluated in terms of gamma functions:

$$\mathbf{k} = \frac{\pi^{1/2}}{\mu^{1/2}} (2)^{(3s-4)/2s} (s-2)^{2/s} (a)^{2/s} (kT)^{(s-4)/2s} \Gamma\left(\frac{s-2}{s}\right) \quad (9\text{-}44)$$

The rate constant for close collision for various values of the index s is given in Table 1.

This derivation is worthy of close study for its clear statement of the relation between collision theory and transition-state theory. The "dividing surface" in the sense of Chapter 8 is placed far from the site of interactions and where the reactants are independent and unperturbed. An examination of the transition state where interactions are large gave the criterion for reaction (close collision) in terms of properties of the reactants, b_c and g. The properties of the transition state gave the transmission coefficient for the colliding reactants to undergo close collision.

(ii) Transition-State Theory

The reactants are separated atoms or spherically symmetrical molecules A and B, of mass m_A and m_B. The products are the two atoms very close together. The separating surface is the maximum of effective potential energy (compare Eq. 40), and one sees that this treatment holds only if s is greater than 2. The origin of energy is the same for reactants and transition state.

For this case, one finds that the usual final rate expression (Eq. 8-32) cannot be used, and the molecular rate is not dependent on one and only one coordinate. In this case activated-complex theory is applied to each angular momentum state. The location of the maximum in effective potential energy depends on the angular momentum (compare Fig. 7-10), and the velocity of crossing the strip depends on the radial momentum. This problem will be treated in full detail, going back to Eq. 8-24 for a rate expression and writing out the full Lagrangian and Hamiltonian functions for the problem.

The coordinates chosen are center of mass, X, Y, Z, and relative polar R, θ, Φ. The potential energy depends only on R, so that the complete Lagrangian function is (compare Eq. 7-15)

$$L = \tfrac{1}{2}(m_A + m_B)(\dot{X}^2 + \dot{Y}^2 + \dot{Z}^2) + \tfrac{1}{2}\mu(\dot{R}^2 + R^2\dot{\theta}^2 + R^2 \sin^2\theta\dot{\Phi}^2) + a/R^s$$
$$= L_{\text{cm}} + L_{\text{int}} \quad (9\text{-}45)$$

Any momentum p_i is defined as $\partial L/\partial\dot{q}_i$, so the momenta are

$$\begin{aligned} p_X &= M\dot{X} & p_R &= \mu\dot{R} \\ p_Y &= M\dot{Y} & p_\theta &= \mu R^2\dot{\theta} \\ p_Z &= M\dot{Z} & p_\Phi &= \mu R^2 \sin^2\theta\dot{\Phi} \end{aligned} \quad (9\text{-}46)$$

The complete Hamiltonian function is

$$H = \frac{1}{2M}(p_x^2 + p_y^2 + p_z^2) + \frac{p_R^2}{2\mu} + \frac{p_\theta^2}{2\mu R^2} + \frac{p_\Phi^2}{2\mu R^2 \sin^2 \theta} - \frac{a}{R^s} \quad (9\text{-}47)$$

The volume element in phase space is

$$d\tau = dX\, dY\, dZ\, dp_X\, dp_Y\, dp_Z\, dR\, d\theta\, d\Phi\, dp_R\, dp_\theta\, dp_\Phi \quad (9\text{-}48)$$

The effective potential energy is

$$V_{\text{eff}} = \frac{p_\theta^2}{2\mu R^2} + \frac{p_\Phi^2}{2\mu R^2 \sin^2 \theta} - \frac{a}{R^s} \quad (9\text{-}49)$$

If s is greater than 2, the effective potential energy has a maximum. The maximum value of the effective potential energy is given by differentiation of Eq. 49 with respect to $(1/R)$ and setting to zero. The value of R at maximum V_{eff} is given by

$$\frac{1}{R^*} = \left(\frac{p_\theta^2 + p_\Phi^2/\sin^2 \theta}{sa\mu}\right)^{1/(s-2)} \quad (9\text{-}50)$$

The value of the effective potential energy at the maximum is

$$V^* = a\left(\frac{p_\theta^2 + p_\phi^2/\sin^2 \theta}{sa\mu}\right)^{s/(s-2)}\left(\frac{s-2}{2}\right) \quad (9\text{-}51)$$

The frequency of crossing a distance δ over the maximum (compare Fig. 7–10) is given by

$$\nu = P_R/\mu\delta \quad (9\text{-}52)$$

The interaction is a close collision if the internal Hamiltonian exceeds the rotational barrier and only an uninteresting small-angle deflection if the total internal energy is less than the rotational barrier in height. Thus the transmission coefficient for close collisions is

$$\begin{aligned} \kappa &= 0 \qquad \text{if } H_{\text{int}} < V^* \\ \kappa &= 1 \qquad \text{if } H_{\text{int}} > V^* \end{aligned} \quad (9\text{-}53)$$

The internal Hamiltonian is

$$H_{\text{int}} = \frac{p_R^2}{2\mu} + \frac{p_\theta^2}{2\mu R^2} + \frac{p_\Phi^2}{2\mu R^2 \sin^2 \theta} \quad (9\text{-}54)$$

Thus even though the frequency of crossing a strip depends on only one momentum, p_R (Eq. 52), the transmission coefficient κ depends on three momenta and two coordinates:

$$\kappa = \kappa(p_R, p_\theta, p_\phi, R, \theta) \quad (9\text{-}55)$$

The rate of close collision (Eq. 53) is

$$k = \frac{(f_t^3)_{+}}{f_A f_B} \frac{1}{h^3} \int \cdots \int_6 \exp\left[-(V^* + p_R^2/2\mu)/kT\right] \frac{p_R}{\mu\delta}\, d\tau \qquad (9\text{--}56)$$

To evaluate the integral, it is convenient to define two new variables

$$p^2 = p_\theta^2 + p_\Phi^2/\sin^2\theta$$
$$\tan\chi = \sin\theta(p_\theta/p_\Phi) \qquad (9\text{--}57)$$

or the inverse transformations are

$$p_\Phi = p\cos\chi\sin\theta$$
$$p_\theta = p\sin\chi \qquad (9\text{--}58)$$

In these variables the volume elements are

$$d\tau = dR\, d\theta\, d\Phi\, dp_R\, dp_\theta\, dp_\Phi$$
$$= \sin\theta\, d\theta\, d\chi\, d\Phi\, p\, dp\, dR\, dp_R \qquad (9\text{--}59)$$

The sixfold integral in Eq. 56 is reduced to

$$\frac{1}{h^3}\int_0^\pi \sin\theta\, d\theta \int_0^{2\pi} d\chi \int_0^{2\pi} d\Phi \int_{R^*}^{R^*+\delta} \frac{dR}{\delta}$$
$$\times \int_0^\infty \exp\left[-\frac{p^{2t}}{kT(sa\mu)^t 2t}\right] p\, dp \int_0^\infty \exp\left(-p_R^2/2\mu kT\right)\frac{p_R\, dp_R}{\mu} \qquad (9\text{--}60)$$

where $t = s/(s-2)$. These integrals reduce respectively to

$$\frac{1}{h^3}(2)(2\pi)(2\pi)(1)(I)(kT) = \frac{8\pi^2 kT}{h^3}(I) \qquad (9\text{--}61)$$

where I is the integral over angular momentum p. Although this integral can be evaluated in general (for s greater than 2), it is convenient to leave it as I and write the rate constant expression (with some condensing of terms) as

$$\mathbf{k} = \left(\frac{8kT}{\pi\mu}\right)^{1/2}\left[\frac{\pi}{\mu kT}\int_0^\infty \exp\left[-V^*(p)/kT\right]p\, dp\right] = \bar{g}\pi\left(\frac{I}{\mu kT}\right) = \bar{g}\pi d_{\text{eff}}^2 \qquad (9\text{--}62)$$

Thus the integral I multiplied by π and divided by μkT gives the effective cross-section πd_{eff}^2 for the collision, or the equivalent hard-sphere collision diameter is

$$d_{\text{eff}} = \left(\frac{I}{\mu kT}\right)^{1/2} \qquad (9\text{--}63)$$

The value of the integral in Eq. 60 is simply

$$I = \left(\frac{s-2}{2s}\right)\left[\frac{2kT}{a(s-2)}\right]^{(s-2)/s}(sa\mu)\Gamma\left(\frac{s-2}{s}\right) \qquad (9\text{--}64)$$

When all terms are collected, the final rate expressions for various values of the index s are the same as those of Eq. 44.

For this particular example, the collision-theory formulation is computationally simpler than the transition-theory formulation. For equilibrium distributions of reactants, both approaches give the same result. It seems that the collision-theory formulation is the easier to generalize for non-equilibrium distribution of reactants.

This problem can be set up in terms of quantized angular momenta[52] instead of the classical-mechanical form considered above. Angular momentum is quantized and its magnitude is given by the quantum number J. For a fixed value of the angular momentum, conserved in spite of expansion or contraction of the intermolecular distance R, and for inverse R^6 potential-energy function, $V = -a/R^6$, there is only one internuclear distance R_c at which attractive and centrifugal forces are balanced. At larger separations the complex spirals apart. At shorter separations the complex spirals inward, and the radicals or molecules undergo a close encounter. Activated-complex theory calculates the rate at which complexes cross into a spherical shell of diameter R_c for a given value of J, and then sums over all values of J. It is assumed that the distance R_c is so great that the radicals in the complex have about the same vibrational and rotational energy levels as for the free reactants.

The magnitude of the angular momentum is M where

$$M^2 = J(J + 1)\alpha^2$$

where α is $h/2\pi$. The multiplicity of the quantum number J is $2J + 1$. If the intermolecular attraction is given by $-a/R^6$, the critical diameter is

$$R_c = (6a\mu/M^2)^{1/4}$$

where μ is the reduced mass. The potential energy at this distance is

$$V(R_c) = 2M^3/(6\mu)^{3/2}a^{1/2}$$

and the relative rate from one rotational state to another is given by

$$\beta(J) = (2J + 1) \exp\left[-2\{J(J + 1)\alpha^2\}^{3/2}/(6\mu)^{3/2}a^{1/2}kT\right]$$

If the quantum-mechanical sum over rotational states can be approximated by an integration, then the integral gives the gamma function of 2/3. The final expression for the rate of collision is as before

$$k = \frac{2^{11/6}\pi^{1/2}a^{1/3}(kT)^{1/6}\Gamma(2/3)}{\sigma\mu^{1/2}}$$

D. BIMOLECULAR COMBINATION OF IONS[53]

(i) Collision Theory

At large distances apart two monovalent ions of opposite charge have the potential-energy function $-\varepsilon^2/R$, but at some close distance D short-range chemical bonding sets in. A simplified model for combination of ions is that reaction occurs if the particles reach the distance D but does not occur if the distance of closest approach exceeds D. For separations greater than D, the relation of conservation of energy is

$$\tfrac{1}{2}\mu g^2 = \tfrac{1}{2}\mu \dot{R}^2 + \tfrac{1}{2}\mu g^2 (b/R)^2 - \varepsilon^2/R \qquad (9\text{-}65)$$

If at the entrance to the "reaction shell" of particle separation D, the radial velocity is zero, one can evaluate the critical impact parameter (compare Eq. 7–36):

$$b_c^2 = D^2 \left(1 + \frac{\varepsilon^2/D}{\mu g^2/2}\right) \qquad (9\text{-}66)$$

For this particular value of initial velocity, any impact parameter equal to or less than b_c leads to a collision on the surface of the shell D, but any impact parameter greater than b_c merely gives a deflection with distance of closest approach greater than D. Thus the rate for initial relative velocity between g and $g + dg$ is

$$\mathbf{R}(g) = \pi b_c^2(g)g[dn(g)] \qquad (9\text{-}67)$$

The total rate of reaction is the integral of Eq. 67 over all values of the velocity:

$$\mathbf{R} = \pi \int_0^\infty b_c^2(g)g[dn(g)] \qquad (9\text{-}68)$$

For an equilibrium distribution of reactants one again uses the Maxwell-Boltzmann relation:

$$k = 4\pi^2 \left(\frac{\mu}{2\pi kT}\right)^{3/2} D^2 \int_0^\infty \left(1 + \frac{2\varepsilon^2}{\mu D g^2}\right) g^3 \exp\left(-\mu g^2/2kT\right) dg \qquad (9\text{-}69)$$

Evaluating these integrals and collecting terms, one has

$$k = \pi D^2 \left(\frac{8kT}{\pi\mu}\right)^{1/2} \left[1 + \frac{\varepsilon^2}{DkT}\right] \qquad (9\text{-}70)$$

The first term in the bracket corresponds to the "hard-sphere" rate (Eq. 15), and the second term gives the increase in rate brought about by the attractive potential-energy function. If D is about 2×10^{-8} cm, at room temperature the "attractive contribution" exceeds the "hard-sphere" term by about a factor of 300 or the collision diameter exceeds the hard-sphere diameter by about a factor of 17.

(ii) Transition-State Theory

The reactants are two monovalent, oppositely charged, gaseous ions, A and B. The product is the ion pair inside a sphere of radius D. The potential-energy function is simply Coulomb's law, for separations greater than D:

$$V = -\varepsilon^2/R \qquad R > D \qquad (9\text{-}71)$$

and it breaks off in some undefined manner as multidimensional, short-range chemical forces become important where R is less than the distance D. The transition state is the surface of the sphere of radius D, that is, the surface of the area of chemical interaction. The effective potential energy is

$$V_{\text{eff}} = \frac{\mu g^2 b^2}{2R^2} - \frac{\varepsilon^2}{R} \tag{9-72}$$

On the sphere of radius D, the potential energy is ε^2/D and the centrifugal energy is $\mu g^2 b^2/2D^2$. The effective potential energy in multiple of the potential energy at the dividing surface is

$$\frac{V_{\text{eff}}}{\varepsilon^2/D} = \frac{(\mu g^2 b^2/2D^2)}{(\varepsilon^2/D)} \left(\frac{D}{R}\right)^2 - \left(\frac{D}{R}\right) \tag{9-73}$$

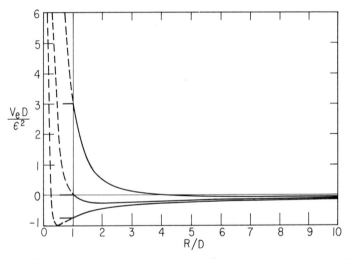

Fig. 9-1. Combination of ions. Reduced, effective potential energy (Eq. 73), for various values of reduced centrifugal energy, 1/4, 1, 4.

This reduced, effective potential energy is plotted against R/D for various values (1/4, 1, 4) of the reduced centrifugal energy in Fig. 1. The effective-potential-energy function for the long-range Coulomb potential is quite different from that for the short-range a/R^6 (compare Figs. 7–10 and 9–1). The Coulomb effective potential shows a shallow well below zero total energy, and a steeply rising centrifugal barrier at close distances. The dividing surface, $R = D$, cuts the inaccessible negative energy curve for reduced centrifugal energies less than one, and the centrifugal barrier repels incoming systems with total energy less than

$$V^* = \frac{\mu g^2 b^2}{2D^2} - \frac{\varepsilon^2}{D} \tag{9-74}$$

In Fig. 1, the effective-potential-energy function, Eq. 72, is continued as a dashed line for R less than D, and it is continued as a short flat solid line for a short distance. The transition state is a narrow range of R just below D, where the chemical forces are assumed to give a flat segment to the effective potential energy. It is clear from Fig. 1 that all particles enter the figure from the right with total energy greater than zero, and thus states of the activated complex with energies below zero are unoccupied. Even if the reactants have an equilibrium distribution of energies, the transition state has a truncated non-equilibrium distribution function. The rate is the same as that of Eq. 60, except that the fifth integral is different. The fifth integral over angular momentum is replaced by the sum of two integrals:

$$I = \int_0^{p_0} p\, dp + \int_{p_0}^{\infty} \exp\left(-V^*/kT\right)p\, dp \qquad (9\text{-}75)$$

where V^* is given by Eq. 74 and p_0 is the angular momentum that gives unit reduced centrifugal energy:

$$p_0^2 = 2\mu D\varepsilon^2 \qquad (9\text{-}76)$$

The surprising thing about Eq. 75 is the absence of the Boltzmann factor in the first integral; this feature arises because of the truncated non-equilibrium distribution of total energies of the transition state. The integral Eq. 75 is readily evaluated, and when substituted in Eq. 60, Eq. 70 is derived again.

For recombination of ions, collision theory is much simpler than transition-state theory. The example is instructive in showing that the "transition state" need not be at a maximum in the effective-potential-energy curve and the reaction coordinate need not be separable from the other rotational coordinates (as with the example of Section C).

E. NUMERICAL EXAMPLES AND COMPARISON WITH EXPERIMENT

(i) Rate of Recombination of Radicals[54]

The rate of recombination of free radicals is extremely fast, and it provides a test of the calculated collision rates. This fast reaction is followed not by direct observation of disappearance of reactants, but rather by indirect methods.

$$CH_3 + CH_3 \longrightarrow C_2H_6^* \xrightarrow{M} C_2H_6 \qquad (9\text{-}77)$$

The rate constants for many radical-recombination reactions have been obtained and also for many radical disproportionations, such as

$$C_2H_5 + C_2H_5 \rightarrow C_2H_4 + C_2H_6 \qquad (9\text{-}78)$$

These reactions occur with zero (0 ± 1 kcal) activation energy, and it is of interest to compare these bimolecular reaction-rate constants with the bimolecular collision-rate constants as derived above. However, first it must be remembered that radicals have an odd number of electrons, and triplet products are usually highly unstable relative to singlet products. Radicals with one unpaired spin are typically $^2S_{1/2}$, $^2P_{1/2}$, or $^2P_{3/2}$, with spin multiplicity g respectively 2, 2, and 4. Stable molecular products (with O_2 as an exception) with an even number of electrons typically have spin multiplicity g of one. Out of a large number of collisions between reactants A and B to form singlet products, only the fraction

$$B_g = 1/g_A g_B \qquad (9\text{--}79)$$

can lead to stable products.

The rate of radical-radical reactions can be calculated by the hard-sphere model with "collision diameters" obtained from the Lennard-Jones σ parameter of "similar" stable molecules, that is, CH_4 is used as a model for CH_3, $CHCl_3$ for CCl_3, Ar for Cl, etc. These values of σ are listed in Table 7–1. The collision-rate constants from Eq. 7–11 are multiplied by B_g and entered in Table 2 for comparison with experimental rate constants.

At close distances, recombining radicals attract with strong short-range "chemical" forces, but far apart the attraction is the London force or the

TABLE 9–2

Bimolecular Reactions with Zero Activation Energy: Observed and Calculated Rate Constants at 400°K

			log **k**, cc/mole-sec		
Reactants		Obs.	Calc. (Eqs. 9–44 and 4–7)	Calc. (Eqs. 9–44 and 4–8)	Calc. (Hard-sphere Eq. 9–18)
A	B				
CH_3	CH_3	13.5	13.8	13.9	13.6
CH_2Cl	CH_2Cl	12.6	13.7	13.8	13.3
$CHCl_2$	$CHCl_2$	12.4	13.7	13.9	13.5
CCl_3	CCl_3	11.8	13.7	13.8	13.4
C_2H_5	C_2H_5	13.5	13.8	13.9	13.5
C_2H_4Cl	C_2H_4Cl	13.1	13.7	—	—
$C_2H_3Cl_2$	$C_2H_3Cl_2$	13	13.7	—	—
$C_2H_2Cl_3$	$C_2H_2Cl_3$	13	13.7	—	—
C_2Cl_5	C_2Cl_5	11.7	13.7	—	—
CH_3	Cl	14.6	13.7	13.8	13.4
CH_2Cl	Cl	14.4	13.6	13.7	13.2
$CHCl_2$	Cl	14.4	13.6	13.7	13.3
CCl_3	Cl	14.4	13.7	13.9	13.5
C_2H_5	Cl	14.3	13.7	13.8	13.4
C_2H_4Cl	Cl	14.3	13.7	—	—
$C_2H_3Cl_2$	Cl	14.3	13.7	—	—
$C_2H_2Cl_3$	Cl	14.3	13.7	—	—
C_2HCl_4	Cl	14.2	13.7	—	—
C_2Cl_5	Cl	14.3	13.7	—	—
C_2H_4	Cl	13.2	14.3	14.4	14.0
C_2H_3Cl	Cl	13.2	14.2	—	—
C_2HCl_3	Cl	13	14.3	—	—
C_2Cl_4	Cl	12.6	14.3	—	—

TABLE 9–3

Bimolecular Reactions with Zero Activation Energy: Parameters Used To Evaluate Coefficient of Inverse R^6 Attraction

Reactants		Semiempirical Theory					Lennard-Jones 6–12			Spin Factor	Sym. No.
A	B	α_1	α_2	N_1	N_2	$a^{1\,3}$ (Eq. 4–7)	σ	ε/k	$a^{1/3}$		
CH_3	CH_3	2.2	2.2	7	7	4.8	3.9	137	6.4	4	2
CH_2Cl	CH_2Cl	4.0	4.0	16	16	7.4	3.4	855	9.0	4	2
$CHCl_2$	$CHCl_2$	5.9	5.9	25	25	9.4	4.8	406	14	4	2
CCl_3	CCl_3	7.8	7.8	34	34	12	5.4	327	17	4	2
C_2H_5	C_2H_5	4.0	4.0	13	13	7.1	4.4	230	9.8	4	2
C_2H_4Cl	C_2H_4Cl	5.8	5.8	22	22	9.4	—	—	—	4	2
$C_2H_3Cl_3$	$C_2H_2Cl_3$	9.5	9.5	40	40	13	—	—	—	4	2
C_2Cl_5	C_2Cl_5	13.3	13.3	58	58	17	—	—	—	4	2
CH_3	Cl	2.2	2.3	12	10	5.2	3.6	222	6.5	8	1
CH_2Cl	Cl	4.0	2.3	16	10	6.2	2.35	555	7.5	8	1
$CHCl_2$	Cl	5.9	2.3	25	10	7.1	4.0	382	9.5	8	1
CCl_3	Cl	7.8	2.3	34	10	7.7	4.4	343	11	8	1
C_2H_5	Cl	4.0	23	13	10	6.2	3.9	288	8.2	8	1
C_2H_4Cl	Cl	5.8	2.3	22	10	7.0	—	—	—	8	1
$C_2H_3Cl_2$	Cl	7.7	2.3	31	10	7.7	—	—	—	8	1
$C_2H_2Cl_3$	Cl	9.5	2.3	40	10	8.3	—	—	—	8	1
C_2HCl_4	Cl	11.4	2.3	49	10	8.8	—	—	—	8	1
C_2Cl_5	Cl	13.3	2.3	58	10	9.3	—	—	—	8	1
C_2H_4	Cl	4.1	2.3	12	10	6.0	3.75	272	7.5	2	1
C_2H_3Cl	Cl	6.0	2.3	21	10	7.0	—	—	—	2	1
C_2HCl_3	Cl	9.7	2.3	39	10	8.3	—	—	—	2	1
C_2Cl_4	Cl	10.6	2.3	48	10	8.7	—	—	—	2	1

α in units of 10^{-24} cm^3; α and N from Eq. 4–7; Lennard-Jones parameters from corresponding molecule with one H atom in addition to radical; $\sigma_{AB} = (\sigma_A + \sigma_B)/2$, $\varepsilon_{AB} = (\varepsilon_A \varepsilon_B)^{1/2}$; a in c.g.s. units times 10^{60}.

potential energy of attraction is $V = -a/R^6$. A reasonable next step beyond the ultrasimple hard-sphere model is to assume that this potential function determines which collisions are to be close. As shown before, either collision theory or transition-state theory then leads to the same expression, given in Table 1. The proportionality constant a can be found theoretically for hydrogen or helium atoms; it can be found semiempirically (Eq. 4–7) for more complicated atoms, molecules, or radicals; or it can be evaluated purely empirically (Eq. 4–8) as $4\varepsilon\sigma^6$ if the Lennard-Jones constants are known, either directly or by analogy. The parameters used to evaluate a semiempirically and empirically for a set of radical-radical reactions are listed in Table 3. The values of $a^{1/3}$ as found from the Lennard-Jones parameter for RH is about 20 percent to 50 percent larger than that found for the radical R by the semiempirical method (Eq. 4–7). The collision constants were calculated by the appropriate expression from Table 3, were multiplied by the spin factor B_g, divided by the symmetry number of the two reactants, and are entered in Table 2 for comparison with observed rate constants.

Table 2 lists the observed radical-radical rate constants[56,57] and the close-collision rate constants as found by three methods: hard-sphere; a from Eq. 4–7; and a from Eq. 4–8. There is very little spread in the calculated close-collision rate constants for the entire series, and the differences between the three methods is small (factor of 2 or 3 at most). There is considerable spread in the observed rate constants, some are higher than theoretical (factor of 5) and some are lower than theoretical (factor of 100). The values higher than the theoretical values indicate that the formation of chemical bonds causes stronger attractions at intermediate distances than the London term $-a/R^6$; these reactions are examples of Fig. 7–9D, and thus some of the rotational barriers are lowered below that indicated by Fig. 7–10. This feature is probably general, and this theory must basically underestimate the rate of close collisions by more or less a factor of 10. In cases where theory and experiment are in agreement, it must be true that the other requirements for reaction (favorable orientation of the various internal coordinates of the reactants at time of collision, favorable phases of internal vibrations, etc.) accidentally balance the factor of 10 or so that the theory misses. In cases where experimental values are far less than theoretical values, the factors preventing reaction (orientations, phases, etc.) are much more important than the basic error of the theory itself. In summary, when reactions occur to *form* a chemical bond, the forces of attraction between the reactants are poorly given by Lennard-Jones functions; the actual number of close collisions exceeds that calculated by more or less a factor of 10. Furthermore, there are many requirements that polyatomic radicals and molecules must meet (besides the two-body close-collision requirements) that tend to reduce the rate below the collision rate. A theory, such as that considered here, that underestimates the true collision rate is sure to have some glorious, accidental successes (for example, re-combination of methyl radicals), but for the group of observed reactions as a whole it overestimates some rates and underestimates others.

Unless one is prepared to consider the realistic potential-energy function, that is, the formation of the chemical bond at intermediate and close distances, one might just as well use the simple hard-sphere model for collision rates as the more complicated models involving an attractive potential.

(ii) Ion-Molecule Reactions in the Gas Phase[58]

It has long been obvious that reactions between ions and molecules in the gas phase must be important in many processes, for example, radiation chemistry, electric discharges, photochemistry in the far ultraviolet, reactions in the upper atmosphere, microwave pulses, shock waves, and flames.   From time to time special methods have been used to detect ions and free electrons in such systems, and in recent years the quantitative measurement of rate constants and reaction cross-sections has become possible.   The products of ion-molecule reactions in the mass spectrometer have been recognized for several years, for example, CH_5^+ and H_3^+; often these reactions have been regarded as nuisances, and the products regarded as hazards to the correct identification of mass spectra.   However, recently the emphasis has been turned around; these reactions have been studied directly; and in the mass spectrometer the second-order rate constants have been evaluated for reactions such as:

a. $H_2^+ + H_2 \rightarrow H_3^+ + H$

b. $CH_4^+ + CH_4 \rightarrow CH_5^+ + CH_3$

c. $HCl^+ + HCl \rightarrow H_2Cl^+ + Cl$

d. $CH_3OH^+ + CH_3OH \rightarrow CH_3OH_2^+ + CH_3O$ $\qquad$ (9–80)

e. $C_3H_5^+ + C_3H_6 \rightarrow C_4H_7^+ + C_2H_4$

f. $Kr^+ + H_2 \rightarrow KrH^+ + H$

g. $H_2^+ + O_2 \rightarrow HO_2^+ + H$

h. $CH_3^+ + CH_4 \rightarrow C_2H_5^+ + H_2$

The evaluation of the rate constant involves detailed knowledge of the mass spectrometer, its geometry, the "repeller" potential, the relation between pressure measured outside the ionization zone and that actually present inside the ionization zone, the appearance potential of the ions, etc. The quantity measured is the reaction cross-section as a function of ion-repeller voltage, and with further assumptions the bimolecular rate constant is evaluated.

The attraction of an ion for a polarizable spherical molecule is

$$V = -a/R^4 \qquad (9\text{–}81)$$

The coefficient a is simply related to the polarizability α of the molecule:

$$a = \alpha\varepsilon^2/2 \qquad (9\text{–}82)$$

where ε is the charge of the ion.   Polarizabilities of the various molecular reactants, Eq. 80, are listed in Table 4 and hard-sphere diameters are estimated from values of Lennard-Jones σ for similar molecules.   The algebraic expression for the collision-rate constant for this model is given in Table 1.   For the eight reactions given by Eq. 80, the collision-rate constant was calculated by hard-sphere model and from the inverse R^4 model, and these collision-rate constants are compared with the observed rate constants in Table 4.   Rate constants for the hard-sphere model vary only slightly, from 1.5 to 5.1 $\times$ 10^{-10} cc/molecule-sec. Rate constants calculated from the ion-molecule model, Eq. 81, also show only a small spread, 8.8 to 22 $\times$ 10^{-10}, but these values are typically about 4 or 5 times as large as the hard-sphere values. The observed rate constants show much greater variation, from 4.2 to 111 $\times$ 10^{-10}. In general, the agreement between calculated (ion-molecule) and observed rate constants is fairly good (within a factor of

TABLE 9–4

Rate Constants[58] for Ion-Molecule Reactions Compared with
Theoretical Values Using Inverse R^4 Attraction

Reactants		d Hard-Sphere (Å)	$10^{24}\alpha$ (cm³)	$10^{10}k$, cc/molecule-sec		
Ion	Molecule			Calc. Eq. 9–44	Obs.	Calc. (Hard-Sphere)
H_2^+	H_2	2.9	0.79	20.7	21	5.1
CH_4^+	CH_4	3.8	2.60	13.3	8.5	3.1
HCl^+	HCl	3.3	2.63	8.8	4.2	1.5
CH_3OH^+	CH_3OH	3.6	3.23	10.5	111	2.0
$C_3H_5^+$	C_3H_6	5.1	5.6	12.1	21	3.5
Kr^+	H_2	3.1	0.79	14.7	5.0	4.6
H_2^+	O_2	3.1	1.60	22	96	4.5
CH_3^+	CH_4	3.8	2.60	13.5	41	2.2

α: Ref. 29, p. 950.

4), but in some cases the observed rates are very much higher, probably an effect of short range chemical forces overriding Eq. 81 at important distances.

(iii) Recombination of Ions[59]

Association of ions, such as $H^+ + e^- \rightarrow H$, is necessarily a three-body, third-order reaction. However, dissociative recombination of ions such as

$$NO^+ + e^- \rightarrow N + 0 \qquad (9\text{–}83)$$

may be a second-order process. It has been found experimentally that for neutralization of heavy ions such as

$$NO^+ + SF_6^- \rightarrow \qquad (9\text{–}84)$$

the rate may be of mixed second and third order:

$$\mathbf{R} = (\mathbf{k}_2 + \mathbf{k}_3[M])[NO^+][SF_6^-]$$

By extrapolation to zero total pressure, one may separately evaluate both constants. The theory of second-order recombination of ions was reviewed in section D above, and that for third-order recombination has been given by Mahan and co-workers[59].

The second-order rate constant at room temperature for reaction 84 was found to be 1.5 to 2×10^{-7} cc^{-1} sec^{-1}. For a diameter of 4.6 Å, which is based on viscosity data for neutral SF_6 and NO, the hard-sphere collision-rate constant is 2.2×10^{-10} cc^{-1} sec^{-1}. If the diameter of interaction, D of Eq. 70, is taken to be this hard-sphere diameter, then the calculated rate constant is 0.26×10^{-7} cc^{-1} sec^{-1}. Thus the simple model considered in section D above predicts the correct order of magnitude of this extremely large rate constant, the observed value being only 6 to 8 times larger than that calculated. For this case, the hard-sphere relation is a total failure.

PROBLEMS

(1) Calculate an average time between successive collisions for each of the following situations where helium is the gas, hard-sphere model:

(a) on one cm^2 of surface, 300°K, one atm. pressure
(b) on one cm^2 of surface, 1000°K, one atm. pressure
(c) on one cm^2 of surface, 300°K, 10^{-6} atm. pressure
(d) helium-helium collision, 300°K, one atm.
(e) helium-helium collision, 1000°K, one atm.
(f) helium-helium collision, 300°K, 10^{-6} atm.

(2) For cases (d), (e), and (f) above, calculate the mean free path between collisions.

(3) If a of the London attractive potential is taken to be the "empirical" valve $4\epsilon\sigma^6$ and if σ is taken to be the hard-sphere diameter, find an algebraic expression for the ratio of close-collision rate as calculated by Eq. 9-44 and the hard-sphere rate. Evaluate this ratio at 300°K for helium-helium collisions and for xenon-xenon collisions (see Table 4-1).

10

Bimolecular Atom-Transfer Reactions, H—H—H

A. EXPERIMENTAL DATA[60]

Insofar as theory is concerned, the simplest bimolecular chemical reaction is that of hydrogen atom-molecule exchange:

$$H + H—H \xrightarrow{\ k\ } H—H + H \tag{10-1}$$

However, the experimental determination of this rate is extremely difficult, and the experimental data are subject to a disappointingly high degree of scatter and uncertainty. Simply as written, the reaction above is un-observable; some labeling of reactants and products is required. Such labelings to obtain observable kinetics include:

(i) Conversion of para-hydrogen to ortho-hydrogen.
(ii) Conversion of ortho-deuterium to para-deuterium.
(iii) Conversion of H_2 and D_2 to HD.

It is well to define the abstract, non-observable exchange-rate constant k in Eq. 1, and then carefully relate it to the various observable processes. Suppose all hydrogen atoms to be distinguishable; suppose every process such as reaction (1) could be observed directly; then the total rate of all exchange reactions defines the rate constant k:

$$R = k[H][H_2] \tag{10-2}$$

The non-observable total rate of exchange is proportional by the factor k to the product of macroscopic concentrations of hydrogen atoms and hydrogen molecules; specifically, note that no reduction in k has been made by virtue of the nature or distribution of labels.

(i) Conversion of Para-H_2 to Ortho-H_2

Normal "chemical" hydrogen is a mixture of one part of para-hydrogen (antisymmetric nuclear spins and even rotational quantum numbers) and three parts of ortho-hydrogen (symmetric nuclear spins and odd rotational quantum numbers). Almost pure para-hydrogen can be obtained by use of active charcoal or other catalysts at liquid-hydrogen temperatures. When warmed to room temperature in glass, quartz, or certain other containers, pure para-hydrogen can be maintained in a metastable state for many hours or days. At an elevated temperature some H_2 dissociates to produce atomic hydrogen H, which brings about para-to-ortho conversion by a chain reaction (Eq. 1). If one considers all possible exchange-collisions involving a hydrogen atom and a para-hydrogen molecule, one sees that the exchange can lead to ortho-hydrogen in three ways or to para-hydrogen in one way; thus the relation of specific changes to the overall exchange-rate constant k is

$$
\begin{aligned}
H + H_2(p) &\rightarrow H_2(p) + H & \tfrac{1}{4}k \\
&\rightarrow H_2(o) + H & \tfrac{3}{4}k \\
H + H_2(o) &\rightarrow H_2(p) + H & \tfrac{1}{4}k \\
&\rightarrow H_2(o) + H & \tfrac{3}{4}k
\end{aligned}
\tag{10-3}
$$

The differential rate equation for formation of ortho-hydrogen is

$$
\frac{d[H_2(o)]}{dt} = \tfrac{3}{4}k[H_2(p)][H] - \tfrac{1}{4}k[H_2(o)][H]
\tag{10-4}
$$

Under conditions of equilibrium distribution of spin states (at moderately high temperature), the rate of change of ortho-hydrogen is zero, so that the rate Eq. 4 gives the correct equilibrium result

$$
[H_2(o)]_{eq} = 3[H_2(p)]_{eq}
\tag{10-5}
$$

Under any conditions, equilibrium or not, the total molecular species are the sum of ortho- and para-hydrogen:

$$
[H_2(\Sigma)] = [H_2(o)] + [H_2(p)]
\tag{10-6}
$$

Thus the rate Eq. 4 can be expressed in terms of one variable, the concentration of ortho-hydrogen:

$$
\frac{d[H_2(o)]}{dt} = k[H]\{\tfrac{3}{4}[H_2(\Sigma)] - [H_2(o)]\}
\tag{10-7}
$$

This equation is readily integrated:

$$
\ln \{\tfrac{3}{4}[H_2(\Sigma)] - [H_2(o)]\} = -k[H]t + \text{constant}
\tag{10-8}
$$

At zero time, the initial concentration of ortho-hydrogen is $[H_2(o)]_i$, and at infinite time the concentration of ortho-hydrogen is the equilibrium value, $[H_2(o)]_{eq} = \tfrac{3}{4}[H_2(\Sigma)]$.

$$
\ln \frac{[H_2(o)]_{eq} - [H_2(o)]}{[H_2(o)]_{eq} - [H_2(o)]_i} = -k[H]t
\tag{10-9}
$$

The quantity most often reported in the literature is the half-time $\tau_{1/2}$ for the conversion of ortho-hydrogen to the equilibrium mixture:

$$\ln \tfrac{1}{2} = -k[H]\tau_{1/2} \qquad (10\text{--}10)$$

Thus the rate constant for total exchange can be evaluated in terms of the half-time of reaction

$$k = k_1 = 0.693/[H]\tau_{1/2} \qquad (10\text{--}11)$$

At low temperature, 10–100°C, Geib and Harteck produced a high mole fraction, 0.03 to 0.19, of hydrogen atoms in an electric discharge, and the rate of exchange was determined in a fast-flow system. Two series of data were taken: one with high mole fraction of atoms, 0.19, and large degrees of para-ortho conversion, 35 to 85 percent; a second series with small mole fraction of atoms, 0.03, and much smaller degrees of conversion, 6 to 35 percent. The rate constants were evaluated in terms of two extreme assumptions: "slug-travel" of the gaseous sample in the 1-liter reaction vessel or complete diffusive mixing of species in the reaction vessel. For the first series of runs, the estimated rate constant k_1 varied by as much as a factor of 3, depending on the assumption as to the degree of diffusion; for the second series (runs 9–13), the maximum variation in estimated rate constant is 25 percent. The rate constants for this second series are listed in Table 1; and the data for the first series (runs 1–8) are omitted entirely.

In a recent study, Schulz and LeRoy[60f] generated hydrogen atoms in one chamber, and by fast-flow techniques they mixed them with a stream of hydrogen molecules to study the para-ortho conversion between 300 and 444°K. The hydrogen-atom concentration in the reaction system was measured by a calorimetric (heat of atom recombination) probe. Ortho- and para-hydrogen were separated by gas chromatography and measured relative to helium. Schulz and LeRoy reported their rate constant as $\tfrac{3}{4}k_{obs}$ (compare Eq. 3). Their rate constant has been multiplied by 4/3 and entered in Table 1.

At elevated temperature, Farkas, at 873–1023°K, and van Meersche, at 723–874°K, studied para-ortho hydrogen conversion by thermal production of hydrogen atoms. It has recently been shown[60e] that chemical equilibrium between molecular and atomic hydrogen is brought about by catalysis of the walls of the vessel:

$$H_2 + W \rightleftharpoons 2H + W \qquad (10\text{--}12)$$

but also, that atmospheric oxygen slowly diffuses through silica tubes around 1000°K to produce additional para-ortho exchange, perhaps by way of HO radicals. These recent studies indicate that Farkas' results may be too high by as much as a factor of two. However, the uncertainty is such that the data cannot be rescued simply by applying a factor of two. Farkas'

TABLE 10–1

Rate Constants for Para-Ortho Conversion of Hydrogen and Deuterium[a]

Reaction	$T°K$	$1000/T$	P (mm)	log k	Ref.
1	873	1.145	400	12.18	60a
			200	12.20	
			100	12.16	
			50	12.17	
	923	1.082	400	12.10	
			200	12.13	
			100	12.12	
			50	12.10	
	973	1.027	400	12.32	
			200	12.28	
			100	12.33	
			50	12.35	
	1023	0.977	400	12.43	
			200	12.46	
			100	12.43	
			50	12.38	
1	283	3.532	0.57	7.78	60b
	284	3.520	0.53	7.88	
	330	3.030	0.56	8.57	
	373	2.680	0.56	9.13	
	373	2.680	0.53	9.12	
1	720	1.389	107	12.17	60c
	723	1.382	403	12.09	
	723	1.382	398	11.95	
	746	1.340	397	12.11	
	746	1.340	408	12.03	
	748	1.337	124	12.06	
	748	1.337	111	12.06	
	767	1.302	94	12.09	
	767	1.302	114	12.16	
	774	1.292	389	12.05	
	777	1.286	401	12.13	
	800	1.250	443	12.16	
	800	1.250	100	12.12	
	800	1.250	127	12.11	
	802	1.246	357	12.14	
	805	1.240	111	12.13	
	806	1.238	108	12.15	
	809	1.237	392	12.10	
	814	1.228	142	12.13	
	851	1.174	103	12.27	
	874	1.144	98	12.27	
1	300.2	3.330	3.1	8.196	60f
	301.2	3.320	2.7	8.220	
	323.2	3.092	3.1	8.457	
	323.8	3.088	3.1	8.472	
	343.9	2.908	3.1	8.668	
	343.6	2.911	3.1	8.661	
	364.4	2.743	3.0	8.920	
	364.2	2.745	3.0	8.883	
	383.7	2.606	3.2	9.088	
	383.4	2.609	3.3	9.060	
	404.0	2.473	4.3	9.286	
	404.1	2.472	4.3	9.293	
	423.5	2.360	4.3	9.486	
	423.4	2.361	4.3	9.485	
	443.4	2.253	4.3	9.639	
	444.3	2.250	4.3	9.670	

TABLE 10–1 (Continued)

Reaction	$T°K$	$1000/T$	P (mm)	log k	Ref.
2	903	1.107	29	11.79	60d
	927	1.079	29	11.81	
	931	1.074	74	11.76	
	931	1.074	15	11.84	
	932	1.073	31	11.90	
	933	1.072	11	11.94	
	933	1.072	9	11.94	
	945	1.058	14	11.86	
	969	1.032	13	11.85	
	971	1.030	18	11.83	
	973	1.028	8	12.00	
	981	1.019	12	11.87	
4	368.2	2.714	3.4	8.34	60g
	368.0	2.716	3.4	8.32	
	368.4	2.712	3.0	8.29	
	368.8	2.710	3.0	8.31	
	386.0	2.590	3.0	8.51	
	386.2	2.588	3.0	8.52	
	404.8	2.471	3.4	8.69	
	404.4	2.473	3.4	8.68	
	420.5	2.378	3.3	8.85	
	421.0	2.375	3.3	8.84	
	439.1	2.277	3.8	8.99	
	439.7	2.273	3.8	9.01	
	449.9	2.222	3.8	9.12	
	449.1	2.226	3.8	9.08	
	467.7	2.138	3.3	9.24	

[a] k in units of cc/mole-sec.

rate constants were recomputed from an extension of Eq. 11:

$$k_1 = 0.693/(K[H_2])^{1/2}\tau_{1/2} \tag{10–13}$$

using Farkas' half-times and modern values of the chemical equilibrium constant for reaction 12. Each of Farkas' rate constants is an average for four different initial pressures, 50, 100, 200, and 400 mm; and the second-order rate constant shows very good precision with respect to pressure variation. These four average rate constants are also given in Table 1 as k_1. Also, the results of van Meersche on para-ortho hydrogen conversion were recomputed by Eq. 13, and the rate constants are entered in Table 1 as k_1.

The points in Table 1 are too numerous and too close together to present clearly on one graph; they are grouped in blocks of more or less constant temperature and average rate constants. These averages are given in Table 2 and plotted in Fig. 1. The line is the Arrhenius function, log k = log A $-$ E/RT, where the value of log A is 14.71 and the Arrhenius activation energy is 8.7 kcal. The high temperature points of Farkas were also fitted to the Arrhenius equation to give log A = 13.98 and E = 7.4 kcal. This

TABLE 10–2

Rate Constants for Para-Ortho Conversion of Hydrogen
into Constant-Temperature Sets

$1000/T$	$\log k_1$	Ref.
0.977	12.42	60a
1.027	12.32	
1.082	12.11	
1.145	12.18	
1.160	12.27	60c
1.240	12.16	
1.295	12.11	
1.340	12.05	
1.382	12.02	
2.680	9.12	60b
3.030	8.57	
3.526	7.83	
3.32	8.21	60f
3.09	8.46	
2.91	8.66	
2.74	8.90	
2.61	9.07	
2.47	9.29	
2.36	9.48	
2.25	9.65	

function provides an interpolation formula for comparing the rate of HHH
with that of DDD. (Units of $\mathbf{A}$ are cc/mole-sec.)

(ii) Conversion of Ortho-Deuterium to Para-Deuterium

In a similar manner, Farkas and Farkas studied the rate of transformation
of ortho-deuterium to para-deuterium between 903 and 981°K. The rate
constants were re-evaluated by means of Eq. 13 and are entered in Table 1
as k_2. For these data the temperature range is so narrow and the scatter
so great that it is not useful to try to evaluate Arrhenius rate factors. An
estimate of the kinetic isotope effect was made. For each point k_2 listed in
Table 1, the value of k_1 was computed from the empirical Arrhenius function
for Farkas' study ($\log k_1 = 13.98 - 7400/2.303 \, RT$; see above). The ratio
of k_2 (observed) and k_1 (interpolated) at that temperature is then an estimate
of the kinetic isotope effect. The details of this treatment are given in
Table 3.

(iii) Conversion of H_2 and D_2 to HD

The isotope exchange reaction between H_2 and D_2 is much more complicated chemically than the para-ortho conversion discussed above. The

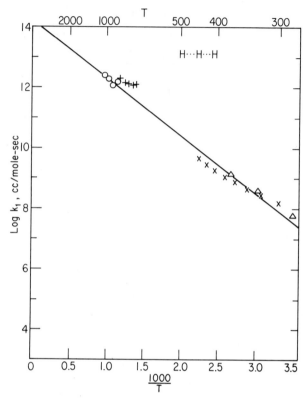

Fig. 10–1. Experimental points and least-squares Arrhenius line for HHH reaction: data from Table 2 and Table I; ○—Ref. a, △—Ref. b, +—Ref. c, f; all references from Table I.

TABLE 10–3

Kinetic Isotope Effect: $k(HHH)/k(DDD)$ or k_1/k_2

T	$1000/T$	$\log k_2$	$\log k_1{}^*$	k_1/k_2
903	1.107	11.79	12.18	2.5
927	1.079	11.81	12.22	2.6
931	1.074	11.76	12.23	2.9
931	1.074	11.84	12.23	2.5
932	1.073	11.90	12.24	2.2
933	1.072	11.94	12.24	2.0
933	1.072	11.94	12.24	2.0
945	1.058	11.86	12.26	2.5
969	1.032	11.85	12.30	2.8
971	1.030	11.83	12.30	2.9
973	1.028	12.00	12.31	2.0
981	1.019	11.87	12.32	2.8

* Interpolated.

overall reaction is

$$H_2 + D_2 = 2HD \qquad K_0 = \frac{[HD]^2}{[H_2][D_2]} \qquad (10\text{--}14)$$

The walls, usually of silica coated with phosphoric acid, catalyze the dissociative equilibria

$$H_2 + W = 2H + W$$
$$D_2 + W = 2D + W \qquad (10\text{--}15)$$
$$HD + W = H + D + W$$

for which the chemical equilibrium constants are

$$K_{HH} = [H]^2/[H_2]$$
$$K_{DD} = [D]^2/[D_2] \qquad (10\text{--}16)$$
$$K_{HD} = [H][D]/[HD]$$

The exchange reactions occur by way of the chain reactions

$$D + H_2 \underset{k_5}{\overset{k_3}{\rightleftarrows}} DH + H \qquad (10\text{--}17)$$

$$H + D_2 \underset{k_6}{\overset{k_4}{\rightleftarrows}} HD + D \qquad (10\text{--}18)$$

The following non-observable reactions are sometimes discussed in accounting for the statistics of the collision processes:

$$H + DH \xrightarrow{k_7} HD + H \qquad (10\text{--}19)$$

$$D + HD \xrightarrow{k_8} DH + D \qquad (10\text{--}20)$$

The following relations between rate constants and equilibrium constants are useful:

$$K_{35} = k_3/k_5 \qquad K_{46} = k_4/k_6 \qquad (10\text{--}21)$$

$$K_0 = K_{35}K_{46} \qquad (10\text{--}22)$$

The differential rate equation for formation of product is

$$\frac{d[HD]}{dt} = -\frac{2\,d[H_2]}{dt} \qquad (10\text{--}23)$$
$$= 2k_3[D][H_2] - 2k_5[H][HD]$$

The differential rate equations for the atomic intermediates are

$$\frac{d[H]}{dt} = -\frac{d[D]}{dt} = k_3[D][H_2] - k_5[H][HD] - k_4[H][D_2] + k_6[D][HD]$$

$$(10\text{--}24)$$

From the steady-state approximation for atoms, it follows that the ratio of atomic species is

$$\frac{[H]}{[D]} = \frac{k_3[H_2] + k_6[HD]}{k_4[D_2] + k_5[HD]} \tag{10-25}$$

and the sum of the rate of change of atomic species is zero:

$$\frac{d[H]}{dt} + \frac{d[D]}{dt} = 0 \tag{10-26}$$

so that the sum of atoms is constant:

$$[H] + [D] = [H]_i + [D]_i \tag{10-27}$$

$$= (K_{HH}[H_2]_i)^{1/2} + (K_{DD}[D_2]_i)^{1/2} = X \tag{10-28}$$

In terms of X defined by Eq. 28, the concentrations of atoms are

$$\frac{[H]}{X} = \frac{k_3[H_2] + k_6[HD]}{k_3[H_2] + k_4[D_2] + (k_5 + k_6)[HD]}$$

$$\frac{[D]}{X} = \frac{k_4[D_2] + k_5[HD]}{k_3[H_2] + k_4[D_2] + (k_5 + k_6)[HD]} \tag{10-29}$$

These expressions, when substituted into Eq. 23, give the differential rate equation

$$\frac{d[HD]}{dt} = 2X \frac{k_3k_4[H_2][D_2] - k_5k_6[HD]^2}{k_3[H_2] + k_4[D_2] + (k_5 + k_6)[HD]} \tag{10-30}$$

When the stoichiometric relations

$$[H_2] = [H_2]_i - [HD]/2$$

$$[D_2] = [D_2]_i - [HD]/2 \tag{10-31}$$

are substituted in the rate equation, it assumes the form

$$\frac{dz}{dt} = \frac{A + Bz + Cz^2}{D + Ez} \tag{10-32}$$

where z is [HD] and

$$A = 2Xk_3k_4[H_2]_i[D_2]_i$$

$$B = -k_3k_4X([H_2]_i + [D_2]_i)$$

$$C = k_3k_4\left(\frac{1}{4} - \frac{k_5k_6}{k_3k_4}\right) \tag{10-33}$$

$$D = k_3[H_2]_i + k_4[D_2]_i$$

$$E = k_5 + k_6 - (k_3 + k_4)/2$$

In the constant C the product k_5k_6/k_3k_4 is simply related to the equilibrium constant for reaction 14 (compare Eq. 22):

$$K_0 = k_3k_4/k_5k_6 \tag{10-34}$$

The value of this equilibrium constant approaches 4 at high temperatures and can readily be found from simple statistical thermodynamics. For the first one or two half-lives of the reaction, the term C in Eq. 32 may be neglected. By use of any of the theoretical methods of the next section, one can estimate the four rate constants appearing in E of Eq. 33 and one also finds the constant E to be very nearly zero at $1000°K$. Finally, as an excellent approximation for at least one half-life, the differential rate equation is

$$\frac{d[HD]}{dt} = X \frac{2k_3k_4[H_2]_i[D_2]_i - k_3k_4([H_2]_i + [D_2]_i)[HD]}{k_3[H_2]_i + k_4[D_2]_i} \qquad (10\text{-}35)$$

The integrated rate equation is

$$\ln\left\{1 - \frac{1}{2}\left(\frac{[HD]}{[H_2]_i} + \frac{[HD]}{[D_2]_i}\right)\right\} = \frac{k_3k_4X([H_2]_i + [D_2]_i)t}{k_3[H_2]_i + k_4[D_2]_i} \qquad (10\text{-}36)$$

For equal initial pressure of hydrogen and deuterium (the usual experimental conditions), the integrated equation is

$$\ln\left(1 - \frac{[HD]}{[H_2]_i}\right) = \frac{2k_3k_4Xt}{k_3 + k_4} \qquad (10\text{-}37)$$

Thus the experimental data yield the function of rate constants $k_3k_4/(k_3 + k_4)$ and not any elementary constant or constants.

It should be re-emphasized that Eqs. 35, 36, and 37 are approximate; the approximation is excellent for small degrees of reaction at any temperature, and it becomes good even for fairly large degrees of reaction at high temperature. It does not, however, correctly give the approach to equilibrium. For very large degrees of reaction the approximation of setting E of Eq. 33 to zero should not be made; the full differential Eq. 32 can be integrated exactly, but the result is quite complicated. The experimental data in the literature were recomputed by means of Eqs. 37 and 28, and these values are entered in Table 4.

(iv) Direct Observation of Reactions 4 and 3

By experimental methods similar to those used in their study of para-ortho hydrogen conversion, Schulz and LeRoy[60g] made a direct determination of the rate constant for reaction 4, $H + D_2 \rightarrow HD + D$. The range of temperature was 368 to $468°K$. These data are given in full in Table 1.

In a system of crossed molecular beams, the occurrence of reaction 4, $H + D_2 \rightarrow HD + D$, has been demonstrated by Fite and Brackman.[60h] Similarly, Datz and Taylor have detected reaction 3, $D + H_2 \rightarrow HD + H$, in a system of crossed molecular beams. These experiments are to be regarded as pioneering demonstrations of feasibility of the molecular beam

TABLE 10–4

Rate Constant $k_3k_4/(k_3 + k_4)$, for Initial Hydrogen-Deuterium Exchange Reaction[a]

$T°K$	$1000/T$	P_{mm}	$\log \dfrac{k_3 k_4}{k_3 + k_4}$	Ref.
855	1.170	30	11.63	60d
887	1.128	28	11.62	
889	1.126	17	11.64	
893	1.120	10	11.55	
893	1.120	10	11.61	
897	1.116	16	11.60	
946	1.057	32	11.61	
946	1.057	12	11.61	
946	1.057	8	11.63	
946	1.057	4	11.65	
1004	0.996	3	11.71	
1008	0.993	8	11.80	
1008	0.993	4	11.71	
1008	0.993	4	11.79	
724	1.380	133	11.47	60c
746	1.340	116	11.50	
772	1.293	98	11.40	
772	1.293	104	11.51	
774	1.291	99	11.93	
800	1.250	100	11.55	
800	1.250	114	11.54	
800	1.250	127	11.61	
813	1.230	122	11.55	
850	1.177	109	11.69	
876	1.140	133	11.75	
916	1.091	58	11.25	
925	1.080	29	11.27	
925	1.080	58	11.28	
925	1.080	87	11.29	
927	1.078	29	11.28	
945	1.059	30	11.34	
952	1.050	30	11.34	
952	1.050	21	11.34	
952	1.050	45	11.36	
961	1.040	29	11.36	
961	1.040	29	11.35	
976	1.023	16	11.34	
990	1.010	24	11.42	
999	1.001	23	11.38	
1010	0.990	17	11.45	
949	1.053	25	11.34	
950	1.052	25	11.35	
990	1.010	11	11.43	
1006	0.994	11	11.51	
1010	0.990	12	11.43	

[a] k in units of cc/mole-sec.

technique for these reactions. With further improvement of signal-to-noise ratio, it is to be expected that significant data concerning elementary physical and chemical-physical rate constants will be obtained.

B. POTENTIAL ENERGY OF ACTIVATION

The Arrhenius activation energy is the measure of how fast the rate constant changes with temperature:

$$\mathbf{E} = -Rd \ln \mathbf{k}/d(1/T) \qquad (10\text{-}38)$$

and the Arrhenius pre-exponential factor is defined at a temperature by

$$\mathbf{A} = \mathbf{k} \exp(\mathbf{E}/RT) \qquad (10\text{-}39)$$

Over a narrow range of temperature $\mathbf{E}$ and $\mathbf{A}$ are almost constant, and the integrated form of the Arrhenius equation is

$$\mathbf{k} = \mathbf{A} \exp(-\mathbf{E}/RT) \qquad (10\text{-}40)$$

Experimental data are often given in terms of the integrated Arrhenius equation. Theoretical rate expressions usually take the form

$$\mathbf{k} = \mathbf{B}(T) \exp(-V^*/RT) \qquad (10\text{-}41)$$

where V^* is the potential energy of activation, the difference in energy between the minimum potential energy of reactants and the saddlepoint or lowest pass in a potential-energy surface between reactants and products. $\mathbf{B}(T)$ includes corrections for zero-point energies and other temperature-dependent factors. To find the relation between theoretical $\mathbf{B}$ and V^* on the one hand and experimental $\mathbf{A}$ and $\mathbf{E}$ on the other hand, one defines the function

$$\Theta = d \ln \mathbf{B}/d \ln T \qquad (10\text{-}42)$$

and then one readily sees that

$$\mathbf{E} = V^* + \Theta RT$$
$$\mathbf{A} = \mathbf{B} \exp \Theta \qquad (10\text{-}43)$$

The "activation energy at absolute zero," $\mathbf{E}_0$, is another term often used,[33] and it is a limiting case of Eq. 43. At the absolute zero, ΘRT is simply the zero-point vibrational energy of the transition state minus the sum of the zero-point vibrational energies of the reactants:

$$\mathbf{E}_0 = V^* + \sum^{3N-7} \frac{hc\omega^{\ddagger}}{2} - \sum_{\text{reactants}} \frac{hc\omega}{2} \qquad (10\text{-}44)$$

The relation between these three ways of expressing activation energy is given by a formal, specially defined telescoping together of the three-dimensional R_1–R_2 potential-energy surface into a two-dimensional energy profile. A potential-energy surface for a slightly exothermic bimolecular

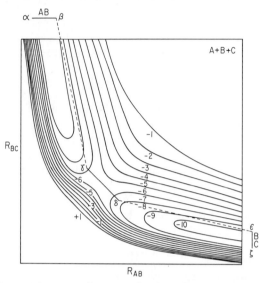

Fig. 10–2. Potential-energy function for bimolecular atom-transfer reaction with five straight-line segments defined on this figure and used in the next figure.

reaction is given by Fig. 2, with five straight-line segments indicated, $\alpha\beta$, $\beta\gamma$, $\gamma\delta$, $\delta\varepsilon$, and $\varepsilon\zeta$. The energy profile along these line segments is given by Fig. 3. The energy scale in the two figures is the same, but the distance variables in Fig. 3 are freely contracted and expanded and have no quantitative meaning. For the reactant molecule AB and the product molecule BC, the zero-point energy of vibration is shown. For the saddle-point, the zero-point energy of the symmetric stretch vibration and of the

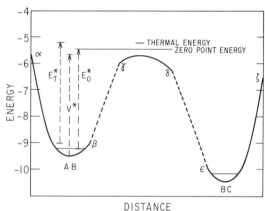

Fig. 10–3. Potential-energy profile along the five straight-line segments of Fig. 2. This figure illustrates the potential energy of activation, **V***; activation energy at absolute zero, **E₀***; and activation energy at any temperature, **E**$_T$ *.

two bending vibrations of the complex is shown above the saddlepoint. The average internal thermal energy (vibrations, rotations, translations of mutual approach but not of center of mass) for reactant and complex is shown by a short horizontal line. The observed activation energy is $\mathbf{E}_T$, "the average energy of the complexes that react minus the average energy of the pairs of reactants" (R. C. Tolman). Theoretical potential-energy surfaces give the potential energy of activation $\mathbf{V}^*$, and after a vibrational analysis one can compute the activation energy at absolute zero $\mathbf{E}_0$ by applying corrections for zero-point energy. To calculate the Arrhenius activation energy $\mathbf{E}_T$ from a theory in order to compare with experiment, one must set up the theoretical expression, Eq. 41, evaluate the temperature dependence of its pre-exponential factor $\mathbf{B}(T)$ (Eq. 42), and then substitute into Eq. 43.

Potential energies of activation for the H—H—H reactions have been calculated by various approaches, which can be classified as: (i) theoretical, (ii) semiempirical, and (iii) 100-percent empirical with the empircism outside the field of kinetics. All of these methods will be reviewed here.

(i) Theoretical Estimate of Potential Energy of Activation

Calculations based on purely theoretical methods have been carried through only for the simplest bimolecular reaction:

$$H + H_2 \rightarrow H_3 \rightarrow H_2 + H \qquad (10\text{--}45)$$

At that, the wave functions used were necessarily simpler than the (still unknown) real wave function. This discussion will review (a) the first quantum-mechanical treatment of this problem, and (b) a recent detailed theoretical treatment; and (c) other theoretical work, summarized in Table 5.

(a) London Theory. The first theoretical treatment of this reaction was given by F. London[61] in 1928. The detailed derivation was clarified and presented by L. S. Kassel.[62] London regarded the H_3 complex as the superposition of three diatomic molecules:

$$
\begin{array}{c}
\longleftarrow\ 3\ \longrightarrow \\
\mathrm{H}\cdots\mathrm{H}\cdots\mathrm{H} \\
\leftarrow 1 \rightarrow \leftarrow 2 \rightarrow \\
\mathrm{A} \quad \mathrm{B} \quad \mathrm{C}
\end{array}
\qquad (10\text{--}46)
$$

and with heavy approximations he derived the energy expression

$$E = Q_1 + Q_2 + Q_3 \pm (\alpha_1^2 + \alpha_2^2 + \alpha_3^2 - \alpha_1\alpha_2 - \alpha_2\alpha_3 - \alpha_3\alpha_1)^{1/2} \quad (10\text{--}47)$$

where each Q and each α are given by Eq. 4–15. To the same approximation the energy of the hydrogen molecule is

$$E_{\mathrm{HH}} = Q + \alpha \qquad (10\text{--}48)$$

which is not the same as the Heitler-London expression (Eq. 4–14). A comparison of the results obtained using Eq. 48 and Eq. 4–14 is as follows:

	$D_e(H_2)$ (kcal)	$R_e(H_2)$ (Å)	
$(Q + \alpha)/(1 + \Delta)$	72.4	0.80	Heitler-London
$Q + \alpha$	107.9	0.82	London H_3 theory
Experimental	109.4	0.74	

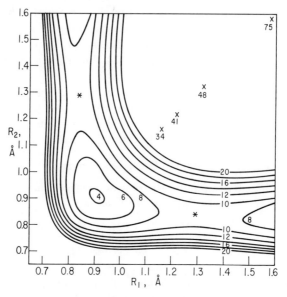

Fig. 10–4. Potential-energy surface for HHH linear complex based on London's theory of H_3 and Heitler-London-Sugiura integrals. The contour lines are kcal/mole; the origin of energy is the minimum potential energy of H_2; the asterisks show the two saddlepoints.

The Heitler-London theory uses an ultrasimple wave function, but from there on the mathematical development is exact. The London theory of H_3 starts with the same ultrasimple waves functions as Heitler-London, but additional mathematical approximations are made to yield the relatively simple expression for H_3, Eq. 47. The amusing fact is (as one sees above) that the dissociation energy for H_2 by the doubly crude Eq. 48 is better than that for the crude Eq. 4–14, and in fact better than some other more refined treatments. On the other hand, the bond length is worse for Eq. 48, and both Eq. 4–14 and Eq. 48 are known to be qualitatively incorrect in a major sense of the word (Ref. 21, pp. 139–143). This example illustrates that a single energy-difference criterion is a very poor basis for judging the correctness of a quantum mechanical, approximate theory.

London found that the linear structure of H_3 is much more stable than nonlinear structures even through the linear structure is unstable with respect to H and H_2. For any linear structure of H_3, one has the three distances R_1, R_2, and $R_3 = R_1 + R_2$. For each of these distances one can find the value of Q and α from the Heitler-London-Sugiura Eq. 4–15. Thus one can readily construct a potential-energy surface for H_3, using H_2 integrals according to London's theory. Such a potential-energy surface[63] is given by Fig. 4, where the origin of energy is the minimum potential energy of H_2, according to Eq. 48, and the energies are in kilocalories per mole. This theory gives a double barrier between reactants and products and a symmetrically placed potential-energy well, that is, it predicts a metastable H_3 complex. The height of this potential energy barrier is 8.8 kcal/mole, and the observed activation energy for the H—H—H para-ortho conversion is 8.7 kcal/mole. As will be seen below, more exact theories remove the "well in the top of the pass" and destroy this good, accidental agreement of theory and experiment.

(b) **Theory of Boys and Shavitt.**[64] A detailed quantum-mechanical treatment of the H_3 complex is that of Boys and Shavitt. For various structures of the H_3 complex, the total energy of the system (that is, the potential energy for motion of the nuclei, to the Born-Oppenheimer approximation) was constructed by "a linear variational calculation of the superposition of configuration type $\cdots 6$ 1^s-orbitals $\cdots 66$ configurations. . . ." Such a calculation is involved, and it was made possible by "the use of an electronic computer for much of the complicated analysis and organization . . . as well as all of the numerical work." In spite of the use of this large electronic computer, the entire potential-energy surface was not obtained; only eight structures near the saddlepoint were evaluated. For each of these eight structures there was variation of a scale factor to locate the lowest energy. The structures were symmetrical and linear (four), unsymmetrical and linear (two), symmetrical and bent (one), and equilateral triangle (one). The bent structure and the equilateral triangle were found to be less stable than the linear structures, in qualitative agreement with London's theory. The four symmetrical linear structures allow construction of an energy profile along the symmetrical axis, $c = 1$ (Eq. 3–19), and the potential energy does show a minimum along this line. This minimum on the R_1-R_2 plane must be either a saddlepoint, a straight parabolic channel, or a minimum. In any of these cases, the normal mode coordinates are symmetrical, $c = 1$, and antisymmetrical, $c = -1$:

$$q_1 = \frac{1}{\sqrt{2}} (r_1 + r_2) \qquad c = 1$$

$$q_2 = \frac{1}{\sqrt{2}} (r_1 - r_2) \qquad c = -1$$

(10–49)

The procedure followed by Boys and Shavitt was to fit their calculated energies for linear structures to the quadratic function in normal-mode coordinates:

$$E = E_0 + \tfrac{1}{2}F_1 q_1^2 + \tfrac{1}{2}F_2 q_2^2 \qquad (10\text{--}50)$$

The values found for the force constants are

$$\begin{aligned} F_1 &= 2.242 \times 10^5 \text{ dynes/cm} \\ F_2 &= -0.366 \times 10^5 \text{ dynes/cm} \end{aligned} \qquad (10\text{--}51)$$

The positive curvature in one direction and the negative curvature in the perpendicular direction at a point on the symmetrical axis establish that the potential-energy surface is a saddlepoint, not a minimum (as given by London's theory, Fig. 4). The theory of Boys and Shavitt indicates that the "well in the top of the pass" of the London theory and related semi-empirical theories is "an artifact of the approximation."

Similarly, Boys and Shavitt evaluated the bending force constant by comparing their linear structures with their bent structure. However, the nonlinear structure was bent by 40°, and this much distortion is far in excess of small vibration theory, the Taylor series expansion, Eq. 4–17. Thus the bending constant is probably too high.

The energy of the H_3 saddlepoint was determined, (E_0 of Eq. 50). The difference in this energy and that of three separated hydrogen atoms gives the binding energy of the H_3 complex. The energy of the hydrogen molecule H_2 was evaluated to the same level of approximation as that used for H_3, and the difference between these two calculated quantities gives the theoretical potential energy of activation, 15.4 kcal/mole.

(c) Other Quantum-Mechanical Theories of H_3. In the years between London's theory of 1928 and 1965, there have been several attempts to evaluate the energy of the H_3 complex. If the binding energies of H_3 and H_2 were evaluated to the same degree of approximation, the difference gives a theoretical estimate of the potential energy of activation V^*. Table 5 gives a series of estimates of the binding energy of H_3 and the activation energy V^*; the method used is identified by the usual alphabetical abbreviations; and the references are given. The methods given as footnotes o and p in Table 5 appear to give the correct energies, but each of these methods is known to fail on other counts and in other regions. Thus still in 1965, there is not a satisfactorily accurate theoretical determination of the binding energy of H_3 or the potential energy of activation V^*, in spite of the large amount of work expended on this problem. The theoretical evaluation of the energy of H_3 illustrates the theorem of R. C. Tolman who, when asked why he had switched from chemistry to astrophysics, replied: "Chemistry is hard."

TABLE 10–5
Theoretical Studies of H_3 System

Method	Energies, kcal/mole		Ref.
	H_3 (binding)*	V (activation)*	
MO	38.5	—	a
MOSCF	41.1	—	b
MOSCF, Koopman's th.	41.8	46	c
VB, Mulliken approx.	45.8	—	d
VB	53.1	19.1	e
VB, screening	56.2	30.7	e
MOSCF, 3 floating orb.	58.0	—	f
MOSCF, Mulliken approx.	59.0	16.1	g
Elliptic orbitals	60.2	—	h
VB, ionic terms	60.4	13.6	e
MOCI	60.7	—	i
LCAO–MOSCF–HFDODS	66.4	—	j
VB, screening, ionic	67.1	25.2	e
CI, ζ variable	67.7	25.1	k
MOCI, 5 floating orb.	72.4	21.0	l
MOCI, 6 s-orb	80.2	15.4	m
MOSCFCI, screening, Mulliken approx.	82.8	9.9	g
MOSCFCI, 27 orb.	91.9	14.3	n
Monte Carlo	104.5	6.2	o
VB, London theory	105	8.8	p
Hückel theory	141	−32	q
"Experimental"	102	8 ± 2	

* Minimum energy at $R_{AB} = R_{BC}$.

a. J. M. Walsh and F. A. Matsen, *J. Chem. Phys.*, **19**, 526 (1951).
b. V. Griffing and B. J. Ransil, U.S. Dept. Com. OTS P.B.R. 138340 (1958).
c. V. Griffing and J. T. Vanderslice, *J. Chem. Phys.*, **23**, 1039 (1955).
d. R. S. Barker, H. Eyring, C. J. Thorne, and D. A. Baker, *J. Chem. Phys.*, **22**, 699 (1954).
e. J. O. Hirschfelder, H. Eyring, and N. Rosen, *J. Chem. Phys.*, **4**, 121 (1936).
f. W. E. Meador, Jr., *J. Chem. Phys.*, **29**, 1339 (1958).
g. L. Oleari, S. Carrá, and M. Simonetta, *Gazz. Chim. Ital.*, **91**, 1413 (1961).
h. J. R. Hoyland, *J. Chem. Phys.*, **41**, 1370 (1964).
i. B. J. Ransil, *J. Chem. Phys.*, **26**, 971 (1957).
j. J. N. Bradley, *Trans. Faraday Soc.*, **60**, 1353 (1964).
k. H. C. Bowen and J. W. Linnett, *Trans. Faraday Soc.*, **60**, 1185 (1964).
l. G. E. Kimball and J. G. Trulio, *J. Chem. Phys.*, **28**, 493 (1958).
m. Ref. 64.
n. C. Edmiston and M. Krauss, *J. Chem. Phys.*, **42**, 1119 (1965).
o. H. Conroy, and B. L. Brunner, *J. Chem. Phys.*, **42**, 4047 (1965).
p. Ref. 63.
q. R. G. Pearson, *J. Chem. Phys.*, **16**, 502 (1948).

(ii) Semiempirical Estimate of Potential Energy of Activation

It is very satisfying to set up a problem in quantum mechanics and to obtain the answer by deduction, even if the last stages involve a large electronic computer. A well-developed method of getting a generation or so ahead of computer developments is the "semiempirical" method. The idealized situation involves two observables, X and Y, with a common function, z, in their Schroedinger equation:

$$X = X(z, \cdots)$$
$$Y = Y(z, \cdots) \tag{10–52}$$

By approximations, the second functional relation is inverted:

$$z = z(Y, \cdots) \tag{10–53}$$

That is, the complicated integral z is formally (and usually approximately) expressed in terms of the observable Y. With additional approximations, the integral z is eliminated from the theoretical expression for X:

$$X = X(Y, \cdots) \tag{10–54}$$

The final result is to express the phenomenon X in terms of the different phenomenon Y. Significant relations can be found this way, although in some cases the approximations required are so severe that the final result is useful over only a very limited range. Advances in this field call for ingenuity, calibrated intuition, and the rare gift for getting the right answer without benefit of a rigorous method. Much of chemistry, good and bad, is of this nature.

(a) **Method of Polanyi and Eyring.** The semiempirical method of Polanyi and Eyring for bimolecular atom-transfer reactions involves the London theory of H_3 (Eq. 47), as one phenomenon (rates) with unknown integrals, Q_1, Q_2, Q_3, α_1, α_2, and α_3. The second phenomenon is the potential-energy function of H_2, involving $Q(R)$ and $\alpha(R)$ (Eq. 48), which is approximated by the Morse function (Eq. 4–16). The approximation that allows these two phenomena to be connected is based on the theoretical result that Q is more or less proportional to α at large values of R; this approximation is expressed by Eq. 4–22. The value of f is 0.14 in Heitler-London-Sugiura theory. Thus, Polanyi and Eyring proposed to calculate the rate of ortho-para hydrogen conversion from the spectroscopically observed dissociation energy and vibration frequency of the H_2 molecule: Eqs. 4–16 to 4–19, and Eqs. 47, 48. This study has received detailed discussion in other books (Ref. 33, pp. 107–115), and only the outstanding features will be mentioned here. This semiempirical theory, based on London's formula for H_3, gives a "well in the top of the pass" just like the London theory itself. The barrier height is about 14 kcal/mole; the "well depth" of H_3 is about 2.5 kcal/mole.

By comparison the barrier height in London's theory is 8.8 kcal/mole, and the well depth of H_3 is about 5 kcal/mole. The barrier height in Boys and Shavitt's model is 15.4 kcal and there is no well in the top of the pass.

Eyring and others have extended this semiempirical method to reactions other than H_3, for example

$$A - B + C \to A \cdots B \cdots C \to A + B - C \qquad (10\text{--}55)$$

by using the London function (Eq. 47), by considering the Morse function of each molecule AB, BC, and AB, and by regarding f of Eq. 4–22 as empirical. The parameter f is fitted to the observed activation energy of Eq. 55. Thus the extended semiempirical function no longer predicts potential energy of activation, but it does still predict A-factors and kinetic isotope effects. An objection to the extended semiempirical method is that Eq. 47 was derived for a system of three $1s$ wave functions, and the extended theory considers reactions of CH_3, Cl, etc., which involve $2p$ and higher orbitals. Probably this objection should not be entertained, since the extended semiempirical theory is just a mechanism for transforming the Morse function of reactant smoothly and continuously into the Morse function of product. A semiempirical theory may free itself from its derivation, and then "it must assume the status and responsibilities of a purely empirical method."[65]

(b) London-Polanyi-Eyring-Sato Method.   A semiempirical method closely related to that of Polanyi and Eyring is that of Sato.[34] By analogy with Eq. 4–14, Sato rewrote London's Eq. 47 as

$$E = \frac{Q_1 + Q_2 + Q_3 \pm (\alpha_1^2 + \alpha_2^2 + \alpha_3^2 - \alpha_1\alpha_2 - \alpha_2\alpha_3 - \alpha_3\alpha_1)^{1/2}}{1 + \Delta} \qquad (10\text{--}56)$$

This equation is based purely on intuition. If one takes the model of Eq. 46 seriously, one would have Δ for each diatomic molecule: Δ_1, Δ_2, and Δ_3. The Δ of Eq. 56 bears no resemblance to the Δ of Eq. 4–14; it is Sato's empirical parameter with no theoretical privileges or obligations. Sato evaluates the functions in Eq. 56 from Eqs. 4–25 and 4–26 for each of the "three" diatomic molecules of Eq. 46. By this method R. Weston[66a] prepared a detailed potential-energy function for the H_3 complex with Sato's parameter Δ adjusted to give the observed activation energy, taken as 8.0 kcal/mole. A portion of this potential-energy surface is given as Fig. 5. There is a symmetrical saddlepoint with no trace of a "well in the top of the pass." Thus Sato's potential-energy surface for H_3 is a complete potential-energy surface that appears to be qualitatively correct.[66b]

With this evaluation one uses the Sato potential-energy surface to see over what distances the theory of small vibrations (Eq. 4–38), is tenable. The curvatures at the saddlepoint give the force constants; and an extended

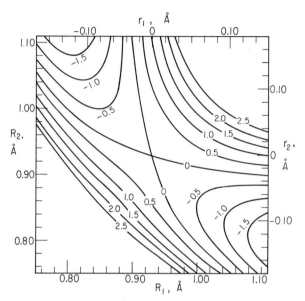

Fig. 10–5. Portion of London-Eyring-Polanyi-Sato potential-energy surface for HHH.

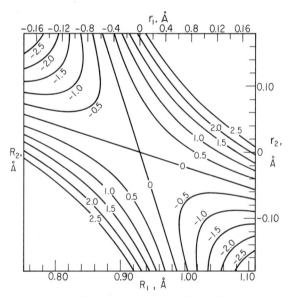

Fig. 10–6. Continuation of quadratic potential based on curvatures at origin of Fig. 6.

quadratic surface based on Eq. 4–38 is presented as Fig. 6 on the same scale as Fig. 5. These two figures provide a two-dimensional analogy to the comparison of the Morse curve and its extended parabola in Fig. 4–1. By superposition of Figs. 5 and 6, one notes that the quadratic surface appears to be a good approximation to the full Sato surface for a diameter of about 0.1 Å around the saddlepoint. Classical-mechanical small-vibration theory with separability of normal modes requires that one consider only small departures from the extremum point. On the other hand, the "Boltzmann-average" de Broglie wavelength for a hydrogen atom,

$$\lambda = h/(2\pi m K T)^{1/2} \tag{10-57}$$

is about 0.5 Å at 1000°K and 1.0 Å at 300°K (Table 2–1). This comparison clearly shows that quantum effects are large in this reaction, and separability of normal mode coordinates is not to be expected.

This semiempirical method does not predict activation energy. Its evaluation of other properties of the saddlepoint will be compared with other methods in a later section, where it will be referred to as the LEPS (London-Eyring-Polanyi-Sato) method.

(c) **Method of Porter and Karplus.**[66b] Porter and Karplus used as semi-empirical formula "the complete formulas for the non-ionic valence-bond treatment for the three-orbital three-electron system corresponding to H_3" as given by J. C. Slater (*Phys. Rev.*, **38**, 1109 [1931]). This set of equations reduces to the London formula for special, highly restricted conditions. As in the Sato method, certain integrals are "evaluated" from singlet and triplet H_2, which were accurately evaluated (W. Kolos and C. C. J. Roothaan, *Rev. Mod. Phys.*, **32**, 219 [1960]) from quantum mechanics. Some integrals were evaluated exactly. Other expressions were modified to bring about agreement with the observed activation energy. By use of a fast electronic computer, Porter and Karplus were able to evaluate full potential-energy surfaces for both linear and nonlinear H_3 complexes. These potential-energy surfaces are similar to Sato surfaces in general appearance and in the values of the second derivatives of the H_3 saddlepoint.

(iii) Bond-Energy–Bond-Order (BEBO) Method[41]

Quantum-mechanical calculations show that a system of 3 protons and 2 electrons forms a stable molecule-ion, which is an equilateral triangle. As noted above, quantum-mechanical calculations show that a system of 3 protons and 3 electrons is unstable and a linear structure is more stable than bent structures. Similar calculations show that a system of 3 protons and 4 electrons is highly unstable. In the language of simple molecular-orbital theory, these calculations show that in the 3-proton system the lowest molecular orbital is bonding and the second molecular orbital is non-bonding and destabilized by electron-electron repulsion. Two electrons with opposite spins go into the lowest molecular orbital to form stable H_3^+; the third electron goes into the excited non-bonding orbital to form the slightly unstable H_3; and the fourth electron also goes into the non-bonding orbital to give highly unstable H_3^-. In the language of simple valence-bond theory, the H_3 complex is, as in Eq. 46, regarded as the superposition of 3 diatomic molecules, and special attention is given to the sign of the electron spin function, $\uparrow$ or $\downarrow$. Two hydrogen atoms form a stable bond if the two electrons have opposite spins, $\uparrow\downarrow$, but they form an unstable pair if the electron spins are parallel, $\uparrow\uparrow$. Referring to Eq. 46, one sees that if the electron on atom A has spin $\uparrow$, then the electron on atom B must have spin $\downarrow$ for molecule 1 to have a stable singlet bond; and the electron on atom C must have spin $\uparrow$ for molecule 2 to have a stable singlet bond. The relatively stable pattern is

$$\begin{array}{ccc} A & B & C \\ \uparrow & \downarrow & \uparrow \end{array}$$

or equally well

$$\begin{array}{ccc} \downarrow & \uparrow & \downarrow \end{array}$$

In either case, "molecule 3" between atoms A and C necessarily has parallel electron spins and forms a triplet, repulsive bond. This simple valence-bond discussion, which regards the pair AC "molecule 3" as if atom B were not there, is highly artificial; and yet it gives a qualitative explanation of why the second molecular orbital in a system of 3 protons is destabilizing. As usual, simple molecular-orbital theory and simple valence-bond theory illuminate slightly different aspects of a problem in molecular binding; the two methods considered together give a better picture than either one taken alone. In the present case, it is the valence-bond viewpoint that suggests an ultrasimple, yet fairly successful, method of calculating potential energy of activation for H_3 and other hydrogen-transfer reactions.

The reactants are one H atom and one H_2 molecule far apart, and the origin of energy is the minimum potential energy of the H_2 molecule. The potential energy of dissociation of H_2 is 109.4 kcal/mole and the activation energy for para-ortho hydrogen conversion is about 8 kcal/mole. Thus the mechanism is certainly not the dissociation of H_2 by hard impact of H and random reassociation of two atoms. Rather, at all stages of the collision, the formation of the second bond must be "paying for" the breaking of the first bond. The bond order in the reactant H_2 is one and the bond order in the product H_2 is one. The very strong correlation between one bond and the other is expressed by the assumption that the path of lowest energy (compare Fig. 4–6) between reactant and product is that along which the sum of bond orders is unity:

$$n_1 + n_2 = 1 \qquad (10\text{--}58)$$

The energy of the linear H_3 complex along the line of constant order is assumed to be composed of three parts:

$$V = E_{HH} - E_1 - E_2 + V_{tr}(R_3) \qquad (10\text{--}59)$$

That is, the energy of the system (relative to zero for reactants) is the bond energy, $-E_1$, of the first bond, plus the bond energy, $-E_2$, of the second bond, plus the triplet repulsion energy between end atoms. If the order of the bond being broken is n, the order of the bond being formed is $1 - n$. The functional relation (Eq. 59) can be re-expressed as

$$V = E_{HH} - E(n) - E(1 - n) + V_{tr}(R_3) \qquad (10\text{--}60)$$

Pauling's relation between bond length and bond order[40] has been given as Eq. 4–49. The index p (Eq. 4–52 and Table 4–4) can be seen to be 1.041. Thus Eq. 60 for the energy along the bottom of the reaction channel is (Eq. 4–50)

$$V = D_e - D_e n^p - D_e (1 - n)^p + V_{tr}(R_3)$$
$$= 109.4[1 - n^{1.041} - (1 - n)^{1.041}] + V_{tr}(R_3) \qquad (10\text{--}61)$$

The "reaction path" or rather the path of minimum potential energy for reaction is determined by the assumed conservation of bond order (Eq. 58), and Pauling's relation defining bond order (Eq. 4–49). The distance of closest approach of the end atoms is 1.84 Å or the minimum value of $r_3 = R_3 - R_{30}$ is 1.10 Å. At distances r between 1 and 2 Å, Sato's Eq. 4–21, Fig. 4–2, is a fair approximation to the theoretical triplet function for H_2. It is assumed that the term $V_{tr}(R_3)$ in Eq. 61 for the H_3 complex is given by Sato's anti-Morse function, Eq. 4–21; for H_2 the Morse parameter β is 1.94 Å^{-1}; and thus for H_3

$$V_{tr} = D_e \tfrac{1}{2} \exp(-\beta r_3)[1 + \tfrac{1}{2} \exp(-\beta r_3)]$$
$$= 109.4 \tfrac{1}{2} \exp(-1.94 r_3)[1 + \tfrac{1}{2} \exp(-1.94 r_3)] \text{ kcal/mole} \qquad (10\text{--}62)$$

Since, for linear complex, R_3 is the sum of R_1 and R_2 and since these two distances can be expressed in terms of the single parameter n, the repulsive term (Eq. 62) can be expressed in terms of bond order:

$$R_3 - R_{3s} = R_1 + R_2 - R_{3s} = R_{1s} + R_{2s} - R_{3s} - 0.26 \ln n_1 n_2 \qquad (10\text{--}63)$$

$$V_{tr} = D_e[\tfrac{1}{2} \exp(-\beta \Delta R_s)(n_1 n_2)^{0.26\beta}][1 + \tfrac{1}{2} \exp(-\beta \Delta R_s)(n_1 n_2)^{0.26\beta}] \qquad (10\text{--}64)$$

where $\Delta R_s = R_{1s} + R_{2s} - R_{3s}$. For algebraic manipulation, it is convenient to define two constant terms

$$B = \tfrac{1}{2} \exp(-\beta \Delta R_s) \rightarrow 0.118 \qquad \text{for } H_3$$
$$\gamma = 0.26\beta \rightarrow 0.504 \qquad \text{for } H_3 \qquad (10\text{--}65)$$

The general expression for the repulsive term is then

$$V_{tr} = D_e B(n - n^2)^\gamma [1 + B(n - n^2)^\gamma] \qquad (10\text{--}66)$$

which for H_3 is

$$V_{tr} = 13.0(n - n^2)^{0.504}[1 + 0.119(n - n^2)^{0.504}] \text{ kcal} \qquad (10\text{--}67)$$

where n_1 is n and n_2 is $1 - n$. With these assumptions the locus of the line of minimum energy between reactants and products on the R_1–R_2 plane is given by the one progress variable n and spectroscopic and structural parameters

$$\frac{V}{109.4} = (1 - n^p) - (1 - n)^p + B(n - n^2)^\gamma [1 + B(n - n^2)^\gamma] \qquad (10\text{--}68)$$

where p is 1.041 and B and γ are given by Eq. 65. The potential energy V as a function of bond order n and as a function of distance along the reaction path ρ is given in Table 6.

TABLE 10–6

Variation of Distances and Energies as a Function of Order of Bond Being Broken for H_3 Reaction

		angstrom units			kcal/mole		
n_1	n_2	R_1	R_2	$-\rho$	V_{bonds}	V_{tr}	V
1.000	0	0.74	∞	∞	0	0	0
0.999	0.001	0.74	2.54	1.66	0.03	0.40	0.43
0.998	0.002	0.74	2.36	1.47	0.06	0.57	0.63
0.997	0.003	0.74	2.26	1.37	0.08	0.70	0.78
0.996	0.004	0.74	2.18	1.29	0.11	0.81	0.91
0.995	0.005	0.74	2.12	1.24	0.13	0.90	1.03
0.994	0.006	0.74	2.08	1.19	0.15	0.99	1.14
0.992	0.008	0.74	2.00	1.11	0.20	1.13	1.33
0.990	0.010	0.74	1.94	1.06	0.24	1.27	1.51
0.985	0.015	0.75	1.84	0.95	0.33	1.57	1.90
0.980	0.020	0.75	1.76	0.87	0.43	1.81	2.24
0.970	0.030	0.75	1.66	0.77	0.57	2.21	2.78
0.960	0.040	0.75	1.58	0.69	0.73	2.56	3.29
0.950	0.050	0.76	1.52	0.64	0.87	2.85	3.72
0.940	0.060	0.76	1.48	0.59	1.01	3.12	4.13
0.920	0.080	0.76	1.40	0.51	1.21	3.57	4.78
0.900	0.100	0.77	1.34	0.46	1.42	3.97	5.39
0.850	0.150	0.78	1.24	0.35	1.92	4.77	6.69
0.800	0.200	0.80	1.16	0.27	2.19	5.34	7.53
0.750	0.250	0.82	1.10	0.21	2.49	5.84	8.33
0.700	0.300	0.84	1.06	0.16	2.69	6.18	8.87
0.650	0.350	0.86	1.02	0.12	2.91	6.46	9.37
0.600	0.400	0.88	0.98	0.08	3.06	6.64	9.70
0.550	0.450	0.90	0.95	0.04	3.06	6.76	9.82
0.500	0.500	0.92	0.92	0.00	3.06	6.79	9.85

By this procedure the potential energy of activation is found to be 9.8 kcal, and the observed activation energy is 8.7 kcal. A direct comparison of these quantities requires evaluation of zero-point energies and other properties of the collision complex, H_3.

C. RATE CONSTANT EXPRESSIONS

(i) Collision Theory

(a) Hard-Sphere Model with Wigner's Steric Factor.[67] The rate of collision of two hard-sphere molecules with a Boltzmann distribution of energies has been given by Eq. 7–11. London[61] and later workers showed that the most favorable orientation of three atoms is linear. For a linear three-atom collision, the probability of reaction is zero if the kinetic energy of mutual approach is less than E_0 and unity if this "internal" kinetic energy is greater than this critical energy. However, the probability of precisely linear approach is itself zero. One must examine the probability of reaction for nonlinear approaches. The critical energy for approach at an angle θ is

$$E = E_0 + E(\theta) \tag{10-69}$$

The probability of reaction is assumed to be zero if the kinetic energy of approach is less than the critical energy and unity if greater than E. However, from Eq. 7–36 one sees that the cross-section (πb^2) for contact collision by hard-sphere molecules of diameter D in a repulsive force field (the activation energy) is given by

$$\pi b^2 = \pi D^2 [1 - 2E/\mu g^2]$$

The reaction rate according to a hard-sphere model (with, however, a defined molecular axis) is thus

$$\mathbf{R} = n_0 \int_0^{2\pi} \int_0^{\pi} \int_{g(E)}^{\infty} \pi b^2 g \, dn(g, \theta, \Phi) \tag{10-70}$$

For a Boltzmann distribution of velocities (Eq. 7–4), the rate is

$$\frac{\mathbf{R}}{[n_H n_{HH}]} = (\pi D^2)(\bar{g}/2) \exp(-E_0/kT) \int_0^{\pi} \exp(-E(\theta)/kT) \sin\theta \, d\theta \tag{10-71}$$

Wigner evaluated the integral over angle of approach with the approximations that

$$E(\theta) \approx (\tfrac{1}{2}) F_\theta \, \theta^2 \qquad \sin\theta \approx \theta$$

$$\int_0^{\pi} \exp[-E(\theta)/kT] \sin\theta \, d\theta \approx 2 \int_0^{\infty} \exp(-F\theta^2/2kT)\theta \, d\theta \tag{10-72}$$

$$= 2\frac{kT}{F_\theta}$$

Thus the rate of reaction is

$$\mathbf{R} = (\pi D^2)\left(\frac{8kT}{\pi\mu}\right)^{1/2}\left(\frac{kT}{F_\theta}\right)\exp\left(-E_0/kT\right)[n_{\mathrm{H}}][n_{\mathrm{HH}}] \qquad (10\text{--}73)$$

$$= (\text{rate of collision})\left(\frac{kT}{F_\theta}\right)\exp\left(-E_0/kT\right)$$

The temperature dependence is $T^{3/2}$. The activation energy is thus

$$\mathbf{E} = E_0 + \tfrac{3}{2}RT \qquad (10\text{--}74)$$

The "steric factor" is

$$P(\xi) = kT/F_\theta \qquad (10\text{--}75)$$

The value of F_θ found by London for the H_3 complex is about 0.15×10^{-11} ergs/radian², so that the steric factor is 0.09. For molecular diameters, Wigner and Farkas used 2.14 Å for H and 2.3 Å for H_2. The collision rate constant in this case is 1.1×10^{-9} cc/sec or 6.8×10^{14} cc/mole-sec. The activation energy at $1000°K$ can be evaluated from Eqs. 73, 74 and 75 and from Farkas' experimental rate constant, 2.4×10^{12} cc/mole-sec. The value so determined is 9.5 kcal/mole. It will be recalled that the experimental value between room temperature and $1000°K$ is 8.7 kcal/mole.

(b) Collision Dynamics of Three Particles. The simplest possible chemical reaction demands at least three "particles." By regarding the total energy of the electrons as giving the potential energy for motions of the nuclei, the H—H—H reaction can be regarded as a three-particle system with a potential-energy surface depending on only three variables, R_{AB}, R_{BC}, and R_{AC}, or two internuclear distances and one angle. The dynamics of the system does not depend on position or velocity of center of mass, and thus the problem can be reduced to one involving potential energy that depends on three coordinates and kinetic energy that depends on six momenta. Conservation of energy, momentum, and angular momentum can lead to further reductions in the number of independent variables. However, a difficult aspect of chemical dynamics is that reactants, complex, and products all have different sets of separable coordinates. Energy in a pure normal coordinate of reactants will, typically, show up in two or more normal coordinates of the collision complex, and the degree of mixing depends on phase relations in the coordinates of the reactant.

It is of great interest to take a multidimensional potential-energy surface, transcribe it to classical phase space, and follow the detailed trajectory of atoms for wide range of initial conditions. A single calculation of this sort was made by hand by Hirschfelder, Eyring, and Topley[68] in 1936, using the London-Polanyi-Eyring potential-energy surface. The representative point was shown wandering around the "well in the top of the pass," but the calculation was not continued far enough to see whether reaction would occur. The development of electronic computers has made such calculations practicable.   Between 1958 and 1963, F. T. Wall[69a] and co-workers made a large number of computations of classical reaction trajectories on the London-Polanyi-Eyring and certain empirical potential-energy surfaces. M. Karplus[69b] and co-workers have made a much more extensive computer study of the reaction, with the relatively realistic, semiempirical, potential-energy surface of Porter and Karplus.[66b]   The work of Karplus will be discussed below.

The reactant H_2 has substantial zero-point energy, and is capable of being in only a discrete set of vibrational quantum states, $v = 0, 1, \ldots$.   Similarly, the rotations are quantized $J = 0$, 2, 4, etc. (para), or $J = 1$, 3, 5, etc. (ortho).   The relative translation of H and H_2 is essentially classical.   A classical distribution of energy over vibrations and rotations of reactants does not represent the actual distribution, and yet most of the reaction arises from the classical translational energy.   Karplus solved the dynamic reaction problem using classical mechanics throughout, but the initial classical vibrational energy was assigned the magnitude of the quantum-mechanical states ($v = 0, 1, 2, \ldots$) and the initial rotational energy of the reactant H_2 was assigned the magnitude of the quantum-mechanical rotational states ($J = 0, 1, 2, 3, \ldots$).   Complete collision trajectories were calculated for specified v, J, and relative velocity V_R.   Any distribution of velocities V_R could be considered, and in particular the Maxwell-Boltzmann distribution was studied in great detail.   In addition, each computation required a specification of impact parameter b, initial orientation of H_2 relative to the velocity vector, and the phase of the vibration of H_2 relative to initial location of the atom H.   For a given specification of the initial energy, v, J, V_R, the distribution of energy between rotational modes and "bending" vibrational modes of the complex H—H—H depends on impact parameter and initial orientation of H_2; and the distribution of energy between symmetric and antisymmetric "stretching" coordinates of H—H—H depends on the initial phase of the vibration of H_2.   For one collision, a fixed energy (J, v, and V_R), impact parameter, orientation, and vibrational phase of reactants lead to a fixed configuration and energy in each coordinate at the "dividing surface."   For a large number of collisions, an equilibrium distribution of reactant energies (v, J, V_R), with random impact parameters, orientations, and phase is mirrored as an equilibrium distribution (Liouville's theorem) over all *accessible* regions of the dividing surface.

For a given initial condition, reaction either occurs or not.   As calculated by Karplus, Porter, and Sharma,[69b] a non-reactive collision is shown by Fig. 7 and a typical reactive collision is shown by Fig. 8.   The duration of the interaction is about the same for each case.   For a fixed value of v, J, and velocity for appropriately selected random sets of initial phases and orientations, it was possible to vary the impact parameter b to find the average reaction cross section.   This calculation, repeated for fixed v and J, gave

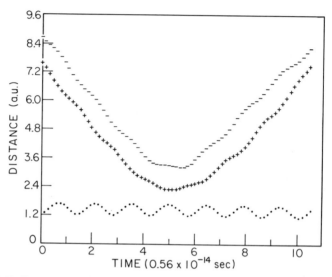

Fig. 10–7. Typical non-reactive H $+$ H$_2$ collision trajectory: $(+ + + + +)R_{AB}$, $(-----)R_{AC}$, $(\cdots\cdots)R_{BC}$; $J = 0$, $v = 0$, $V_R = 1.32 \times 10^6$ cm/sec. From M. Karplus, R. N. Porter, and R. D. Sharma, *J. Chem. Phys.*, **43**, 3259 (1965), Fig. 8a.

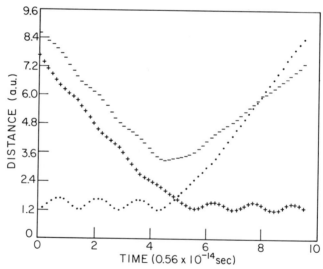

Fig. 10–8. Typical reactive H $+$ H$_2$ collision trajectory. Conditions same as for Fig. 7.

the manner in which the reaction cross-section varies with initial velocity V_R (Fig. 9). There was a fairly sharp threshold, and an increase of reaction cross-section with velocity up to a relatively constant value. The threshold energy was not simply related to the potential energy of activation and initial energies (the averaging over random phases automatically includes in the average some cases with high energy in the "symmetric stretch" coordinate of the complex and thus a subcritical energy along the "reaction

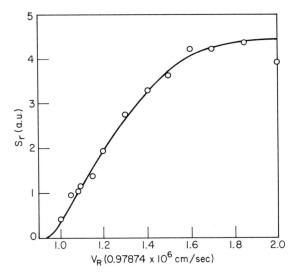

Fig. 10–9. Reaction cross-section $S_r(V_R, J, v)$ as a function of relative velocity V_R for $J = 0$, $v = 0$. From M. Karplus, R. N. Porter, and R. D. Sharma, *J. Chem. Phys.*, **43**, 3259 (1965), Fig. 2a.

path"). The manner in which the reaction cross-section increased with velocity above the threshold was not exactly the same as that predicted by simple collision theories. With improved techniques for molecular beam experiments, one looks forward to experimental testing of this aspect of the calculations.

The calculated reaction cross-sections as a function of initial energies, v, J and V_R, are typical examples of elementary chemical-physical rate constant as defined in Chapter 1. They are averages over initial phases, orientations, and impact parameters. From these cross-sections, one can use the equilibrium distribution of reactants over rotational, vibrational, and relative translational energy at any temperature to calculate the value of the elementary chemical rate constant at that temperature. Karplus and co-workers carried out this calculation, and the values of the chemical rate constants are given in Table 11B.

(ii) Activated-Complex Theory[68]

(a) Rate Constant in Terms of Partition Functions. The normal-mode coordinates of the linear H_3 saddlepoint complex are: 3 translations of center of mass, 2 rotations of linear equilibrium structure, 2 bending vibrations, one symmetrical stretching vibration, and one unstable antisymmetrical stretch. The symbol $\ddagger$ is used for the complex as a whole, and the symbol * for the unstable antisymmetrical vibration or "reaction coordinate." The rate constant expression is then (Eq. 8–32)

$$k = \frac{(f_e f_t^3 f_r^2 f_b^2 f_v)_\ddagger \Gamma^*(kT/h)}{(f_e f_t^3 f_r^2 f_v)_{H_2}(f_e f_t^3)_H} \exp\left(-E_0/kT\right) \tag{10–76}$$

where Γ^* is the correction for tunneling. The partition functions were all reviewed in the section on chemical equilibrium. The molecular parameters needed are: electronic multiplicities for reactants and complex, molecular weights, moments of inertia for H_2 and H_3, and the vibration frequencies of H_2 and H_3. For H_3, the vibration frequencies are found from force constants and bond lengths obtained by theoretical, semiempirical, or BEBO (bond-energy–bond-order) methods.

(b) Rate Constant in Terms of Local Bond Properties. The local or valence-bond coordinates of the H_3 complex are two bonds R_1 and R_2 and two angles Φ and Φ'; the atoms themselves are labeled A, B, C. The rate constant expression in local bond properties is equivalent to Eq. 76 and is given by Eq. 8–70 (with the usual neglect of $\langle\kappa\rangle^B$ and $\langle 1 + \Phi\rangle^T$):

$$k = \frac{W\nu^*(J_A J_B J_C)_\ddagger (l_1 l_2 l_\Phi l_{\Phi'})_\ddagger (\Gamma_s \Gamma_b^2 \Gamma_*)_\ddagger \exp\left(-V^*/kT\right)}{(J_A J_B)_{H_2} l_{H_2} \Gamma_{H_2} (J_C)_H}$$

$$= \frac{W\nu^* V\left[4\pi R_1^2 R_2^2 \dfrac{(2\pi kT)^{4/2}}{(F_1 F_2 F_\Phi F_{\Phi'})^{1/2}} \Gamma_s \Gamma_b^2 \Gamma_*\right]_\ddagger \exp\left(-V^*/kT\right)}{V\left[4\pi R^2 \dfrac{(2\pi kT)^{1/2}}{F^{1/2}} \Gamma\right]_{H_2} V} \tag{10–77}$$

where V is unit volume in the rate constant expression, cubic centimeters or liter; Γ_s, Γ_b, Γ_{H_2} are quantum corrections for the vibrations (Eq. 6–28); R and F are distances and force constants; ν^* is the imaginary frequency. The term W includes several factors:

$$W = \left(\frac{f_\ddagger}{f_{H_2} f_H}\right)_e \left(\frac{\sigma_{H_2}}{\sigma_{H_3}}\right)\left(1 - \frac{F_{12}^2}{F_{11} F_{22}}\right)^{-1/2} \tag{10–78}$$

This expression for electronic partition functions is appropriate only if the rate is the same for all electronic states important in the partition function. So long as f_e is merely the multiplicity of the ground state, the relation given above seems satisfactory. The spin multiplicity of H_2 is one, that of H is 2 and that of H_3 is surely 2 also.   The chemical multiplicity of H on H_2 or D on D_2 is 2; by means of sophisticated arguments one can prove (E. W. Schlag and G. L. Haller, *J. Chem. Phys.*, **42**, 584 [1965]) that carefully interpreted rotational symmetry numbers gives this same result.[69c]   Thus the first two factors in W are respectively 1 and 2.   The molecular parameters needed to evaluate the rate constants are bond lengths of H_3 and H_2, force constants of H_3 and H_2, and normal-mode frequencies of H_3 and H_2.

(c) **Properties of the H_3 Complex.**   From a potential-energy surface one readily locates the saddlepoint in terms of $R_{1\ddagger}$ and $R_{2\ddagger}$, obtains the curvatures or force constants, and evaluates the frequencies.   These properties of the complex have been evaluated by Boys and Shavitt's theoretical method, by the London-Eyring-Polanyi-Sato semiempirical method, and the bond-energy–bond-order method.   These properties as found by each of the three methods are listed in Table 7.   The three methods give essentially the same bond lengths to the H_3 activated complex, but the force constants and vibration frequencies differ substantially.   In spite of the large

TABLE 10–7

Properties of H_3 Activated Complex as Found by Theoretical, Semiempirical, and Bond-Energy–Bond-Order Methods, and Properties of H_2

Complex	Property	Theoretical	Semi-empirical LEPS	BEBO	H_2
	n_1			0.5	1.0
	$V*$	15.4	8.8[a]	9.8	
	R_1 (Å)	0.94	0.93	0.92	0.74
	R_2 (Å)	0.94	0.93	0.92	
	$F_{11} = F_{22}$ (dynes/cm $\times 10^{-5}$)	0.94	0.96	1.320	5.73
	F_{12}	1.31	1.68	1.888	
	F_ϕ (ergs/radian$^2 \times 10^{11}$)	0.0798	0.0657	0.0404	
H—H—H	$\nu*$ (cm^{-1})	$1360i$	$1918i$	$1699i$	
	ν_{str}	1943	2108	2332	4395
	ν_b	950	877	695	
	ZPE (kcal/mole)	5.49	5.52	5.31	6.28
D—D—D	ν_*			$1202i$	
	ν_{str}			1648	3118
	ν_b			492	
	ZPE			3.76	4.46
H—D—D	ν_*			$1276i$	
	ν_{str}			2006	3118
	ν_b			531	
	ZPE			4.39	4.46
H—H—D	ν_*			$1612i$	
	ν_{str}			2006	3817
	ν_b			666	
	ZPE			4.77	5.46

[a] Fitted to experimental data.

differences in individual force constants and frequencies as found by these three methods, the total zero-point energy (ZPE) of the complex is about the same in all three cases. Karplus and co-workers[69b] report similar quantities for their potential-energy surface.[66b]

(d) Tunneling Corrections. The tunneling correction on the reaction rate is not something new and wonderful and unlike all other aspects of reaction-rate theory. It is the quantum-mechanical correction on the reaction coordinate; quantum-mechanical corrections on other internal coordinates are familiar and routine quantities. As noted in Chapter 8, Wigner[35] discussed the general problem of quantum-mechanical corrections in terms of normal-mode coordinates for any potential-energy ridge. A general justification for treating the quantum corrections as separate factors, for example

$$\Gamma = \Gamma_{str}\Gamma_b^2\Gamma_* \qquad (10\text{--}79)$$

could only be given to first approximation

$$\Gamma_i = 1 - u_i^2/24 + \cdots \qquad (10\text{--}80)$$

Meanwhile, kineticists have assumed that for a given vibrational coordinate the quantum correction on the rate of reaction is the same as the quantum correction on the equilibrium partition function (Eq. 6-28):

$$\Gamma = (u/2)/\sinh(u/2) \qquad (10\text{--}81)$$

and that the quantum correction on the reaction coordinate is that of a one-dimensional barrier. For small degrees of tunneling, the correction for an inverted parabolic barrier is

$$\Gamma_* = (|u_*|/2)/\sin(|u_*|/2) \qquad (10\text{--}82)$$

For large degrees of tunneling, the reaction coordinate is replaced by a truncated parabola or an Eckart function. One must prescribe where to truncate the parabola or where to place the base lines of the Eckart function; in either case, one must call on features of the potential-energy surface other than the saddlepoint and its curvatures there.

From a potential-energy surface one can approximately identify the conditions under which the reaction coordinate is (a) classical, (b) separable with Eqs. 79 and 80 sure to be valid or with Eqs. 81 and 82 reasonable postulates, and (c) non-separable, in which case all quantum corrections are very difficult to make, that is, for vibrational normal modes as well as the reaction coordinate. A normal-mode analysis gives the mass along the reaction coordinate m_* and thus the Boltzmann-average de Broglie wavelength $\Lambda_* = h/(2\pi m_* kT)^{1/2}$. (a) The reaction coordinate is classical if the potential-energy profile is essentially flat at the top over a distance large compared to the de Broglie wavelength. (b) The reaction coordinate is separable but not classical if the potential-energy surface near the saddlepoint is well approximated by a quadratic function (Eq. 4–38) over an area whose linear dimensions are all large compared to the de Broglie wavelength. A comparison of Figs. 5 and 6 gives some information of this sort for the H_3 complex, as represented by the semiempirical potential-energy function. It appears that a temperature well above 1000°K is required for separability of coordinates to be assured. (c) The reaction coordinate is non-separable if the de Broglie wavelength is large compared to the quadratic region of the saddlepoint region. For H_3 it appears that kinetic data were taken under non-separable conditions. To carry through the calculation of the rate constant, one must utilize a full potential-energy surface and make several bold assumptions about the appropriate tunneling path or paths.

The theoretical work on H_3 by Boys and Shavitt did not give a complete potential-energy surface, but only a few points. The BEBO method gives a narrow parabolic channel between reactants and products, but not a complete potential-energy surface. The semiempirical method of London-Eyring-Polanyi-Sato, however, does give a complete potential-energy surface. In this section it will be utilized to explore the magnitude of one-dimensional tunneling for several different cuts across the potential-energy surface.

The saddlepoint for H_3 is at 0.93–0.93 Å. The reaction normal mode is a straight line of $-45°$ slope through 0.93–0.93 (EOF of Fig. 10). The energy profile of such a straight line is given to scale in Fig. 11 as EOF. A parabola with the same curvature at 0.93–0.93 is included in Fig. 11, and one sees that the quadratic region along this energy profile is about ±0.3 Å (the thermal de Broglie wavelength of a hydrogen atom at 500°K is 0.78 Å). The extended reaction coordinate EOF encounters side-wall repulsion and eventually turns upward. The minimum energy is 1.4 kcal below the saddlepoint, ΔV_* of Fig. 11, while the energy of reactants is 8.6 kcal below the saddlepoint. Parallel cuts $(-45°)$ at different crossing points, 0.96–0.96 (LM), 0.90–0.90 (GH) are shown in Figs. 10 and 11. For crossing points shorter than the saddlepoint, GH, the curvature is less sharp (smaller F_*), the energy from crossing point to minimum is less deep (smaller ΔV_*), and the crossing point is higher than at the saddlepoint; all of these effects tend to decrease the tunneling for short crossings. For crossing points longer than the saddlepoint, LM, F_* is greater and ΔV_* is greater than at the saddlepoint; these effects tend to give more tunneling than at the saddlepoint. However, the height of the barrier increases as one moves away from the saddlepoint, and this effect via Boltzmann's factor tends to reduce the contribution to the rate by these paths.

A series of cuts at $-45°$ was made for crossing points varying every 0.01 Å from 0.80–0.80; 0.81–0.81; ... ; 0.93–0.93; ... ; 1.09–1.09. For each such cut a value of F and ΔV was found and at each of three temperatures, 333, 500, and 1000°K, u_* and α (compare Eqs. 2–15 to 2–18)

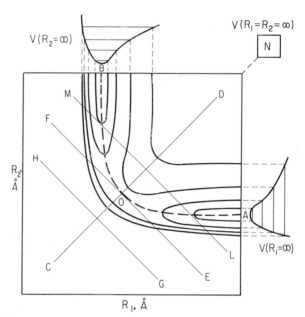

Fig. 10–10. Potential-energy surface with special reference to certain directions and trajectories.

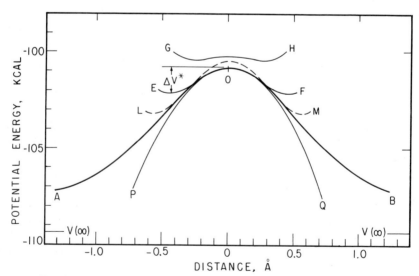

Fig. 10–11. Potential-energy profiles for various cuts across Fig. 10.

were evaluated for H—H—H and D—D—D. For each such cut the Eckart transmission coefficient from Table 2–2 is interpreted as the value for $\kappa(q)$, where q is the crossing point for a $-45°$ motion. The plot of $\kappa(q)$ against q is given in Figs. 12, 13, and 14 for H—H—H and D—D—D at each of three temperatures. The form of the classical curve is given by the Boltzmann factor for the crossing point, and all transmissions are normalized to unity

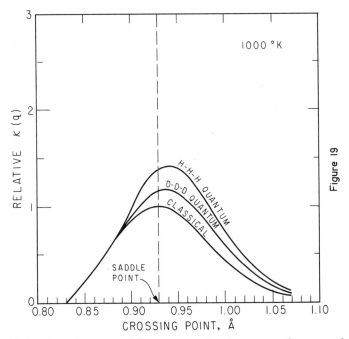

Fig. 10–12. One-dimensional Eckart tunneling factors as a function of crossing point between lines *HG* and *ML* of Fig. 10 for HHH and DDD at 1000°K.

for classical transmission just at the saddlepoint. The ratio of area under the quantum curve to that under the classical curve may be interpreted as the average of the tunneling factor over various crossing points. (However, the dependence of the tunneling factor on the symmetrical-stretch normal mode coordinate is a violation of the assumption of a unique reaction coordinate in Eq. 8–25.) This average tunneling factor is given as entry *a* in Table 8.

Many other tunneling paths may be considered. One may fit an Eckart potential from the minimum in potential energy of reactants to minimum in V of products and with the negative force constant evaluated at the saddlepoint (compare Fig. 3). Corrections based on this model are entered as entry *b* in Table 8. This model is surely incorrect, since no particle ever

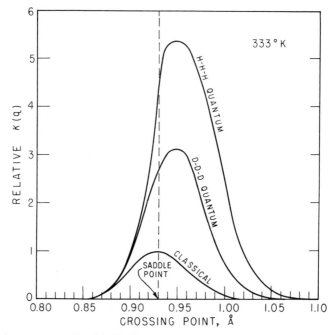

Fig. 10–13. Same as Fig. 12 at 500°K.

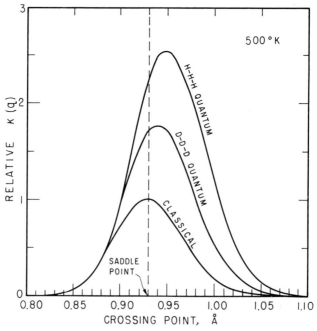

Fig. 10–14. Same as Fig. 12 at 333°K.

TABLE 10–8

Comparison of Various Methods of Obtaining Tunneling Corrections

Reaction	Type of Correction	Tunneling Factor Γ_*		
		333°K	500°K	1000°K
HHH	a	5.8	2.7	1.4
	b	23.0	3.9	1.4
	c	6.7	3.0	1.5
	c′	5.1	2.0	1.2
	c″	5.8	2.6	1.4
DDD	a	3.2	1.8	1.2
	b	5.0	2.0	1.2
	c	3.5	1.6	1.3
	c′	2.2	1.4	1.1
	c″	3.2	1.7	1.2
$\frac{HHH}{DDD}$	a	1.8	1.5	1.2
	b	4.6	1.9	1.2
	c	1.9	1.9	1.2
	c′	2.3	1.4	1.1
	c″	1.8	1.5	1.2

a. $\langle\Gamma_*\rangle_{av}$, Eckart correction averaged over various crossing points, the ratio of areas in Figs. 12, 13, and 14, London-Eyring-Polanyi-Sato (LEPS) potential-energy surface.

b. Eckart function fitted over full reaction path (*BOA* of Fig. 10), from minimum V of reactants to minimum V of products. LEPS surfaces. This method is not a valid one.

c. Eckart function fitted from zero-point energy level of reactants to zero-point energy level of products and through the saddle-point 0. LEPS surface.

c′. Same as c, but Boys and Shavitt's potential-energy function.

c″. Same as c, but BEBO potential-energy function.

hits the barrier or ridge with an energy less than the zero-point energy of the reactant, and it must appear on the other side of the barrier with no lower energy than the zero-point energy of products.

A more reasonable but equally simple approximation is to fit an Eckart potential from the zero-point energy level of reactants to zero-point energy level of products with the negative force constant evaluated along the reaction coordinate at the saddlepoint. With this model one obtains entry c in Table 8. It should be noted that the zero-point energy of the complex is not added to the barrier height in this model; the quantum correction for one supposedly separable coordinate does not constitute potential energy for the reaction coordinate. When the zero-point energy of reactants is greater than the barrier height, this method fails; quantum effects on the reaction coordinate are surely present, but cannot be simply estimated. This method requires less information about the potential-energy surface as a whole than does the first method described above, and it can readily be extended to Boys and Shavitt's potential-energy function or to that of the BEBO method.

These five different ways of estimating large tunneling corrections are given for the HHH and DDD reactions at 333, 500 and 1000°K in Table 8. Method b ignores the quantized vibration of the reactant and is regarded as invalid. The other four methods agree with each other fairly well, but discrepancies as large as 50 percent are common. The method recommended is a, if one has a complete potential-energy surface, or method c when one has only quadratic parameters. When method c appears to give a tunneling correction greater than 10, one usually gives up hope of a simple method to estimate tunneling. On the other hand one must also surrender when the zero-point energy of reactant is greater than the potential-energy barrier V^*.

TABLE 10–9

Tunneling Corrections Using Method c'' of Table 10–8 and Bond-Energy–Bond-Order Potential-Energy Function for Other H_3 Reactions over a Wide Range of Temperature

T	$1000/T$	HHH	DDD	DHH	HDD
2000	0.5	1.2	1.1	1.1	1.1
1000	1.0	1.4	1.2	1.4	1.2
667	1.5	1.9	1.4	1.7	1.5
500	2.0	2.6	1.7	2.3	1.8
400	2.5	4.0	2.3	3.3	2.5
333	3.0	5.8	3.2	5.1	3.6
286	3.5	9.3	4.9	8.3	5.4

An interesting case is predicted by method c. If the zero-point energy of the H reactant is only slightly less than the barrier height, that of the D reactant will be well below the barrier height. In this case, the large value of α for deuterium and small value of α for hydrogen leads to more tunneling by D than H.

By means of method c and the BEBO potential-energy function, a table of tunneling corrections for various H_3 reactions over a wide range of temperature is given by Table 9.

(e) Evaluation of Rate Constants. By means of the usual expression in terms of partition functions (Eq. 76), Shavitt evaluated the rate constant for all hydrogen transfer reactions involving H and D. As a part of this presentation, he gave convenient formulae for moments of inertia and vibration frequencies for two- and three-atom models and he carried out corrections for tunneling using the Eckart relation. This theoretical treatment disagrees with experiment by several orders of magnitude. Therefore, Shavitt semiempirically readjusted the activation energy to agree with experiment at 1000°K. The rate constants for the ortho-para hydrogen conversion as found by Boys and Shavitt's unadjusted theory are given in Table 10. The kinetic isotope effect, k_{HHH}/k_{DDD} or k_1/k_2, is independent of activation energy. Shavitt's values for this quantity are given in Table 10. The other observed quantity is $k_3k_4/(k_3 + k_4)$; this quantity, with the theoretically calculated activation energy, is also given in Table 10.

TABLE 10-10
Theoretical Rate Constants and Rate Constant Ratios Based on Boys and Shavitt's Potential-Energy Function[a]

T	$1000/T$	$\log k_1$	$\log k_3k_4/(k_3 + k_4)$	k_1/k_2
300	3.33	3.81	2.88	10.14
400	2.50	6.05	5.43	5.44
500	2.00	7.47	7.01	3.97
600	1.67	8.44	8.08	3.26
700	1.43	9.17	8.86	2.82
800	1.25	9.72	9.46	2.54
1000	1.00	10.53	10.32	2.19
1200	0.83	11.10	10.62	1.98

[a] Ref. 64.

The rate expression based on local bond properties (Eq. 77) has certain advantages over the usual expression based on normal coordinates (Eq. 76). The BEBO method will be presented in terms of Eq. 77. Maximum cancellation of terms in Eq. 77 reduces the expression to the form of Eq. 8–71:

$$\frac{k}{V} = \underbrace{\left(\frac{R_{\ddagger}}{R_{HH}}\right)^2}_{\substack{\text{that}\\\text{change}}} \left(\frac{F_{HH}}{F_{\ddagger}}\right)^{1/2} \underbrace{\left(\frac{\nu^*}{w}\right)}_{\text{new}} \underbrace{(R_2^2 l_2 l_\Phi^2)_{\ddagger}}_{\text{new}} T^{3/2} \frac{\Gamma_{str}\Gamma_b^2\Gamma_*}{\Gamma_{HH}} \exp\left(-V^*/kT\right) \quad (10\text{-}83)$$

When properties of the activated complex (Table 7), are substituted, the expression is

$$k = 5.22 \times 10^{13}\left(\frac{\omega^*}{1000}\right)\left(\frac{T}{1000}\right)^{3/2} \frac{\Gamma_{str}\Gamma_b\Gamma_*}{\Gamma_{HH}} \exp\left(-V^*/kT\right) \quad (10\text{-}84)$$

where ω^* is in cm^{-1}. From the tunneling corrections given in Table 9 and from the vibration frequencies from Table 7, all quantum-correction factors can be obtained, and the rate constant calculated as a function of temperature (Table 11A). The contribution of each term in Eq. 77 at 1000°K is given in Table 12.

(f) Kinetic Isotope Effect. The expression for the rate constant (Eq. 83) can be factored into terms that depend on isotopic mass and terms that are independent of mass:

$$\frac{k}{V} = \underbrace{\left\{\left(\frac{R_{\ddagger}}{R_{HH}}\right)^2\left(\frac{F_{HH}}{F_{\ddagger}}\right)^{1/2} \frac{R_2^2 l_2 l_\Phi^2 T^{3/2}}{w} \exp\left(-V^*/kT\right)\right\}}_{\text{mass independent}} \underbrace{\left\{\nu^* \frac{\Gamma_{str}\Gamma_b^2\Gamma_*}{\Gamma_{HH}}\right\}}_{\text{mass dependent}} \quad (10\text{-}85)$$

TABLE 10–11A
Rate Constants and Rate Constant Ratios Based on Bond-Energy–Bond-Order Method

T	$1000/T$	$\log k_1$	$\log k_3 k_4/(k_3 + k_4)$	k_1/k_2
286	3.5	8.18	7.00	7.68
333	3.0	8.91	7.87	6.45
400	2.5	9.71	8.78	5.45
500	2.0	10.51	9.71	4.36
667	1.5	11.06	10.70	3.28
1000	1.0	12.31	11.77	2.42
2000	0.5	13.49	13.06	1.70

TABLE 10–11B
Rate Constants as Calculated by Karplus, Porter, and Sharma for HHH

		Calculated Rate Constants[a] $\times 10^{-11}$		
			Activated-Complex Method	
$T°K$	Collision Method	No Tunneling Factor	Tunneling Factor[b]	With Tunneling Factor
300	0.002025	0.0003011	—	—
333	0.0063	0.001245	5.84	0.0073
400	0.03816	0.01112	—	—
500	0.2348	0.09840	2.66	0.262
600	0.8219	0.4299	—	—
700	2.071	1.260	—	—
800	4.229	2.881	—	—
900	7.481	5.584	—	—
1000	11.935	9.640	1.41	13.6

[a] cm^3 mole^{-1} sec^{-1}.
[b] Johnston and Rapp, Ref. 27.

TABLE 10–12
Contribution of Each Term in Eq. 77 for HHH Reaction at 1000°K

Term	Value
$(f_\ddagger/f_{HH}f_H)_e$	1
$(\sigma_{HH}/\sigma_{HHH})$	2
$\omega^*/1000\omega$	$1699i/1023i = 1.66$
$(R_\ddagger/R_{HH})_1^2$	$(0.92/0.74)^2 = 1.54$
$(F_{HH}/F_\ddagger)_1^{1/2}$	$(5.74/1.320)^{1/2} = 2.08$
R_2^2	0.846×10^{-16} cm^2
l_2	0.246×10^{-8} cm
l_ϕ	1.46 radians!
Γ_{str}	0.65
Γ_b^2	0.93
Γ_*	1.42
Γ_{HH}	0.268
$\exp(-V^*/kT)$	7.22×10^{-3}

For the ratio of rate constants for the HHH and DDD reactions, the expression is

$$\frac{k_1}{k_2} = \frac{(\nu^* \Gamma_{str} \Gamma_b^2 \Gamma_* / \Gamma_{HH})_1}{(\nu^* \Gamma_{str} \Gamma_b^2 \Gamma_* / \Gamma_{DD})_2} \qquad (10\text{--}86)$$

The kinetic isotope effect does not depend on the potential energy of activation, but it is fairly sensitive to the force constants. The ratio k_1/k_2 or k_{HHH}/k_{DDD} as found from Boys and Shavitt's theory and from the BEBO method is given in Tables 9 and 10.

Equation 86 is identical to the expression for the kinetic isotope effect as evaluated and discussed by Bigeleisen.[70] However, his ratio expression was derived without benefit of the absolute expression, Eq. 85 or 83. The advantages Bigeleisen pointed out for Eq. 86 for the isotope effect are pertinent to the rate constant expressions, also.

(g) Evaluation of Arrhenius Rate Factors **A** and **E**. It is much more difficult to evaluate the Arrhenius pre-exponential factor from theory than it is to calculate the rate constant **k** at a number of temperatures. One must not only evaluate all of the terms needed for the rate constant, but also the temperature-derivative terms, Θ of Eq. 42. Experimental data are usually fitted to the Arrhenius equation (Eq. 40). Kineticists sometimes falsely argue that some effect is absent because experimental data fail to show curvature on an Arrhenius plot. It requires extraordinarily precise experimental data over a very wide range of temperature to detect a curvature in an Arrhenius plot. The first effect of a non-exponential temperature function is to change the slope of an Arrhenius plot with no apparent curvature, within experimental error. Thus to evaluate Arrhenius **A** and **E** from theoretical **B** and V^*, one must carry out the tedious corrections of Eq. 43.

The rate constant expression (Eq. 84) factors into a temperature-independent term and a temperature-dependent block:

$$k = 8.86 \times 10^{13} \left(\frac{T}{1000}\right)^{3/2} \frac{\Gamma_{str} \Gamma_b^2 \Gamma_*}{\Gamma_{HH}} \exp\left(-V^*/kT\right) \qquad (10\text{--}87)$$

The temperature coefficient of the pre-exponential factor is

$$\Theta = \tfrac{3}{2} + \Theta_{str} + 2\Theta_b + \Theta_* - \Theta_{HH} \qquad (10\text{--}88)$$

For the real vibrations, Γ is $(u/2)\sinh(u/2)$ and the temperature coefficient is

$$\Theta_v = d\ln\Gamma/d\ln T = -1 + (u/2)\coth(u/2) \qquad (10\text{--}89)$$

Values of Γ and Θ as a function of $u/2$ are given in Table 13. The tunneling correction Γ_* is usually available only as a table of values, but it is

TABLE 10–13

Harmonic Oscillator Functions

x	Γ^{-1}	$-\Theta$	x	Γ^{-1}	$-\Theta$
0	1.000	0	2.6	2.575	1.629
0.1	1.002	0.003	2.7	2.743	1.724
0.2	1.006	0.013	2.8	2.926	1.821
0.3	1.015	0.030	2.9	3.124	1.918
0.4	1.027	0.053	3.0	3.340	2.015
0.5	1.042	0.082	3.1	3.574	
0.6	1.061	0.117	3.2	3.828	
0.7	1.084	0.158	3.3	4.103	
0.8	1.110	0.205	3.4	4.403	
0.9	1.141	0.256	3.5	4.726	
1.0	1.175	0.313	3.6	5.080	
1.1	1.214	0.374	3.7	5.462	
1.2	1.258	0.439	3.8	5.879	
1.3	1.306	0.509	3.9	6.331	
1.4	1.360	0.581	4.0	6.822	
1.5	1.419	0.657	4.1	7.356	
1.6	1.485	0.736	4.2	7.938	
1.7	1.557	0.817	4.3	8.567	
1.8	1.634	0.901	4.4	9.255	
1.9	1.720	0.987	4.5	10.000	
2.0	1.814	1.075	4.6	10.813	
2.1	1.915	1.164	4.7	11.696	
2.2	2.026	1.255	4.8	12.656	
2.3	2.147	1.347	4.9	13.702	
2.4	2.278	1.440	5.0	14.840	
2.5	2.420	1.534	$x > 5$	$e^x/2x$	$x - 1$

$$x = u/2 = h\nu/2kT = hc\omega/2kT = 0.7192\ \omega/T$$
$$\Gamma^{-1} = \sinh x/x \qquad \Theta = d \ln \Gamma/d \ln T$$

simple at certain limits.

$$\Gamma_* = 1 + |u_*|^2/24 \qquad \text{as } T \to \infty$$

$$= (|u|/2) \sin(|u|/2) \qquad \text{at high } T \qquad (10\text{–}90)$$

$$= \text{Table 2–2} \qquad \text{at ordinary } T$$

The temperature derivatives for these regions are

$$\Theta_* = -\frac{|u_*|^2/24}{\Gamma_*} \approx -|u_*|^2/24 \qquad \text{as } T \to \infty$$

$$\qquad\qquad\qquad\qquad\qquad\qquad\qquad\qquad\qquad (10\text{–}91)$$

$$\Theta_* = -1 + (|u_*|/2)\cot(|u_*|/2) \qquad \text{at high } T$$

$$\Theta_* \text{ is slope of log } \Gamma_* \text{ vs log } T \qquad \text{at ordinary } T$$

The values of Γ and Θ for temperatures between 333 and 2000°K for the HHH reaction are given in Table 14 (bond-energy–bond-order method).

TABLE 10–14

Evaluation of Arrhenius Rate Factors for HHH Reaction by
Bond-Energy–Bond-Order Method

$T°K$	2000	1000	667	500	400	333
$1000/T$	0.5	1.0	1.5	2.0	2.5	3.0
u_{str}	0.84	1.68	2.52	3.36	4.20	5.04
u_b	0.25	0.50	0.75	1.00	1.25	1.50
u_*	1.22	2.44	3.66	4.88	6.10	7.32
u_{HH}	1.58	3.16	4.75	6.33	7.91	9.49
Γ_{str}^{-1}	1.12	1.54	2.45	4.22	7.93	15.2
Γ_b^{-1}	1.01	1.04	1.10	1.18	1.28	1.42
Γ_*	1.15	1.42	1.90	2.64	3.95	5.75
Γ_{HH}^{-1}	1.47	3.73	12.1	44.2	174	690
Θ_{str}	0.05	0.23	0.48	0.78	1.17	1.56
Θ_b (a)	—	0.02	0.05	0.08	0.12	0.17
Θ_*	−0.15	−0.50	−0.95	−1.5	−2.0	−2.5
Θ_{HH}	0.20	0.71	1.43	2.18	2.95	3.75
Θ'	1.50	1.50	1.50	1.50	1.50	1.50
Θ	1.20	0.56	−0.30	−1.24	−2.04	−2.85
ΘRT (b)	4.8	1.1	−0.40	−1.2	−1.6	−1.9
E (b)	14.6	10.9	9.4	8.6	8.2	7.9
$\log A$ (c)	15.08	14.69	14.44	14.26	14.18	14.11

(a) To be taken twice.
(b) kcal/mole.
(c) cc/mole-sec.

The total temperature correction factor Θ varies from −2.8 to +1.2. The activation energy (Eq. 40) varies from 7.9 to 14.6 kcal/mole (the potential energy of activation is 9.8 kcal/mole). The Arrhenius A-factor (Eq. 41) varies from $10^{14.1}$ to $10^{15.1}$ cc/mole-sec.

D. COMPARISON OF EXPERIMENT AND THEORY

The experimental values for the rate constants for the various reactions are given in Tables 1, 2, and 4. The theoretical functions for the rate constant k_1 by the method of Boys and Shavitt and by the BEBO method are given in Tables 10 and 11A. The values of the rate constant as calculated by Karplus, Porter, and Sharma by the collisional method are listed in Table 11B. These experimental and theoretical quantities are compared in Fig. 15. The theoretical curve of Boys and Shavitt lies far below the experimental points, because the theoretical activation energy is about 6 kcal/mole too high. Karplus' collision model and the bond-energy–bond-order method give very nearly the same calculated values, and they both agree with experiment within a factor of two.

The exchange rate of H_2 and D_2 to HD gives the rate constant function $k_3k_4/(k_3 + k_4)$ (Eq. 37). The experimental and theoretical values are given

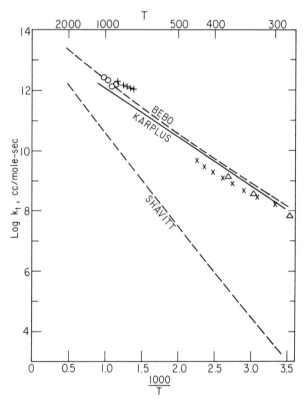

Fig. 10–15. Comparison of experimental rate constants with calculated rate constant functions: ○—Ref. a, +—Ref. c, △—Ref. b; all three from Table I; k_{HHH} or k_1.

in the tables cited above. The experimental points show a very high scatter for one investigator, and large systematic deviations between one investigator and another. The authors of Ref. *e* of Table 1 have shown that much of the systematic error between workers is the diffusion of oxygen through hot silica. If the data entered as + in Fig. 16, Ref. *e*, are regarded as most nearly valid, one sees that the BEBO method is a factor of 3 high and Shavitt's theory is a factor of 10 low.

The HHH reaction was measured at one time, and later the same investigator, Farkas, also measured the DDD reaction. For kinetic isotope effect it is desirable to carry out the reaction of the two isotopic species alternately in the same system or competitively if possible. The intervention of several years makes the kinetic isotope study k_{HHH}/k_{DDD} very

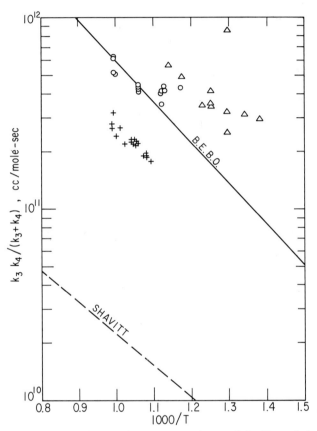

Fig. 10–16. Rate of hydrogen-deuterium exchange, $k_3 k_4/(k_3 + k_4)$, comparison of experiment and theory: ○—Ref. a, △—Ref. c, +—Ref. e; all three from Table I.

uncertain. Nevertheless, as described above, estimates of the ratio k_{HHH}/k_{DDD} were made from Farkas' data, and they are entered in Table 3. Calculated values of this kinetic isotope effect are given in Tables 10 and 11. The activation energy cancels out of the kinetic isotope effect study, so that a good check should be possible for Shavitt's theory. A comparison of theory and experiment is given by Fig. 17. Although the *properties* of

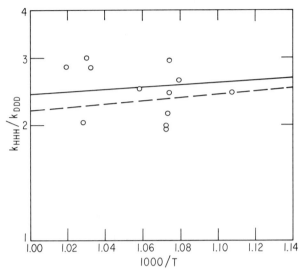

Fig. 10–17. Comparison of experimental and theoretical kinetic isotope effect, k_{HHH}/k_{DDD}.

the activated complex as found by Shavitt and by the BEBO method are rather different (Table 7), the computed kinetic isotope effect is essentially the same for each method (Fig. 17). The two methods agree with each other and with the experimental data.

E. COMPARISON OF COLLISION THEORY AND ACTIVATED-COMPLEX THEORY ON SAME POTENTIAL-ENERGY SURFACE

On the semiempirical potential-energy surface of Karplus and co-workers, the rate constant for the chemical reaction (para-ortho hydrogen exchange) was calculated by two different methods (Table 11B): (1) The phase-average, reaction cross-section was evaluated as a function of initial vibrational, rotational, and mutual kinetic energies by calculation of a large number of collision trajectories, such as those of Figs. 7 and 8. Integration over equilibrium distribution functions for reactants gave the rate constant as a function of temperature. (2) On the same potential-energy surface, the location of the saddlepoint and the second derivatives there are all the data one needs (aside from properties of reactants) to evaluate the rate constant, if one omits the tunneling factor. Karplus and co-workers omitted the tunneling correction from their comparison of activated-complex theory and collision theory, and they tentatively presented several arguments justifying this omission. In Table 11B, Karplus' estimate of the rate constant, according to activated-complex theory, has been multiplied by the tunneling factors worked out by Johnston and Rapp for the same reaction of the

London-Polanyi-Eyring-Sato potential-energy surface. Without the tunneling correction, the activated-complex theory rate constant lies below the collision theory value at all temperatures. With the tunneling correction, the value calculated from activated-complex theory is above that calculated from analysis of molecular dynamics at all temperatures. Thus within the uncertainty of the tunneling correction, the two methods give the same rate constants at all temperatures.

Finally, what are the arguments for and against applying tunneling corrections? Against making this correction, Karplus points out that for bent complexes the barrier is thicker than for the linear complex, so that the methods of this chapter overestimate tunneling; obviously, this consideration is valid, and thus one should average over weighted angles of approach or bending vibrations in a way similar to that used by Johnston and Rapp in averaging over "crossing points." Karplus points out that, in terms of reactants, the de Broglie wavelength is short compared to the barrier width; however, the average velocity above the barrier is quite low and there the wavelength is longer than the width of the flat-topped barrier. The long wavelength at the dividing surface indicates quantum corrections on the reaction coordinate. Finally, Karplus (private communication) points out that the reaction cross-section as a function of energy, as in Fig. 9, shows much the same form and value when evaluated by quantum mechanics as when evaluated by classical mechanics. On this basis, zero-point energy is ascribed to the reactant H_2 and to the symmetric stretch coordinate of the complex, but the relative velocity V_R and the reaction coordinate ρ are regarded as classical. The present author does not accept this argument without qualification. As noted before, a given energy specification (v, J, V_R) is averaged over phases of the vibration of H_2, and depending on the phase of vibration of H_2 the collision is projected variously on the symmetric σ and antisymmetrical ρ coordinates of the complex. Every energy specification (v, J, V_R) therefore represents a complete average over σ and ρ coordinates. In quantum mechanics the zero-point energy in the σ coordinate acts to reduce the calculated rate, and tunneling in the ρ coordinate tends to increase the calculated rate. The averaging of these two opposite terms in the completely quantum-mechanical calculation tends to wipe out the specifically quantum-mechanical effects, and the quantum and classical reaction cross-sections are about the same. A complete, self-consistent classical treatment or a complete self-consistent quantum treatment is almost the same. However, in activated-complex theory it is inconsistent to regard the σ coordinate as quantized and the ρ coordinate as classical. Thus the calculation in Table 11B omitting a tunneling correction is surely. incorrect. Also, as Karplus says, the tunneling correction in Table 11B is probably too large, from the effect of nonlinear structures. If the last column of Table 11B were reduced somewhat, there would be almost precise agreement between the complete collision theory and activated-complex theory, with respect to calculated rate constants for this elementary chemical reaction.

PROBLEM

Between 800 and 3000°K, evaluate the kinetic isotope effect k_{HHH}/k_{DDD} by the London-Eyring-Polanyi-Sato method, using properties of the complex as given in Table 7. The tunneling correction may be approximated by Eq. 10-82.

11

Activation Energies

A. EMPIRICAL RELATIONS

If one examines the total population of gas-phase chemical reactions (complex or elementary; unimolecular, bimolecular, or termolecular; molecule-molecule, molecule-radical, or radical-radical), there is very little correlation between rate of reaction and the thermodynamic properties of reactants and products. Specifically, for such a general population of reactions there is very poor correlation between true activation energy (that is, activation energy for the exothermic direction) and heat of reaction. However, if one considers a series of similar reactions, one often finds a correlation between heat of reaction and activation energy. Such correlations were clearly established by M. G. Evans and Michael Polanyi,[71] and they are heavily documented by N. N. Semenov.[72] The relation used is

$$\mathbf{E} = \mathbf{E_0} - \alpha q \tag{11-1}$$

where $\mathbf{E}$ is the activation energy of a reaction for which the absolute magnitude of the exothermic heat of reaction is q. For a series of similar reactions, one fits two parameters, $\mathbf{E_0}$ and q, to two data; and then the other activation energies are predicted from known bond energies. Alternatively, observed activation energies may be used to evaluate unknown bond dissociation energies. For limited extrapolation or interpolation, this relation is extremely useful.

There are, of course, objections to the Polanyi-Semenov relation: it predicts a negative activation energy for sufficiently exothermic reactions, and one prefers a relation that approaches zero for highly exothermic reactions and that approaches the heat of reaction for highly endothermic processes. For the restricted class of reactions

$$\text{A-B} + \text{C} \rightarrow \text{A} + \text{B-C} \tag{11-2}$$
$$E_1 \qquad\qquad E_2$$

a relation based on a simplified model of the bond-energy–bond-order[41b]

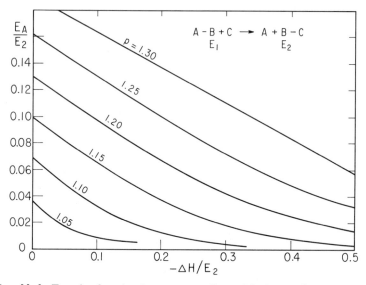

Fig. 11-1. Trend of activation energy, E_A, with heat of reaction, $-\Delta H$, according to Eq. 11-3 based on bond-energy–bond-order method.

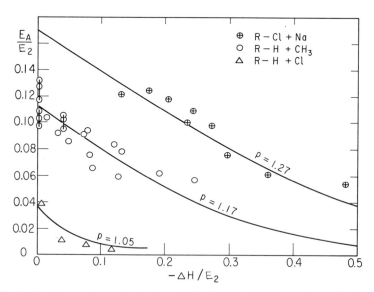

Fig. 11-2. Comparison of calculated (Eq. 11-3) and observed trends for three sets of reactions.

method replaces the Polanyi-Semenov expression by

$$\frac{E}{E_2} = \left(1 - \frac{q}{E_2}\right)\left\{1 - \left[1 + \left(1 - \frac{q}{E_2}\right)^{1/(p-1)}\right]^{1-p}\right\} \qquad (11\text{--}3)$$

where E_1 and E_2 are bond energies. The parameter p is adjusted to any one activation energy in a series of similar reactions, and other values are predicted by the relation. This relation approaches zero for highly exothermic reactions, and it approaches the heat of reaction for highly endothermic reactions. For various values of p (Eq. 3) the trend of activation energy with heat of reaction is shown in Fig. 1. For three sets of reactions from Semenov's book,[72] there is a comparison of Eq. 3 and experimental activation energies in Fig. 2. For the first two cases, R-Cl + Na and R-H + CH$_3$, the cumbersome one-parameter relation 3 is as good as (but no better than) the simple two-parameter equation 1; but for the third case, Cl + R-H, the BEBO relation is clearly superior to Polanyi's rule. Both of these relations are 100-percent empirical with the empiricism in the field of kinetics itself.

B. SEMIEMPIRICAL METHODS

With the London-Polanyi-Eyring-Sato potential-energy function, one can assume that Sato's parameter Δ is constant for a series of similar reactions, (Eq. 2). The parameter Δ can be evaluated from any one activation energy from the series, and all other activation energies can be found. Extensive calculations by the author have shown that this method gives results in close agreement with BEBO (Eq. 3). Since both methods fit one parameter, p or Δ, to one activation energy, since both of these methods have no real theoretical foundation and since Eq. 3 is vastly simpler to use than the Sato potential-energy function, then it is proposed that one use Eq. 3 in this context.

C. BOND-ENERGY–BOND-ORDER METHOD

For the restricted group of reactions such as Eq. 2 where the atom transferred is hydrogen,

$$\text{A-H} + \text{B} \rightarrow \text{A} \cdots \text{H} \cdots \text{B} \rightarrow \text{A} + \text{H-B} \qquad (11\text{--}4)$$

one can do surprisingly well in calculating the activation energy by the BEBO method (compare Chapter 10). This method is 100-percent empirical with the empiricism outside the field of kinetics. The energy of the complex $\text{A} \cdots \text{H} \cdots \text{B}$ is resolved into three parts, E_{AH}, E_{HB}, and E_{AB}. The total bond order in bonds AH and HB is assumed to be unity. From Pauling's rule (Eq. 4–49), one finds the length of each bond, and from Eqs. 4–50 and 4–52 one obtains the energies of these bonds. The repulsive energy between A and B is obtained from Sato's relation 4–21; this extension to general

TABLE 11-1

Bond Energies and Spectroscopic Data Used to
Evaluate Triplet Energies Between End Atoms

Bond R—X	D_e (kcal)	R_s (Å)	$\beta \times 10^{-8}$ (Å^{-1})
H—H	109.4	0.74	1.94
C—H	105.5	1.09	1.78
O—H	114.7	0.96	2.22
F—H	140.5	0.92	2.23
Cl—H	106.4	1.27	1.87
Br—H	90.5	1.42	1.81
I—H	73.9	1.61	1.75
C—C	84.4	1.54	1.94
C—F	107	1.38	2.00
C—Cl	80	1.76	1.81
C—Br	67	(1.91)	(1.81)
C—I	58	(2.10)	1.81
C—O	85.4	1.43	2.05
F—F	38	1.44	2.85
F—Cl	60	1.63	2.34
F—Br	51	1.76	2.39
Cl—Cl	58	1.99	2.02
Cl—Br	52	2.10	2.52
Br—Br	46	2.28	1.98
I—I	36	2.67	1.87
O—O	35	1.47	2.69
O—F	(46)	1.42	(2.77)
O—Cl	50	1.69	2.65
O—Br	(45)	(1.77)	(2.35)

A and B (radicals as well as atoms) has no theoretical basis and is to be regarded simply as a new postulate. The full algebraic detail of the extended BEBO method is given as Appendix E. The energy in terms of single-bond energies, the progress variable n (order of the AH bond), and the spectroscopic terms, p, q, B, and γ (defined in Appendix E) is given by

$$V = E_{1s}(1 - n^p) - E_{2s}(1 - n)^q + E_{3s}B(n - n^2)^\gamma \qquad (11\text{–}5)$$

$$= E(\text{AH}) + E(\text{HB}) + E(\text{AB}) \qquad (11\text{–}6)$$

where the origin of energy is the minimum potential energy of reactant AH. The energy indices p and q have been given in Table 4–4. The structural and spectroscopic data used for bond energies and Morse parameters for the triplet-energy correction are given in Table 1. By assigning orders (n_1 and $n_2 = 1 - n_1$) and by evaluating all the terms in Eq. 5, one can readily find the energy of the complex along the line of constant order. The "bonding terms" are $E_{1s}(1 - n^p) - E_{2s}(1 - n)^q$ and the "repulsive terms" are the remaining functions in Eq. 5. Three examples are given in Table 2 of the values of bonding terms, repulsive terms, and total potential energy as a function of the order of the bond being formed. These examples show that the bonding terms and repulsive terms are about equally important in determining the value of the activation energy. For all cases the repulsive term is symmetrical in bond orders and goes through a maximum at order 0.50. The magnitude of the repulsive term is usually between 2 and 8 kcal/mole. For some cases the bonding contribution also goes through a

TABLE II-2

Examples of Contributions of Bonding and Antibonding Terms
at Various States of Reaction*

	$CF_3 + H{-}CH_3$			$Cl + H{-}C\,me_3$			$F + HF$		
n_2	V_{bonds}	V_{tr}	V	V_{bonds}	V_{tr}	V	V_{bonds}	V_{tr}	V
0	0	0	0	0	0	0			
0.02	0.76	1.69	2.45	−0.96	2.14	1.18	0.48	0.33	0.81
0.03	1.06	2.07	3.13	−1.31	2.58	1.27	0.64	0.45	1.09
0.04	1.34	2.38	3.72	−1.60	2.94	1.34	0.79	0.54	1.33
0.05	1.57	2.70	4.27	−1.87	3.28	1.41	0.96	0.67	1.63
0.10	2.59	3.80	6.39	−2.93	4.53	**1.60**	1.57	1.06	2.63
0.15	3.39	4.47	7.86	−3.77	5.28	1.51	2.11	1.37	3.48
0.20	4.01	5.05	9.06	−4.45	5.94	1.49	2.51	1.60	4.11
0.25	4.48	5.48	9.96	−5.02	6.40	1.38	2.77	1.82	4.59
0.30	4.94	5.84	10.78	−5.51	6.80	1.29	3.02	1.99	5.01
0.35	5.12	6.21	11.33	−6.03	7.21	1.18	3.23	2.18	5.41
0.40	5.24	6.31	11.55	−6.41	7.35	0.94	3.38	2.25	5.63
0.45	5.34	6.47	**11.81**	−6.80	7.48	0.68	3.41	2.29	5.70
0.50	5.26	6.47	11.73	−7.25	7.48	0.23	3.42	2.29	**5.71**

* All energies in kcal/mole.

maximum, but the order of the bond being formed at the maximum is less than 0.5 for exothermic reactions and more than 0.5 for endothermic reactions. The bonding contribution shows a maximum if both p and q are greater than one. For thermo-neutral reactions, the bonding terms show a minimum if p and q are less than one. For exothermic reactions with p or q less than one, the bonding contribution is negative, and the activation energy is due to the triplet repulsion. The maximum values of the potential energy along the path of constant order are printed in boldface type in Table 2. From tables such as these, the potential energy of activation can be readily found by inspection.

This method gives the potential energy of activation, V^*. The observed activation energy (compare Fig. 10–3) differs not only by the difference in zero-point energy between reactants and complex, but also in thermal excitation of the reactant and complex. The zero-point energy of R—H varies from about 4 to 6 kcal. The zero-point energy of a complex R $\cdots$ H $\cdots$ X lies between 1 and 6 kcal, depending on the mass of R and X.

Thus in general, potential energies of activation should be slightly larger than observed energies of activation; for deuterium transfer reactions, the difference between V^* and $\mathbf{E}$ should be less than for hydrogen transfer.

Table 3 gives 130 cases of calculated potential energy of activation.[41a] (The time required to make these calculations with a desk calculator was about three man-days. Thus this method is very simple to carry through.)

TABLE II–3

Calculated Potential Energies of Activation for Hydrogen Transfer Reactions*

D_e (kcal)	RH	F	HO	H	CF$_3$	Cl	CH$_3$	C$_2$H$_5$	Me$_2$CH	Me$_3$C	Br
140	F—H	6	26	33	36	34	38	43	45	49	50
115	HO—H	0.3	4	11	14	9	16	19	20	24	24
109	H—H	2	6	10	14	8	15	18	19	22	21
107	CF$_3$—H	3	7	12	13	9	14	15	18	21	20
106	Cl—H	0.3	0.3	5	8	0	8	10	11	15	16
105	CH$_3$—H	3	6	11	12	7	13	15	16	20	18
100	Et—H	2	4	8	9	4	10	12	13	16	14
98	Me$_2$CH—H	2	4	8	9	3	9	11	12	15	12
93	Me$_3$C—H	2	3	6	7	2	7	9	10	12	8
90	Br—H	0	0.4	2	3	0	3	4	4	5	0
90	\—C—H /	2	2	5	6	1	6	8	9	10	6
85	\—C—H /	2	2	4	5	1	5	6	7	8	2
74	I—H	0	0.7	1	1	0	1	2	2	2	0

* kcal.

The computed activation potential energies vary from zero to 50 kcal, but the activation potential energies for thermoneutral or exothermic reactions vary only from zero to 12 kcal. In general the potential energies of activation in Table 3 agree with established activation energies within 2 or 3 kcal in all cases. Observed activation energies and calculated potential energies of activation are plotted in Figs. 3 and 4. The calculated function shows curvature, approaches zero for highly exothermic reactions, and approaches the heat of reaction for highly endothermic processes. This behavior is more reasonable than Polanyi's linear relationship of activation energy with heat of reaction, but over the range of observations these differences are not important. The calculated curves lie very close to the observed activation energies. The calculated potential energy of activation for fluorine atom attack on hydrocarbons is far less than the zero-point energy of the bond being broken; the observed activation energies are

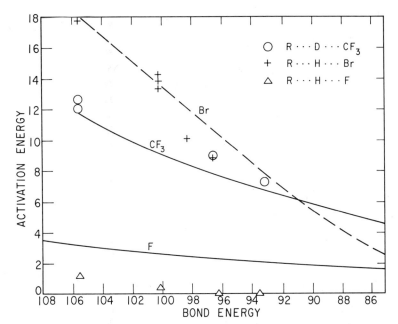

Fig. 11–3. Calculated potential energy of activation and observed Arrhenius activation energy plotted against dissociation energy for carbon-hydrogen bonds: ○—Ref. 21 and unpublished work by Halbert Carmichael; + and △—G. C. Fettis, J. H. Knox, and A. F. Trotman-Dickenson, *Canad. J. Chem.* **38**, 1643 (1960).

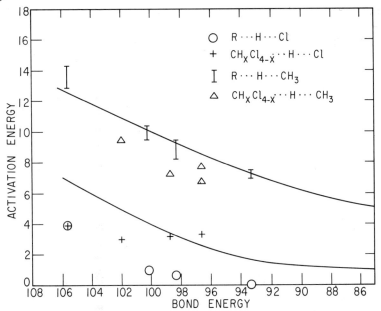

Fig. 11–4. Similar to Fig. 3: ○—Ref. 13 and J. H. Knox and R. H. Nelson; I (showing range of reported values); △—A. F. Trotman-Dickenson, *Gas Kinetics*, Academic Press, Inc., New York (1955).

parallel to the calculated potential energies and about 2 kcal lower. A similar situation applies for the reactions of chlorine atoms and hydrocarbons, but the activation energies are slightly higher. For chlorine atom attack on chlorinated methanes, the observed activation energies do not follow a Polanyi-type relation. For this case, observed activation energies do not parallel the line of computed potential energies of activation.

D. RATE CONSTANTS AS FUNCTION OF TEMPERATURE

Activation energies are primarily defined in terms of the temperature variation of the rate constant, $-R\,d\ln\mathbf{k}/d(1/T)$. The method of calculating rate constants by the BEBO method is given in Appendix E. When this method is applied over a wide temperature range, one sees some curvature

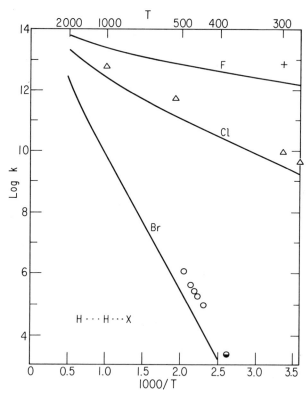

Fig. 11–5. Calculated and observed rate constants for halogen atom attack on H_2: ◉ = Br, + = F—Fettis, Knox, Trotman-Dickenson, Fig. 1 (Chapter 13); ◯ = Br—M. Bodenstein and H. Lutkemeyer, Z. Physik. Chem. **114**, 208 (1924); △ = Cl—H. O. Pritchard, J. B. Pyke, and A. F. Trotman-Dickenson, J. Am. Chem. Soc., **76**, 1201 (1958).

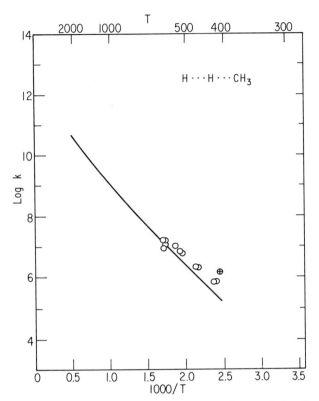

Fig. II–6. Calculated and observed rate constants for methyl radical reaction with H_2: ○—T. G. Marjury and E. W. R. Steacie, *Canad. J. Chem.*, **30**, 800 (1952); ⊕—J. C. Polanyi, *J. Chem. Phys.*, **24**, 493 (1956).

on an Arrhenius plot; and one has a critical test of the BEBO method. Such calculated rate constants as a function of temperature are compared with observed values for halogen atom attack on H_2 in Fig. 5, for CH_3 attack on H_2 in Fig. 6, and for CF_3 attack on methane, ethane, secondary and tertiary hydrocarbons in Fig. 7. These calculations with no adjustable parameters reproduce rate constants at all temperatures with about a factor of 2 for these cases.

E.   GENERAL INTERPRETATION OF ACTIVATION ENERGY

One of the first applications of statistical mechanics to problems in reaction kinetics was R. C. Tolman's general interpretation of activation energy.[94] The rate constant expression may be taken as Eq. 8–18, where the energy is

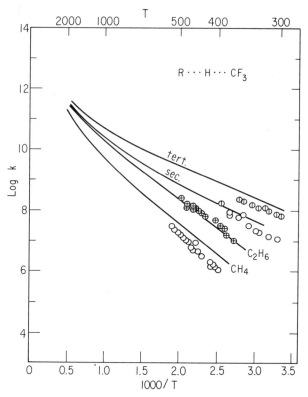

Fig. 11–7. Calculated and observed rate constants for trifluoromethyl radical reaction with hydrocarbons (P. B. Ayscough, J. C. Polanyi, and E. W. R. Steacie, *Canad. J. Chem.*, **33**, 743 [1955]; Ayscough and Steacie, *Canad. J. Chem.*, **34**, 103 [1956]).

that per mole:

$$\mathbf{k} = \frac{h^{-3N}}{f_A^\alpha f_B^\beta f_C^\gamma} \int \cdots \int_{6N} \kappa \nu \exp\left(-E/RT\right) d\tau \tag{11-7}$$

$$= \frac{h^{-3N} I}{f_A^\alpha f_B^\beta f_C^\gamma} \tag{11-8}$$

where I is the integral of Eq. 7. The definition of the Arrhenius activation energy is

$$\mathbf{E} = -R \, d \ln \mathbf{k}/d(1/T) \tag{11-9}$$

When this definition is applied to the theoretical Eq. 8, one obtains

$$\mathbf{E} = -\frac{R}{I}\frac{dI}{d(1/T)} + \frac{\alpha R \, d \ln f_A}{d(1/T)} + \frac{\beta R \, d \ln f_B}{d(1/T)} + \frac{\gamma R \, d \ln f_C}{d(1/T)} \tag{11-10}$$

The statistical mechanical expression for the average energy of molecular systems is

$$\langle E \rangle = -R \frac{d \ln f}{d(1/T)} \tag{11-11}$$

Thus the activation energy is

$$\mathbf{E} = -\frac{R}{I} \frac{d I}{d(1/T)} - (\alpha \langle E_A \rangle + \beta \langle E_B \rangle + \gamma \langle E_C \rangle) \tag{11-12}$$

The function $\kappa \nu$ in Eq. 7 is the state-by-state molecular rate constant, the elementary chemical-physical rate function of Chapter 1. This function $\kappa \nu$ is a purely mechanical property and not a function of temperature. The first term on the right-hand side of Eq. 13 is thus

$$-\frac{R}{I} \frac{d I}{d(1/T)} = \frac{\int \cdots \int E \kappa \nu \exp{(-E/RT)}\, d\tau}{\int \cdots \int \kappa \nu \exp{(-E/RT)}\, d\tau} \tag{11-13}$$

This function has the form of an average, Eq. 6–35; it is the average value of the energy of the $(\alpha A + \beta A + \gamma C)$ system over the "distribution function for reaction." The molecular rate function $\kappa \nu$ modifies the Boltzmann factor to give Tolman's distribution function, the clusters that react. The activation energy is thus

$$\mathbf{E} = \langle E \rangle^T - (\alpha \langle E_A \rangle + \beta \langle E_B \rangle + \gamma \langle E_C \rangle) \tag{11-14}$$

$$\begin{pmatrix} \text{Arrhenius} \\ \text{activation} \\ \text{energy} \end{pmatrix} = \begin{pmatrix} \text{average energy} \\ \text{of clusters} \\ \text{that react} \end{pmatrix} - \begin{pmatrix} \text{average energy} \\ \text{of reactants} \end{pmatrix}$$

This expression can be given a somewhat more concrete physical interpretation. Suppose one could measure the (ensemble) average energy of all reaction products, after reaction had occurred but before any subsequent energy-transfer collisions. The activation energy is the difference in this average energy and the average energy over all states of the reactants.

PROBLEMS

(1) Plot the function

$$\mathbf{k} = 10^{10} T^n \exp{(-2400/T)}$$

as log $\mathbf{k}$ *vs* $1000/T$ for $n = -2, -1, 0, +1, +2$ for temperatures between 400 and 500°K. On a separate graph and with a larger range of $1000/T$, plot these same functions between 300 and 3000°K. For experimental data with 5-percent random error, discuss the possibility of detecting curvature of an Arrhenius plot.

(2) Using the bond-energy–bond-order method, calculate the potential energy of activation for each of the following reactions, assuming $E_{1s} = E_{2s} = 100$ kcal

in all cases and assuming E_{3s} is given by Table 1.   Refer to Table 4–4.

$$Cl{-}H + C{\nwarrow}^{\diagup} \rightarrow Cl + H{-}C{\diagdown}^{\diagup}$$

$$^{\diagdown}O{-}H + C{\nwarrow}^{\diagup} \rightarrow {-}O + H{-}C{\diagdown}^{\diagup}$$

$$_{\diagup}^{\diagdown}C{-}H + C{\nwarrow}^{\diagup} \rightarrow {_{\diagup}^{\diagdown}}C + H{-}C{\diagdown}^{\diagup}$$

The experimental values of these energies of activation are, respectively, 3.8, 6 to 8, and 11 to 14 kcal/mole.

12

Pre-Exponential Factors for Bimolecular Atom Transfer

A. QUALITATIVE TRENDS

For the atom-transfer reaction

$$A - x + B \rightarrow A \cdots x \cdots B \rightarrow A + xB$$

it has long been stated that the Arrhenius $\mathbf{A}$-factor decreases as the "complexity" of the reactant radicals A and B increase for a series of similar reactions. The traditional analysis of this problem has been to compare the theoretical $\mathbf{B}$-factor Eq. 10–41 with the collision-rate constant for the hard-sphere model, Eq. 9–29. In terms of partition functions in normal-mode coordinates, non-linear Ax plus non-linear B to produce non-linear $A - x - B$, the rate constant is (omitting the exponential factor, $\langle \kappa \rangle$, $\langle 1 + \phi \rangle$, etc.)

$$\mathbf{B} = \frac{kT}{h} \frac{(f_t^3 f_r^3 f_v^{3N-7})_{\ddagger}}{f_t^6 f_r^6 f_v^{3N-12}} \tag{12–1}$$

As one can see from Eq. 9–29, the hard-sphere collision-rate constant is

$$\mathbf{k}_{\mathrm{coll}} = \frac{kT}{h} \frac{(f_t^3 f_r^2)_{\ddagger}}{f_t^6} \tag{12–2}$$

The argument is presented that partition functions of a given *type* are usually of about the same order of magnitude; thus one cancels $(f_r)_{\ddagger}$ against $(f_r)_A$, for example. The important item is said to be the *number* of each type of partition function, and thus the ratio of the reaction-rate factor $\mathbf{B}$ and the collision constant may be written

$$\frac{\mathbf{B}}{\mathbf{k}_{\mathrm{coll}}} = \left(\frac{f_v}{f_r}\right)^5 \tag{12–3}$$

For reactants and complexes of various degrees of complexity, that is, atom,

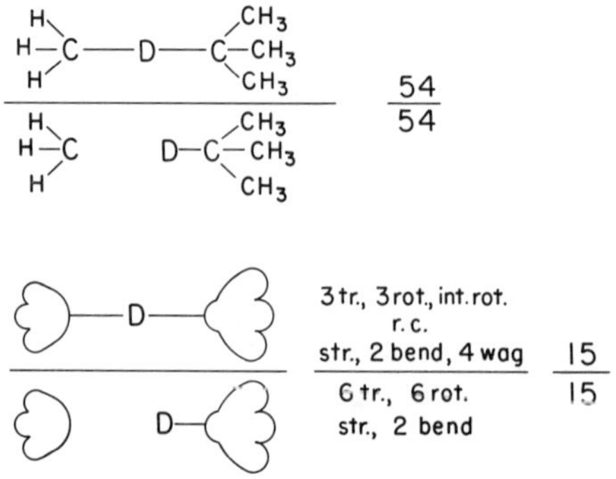

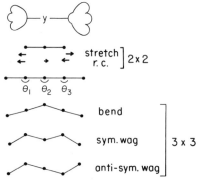

Fig. 12–1. Degrees of freedom that change strongly in going from reactants to activated complex: the 39 degrees of freedom that do not change are replaced by rigid bodies; the 15 degrees of freedom that change strongly are labeled.

linear molecule, non-linear molecule, one always obtains an expression of the form

$$\frac{\mathbf{B}}{\mathbf{k}_{\text{coll}}} = \left(\frac{f_v}{f_r}\right)^s \tag{12-4}$$

where s varies from 0 for two reactant atoms to five for the case derived above. The analysis so far is reasonable enough. However, many authors now proceed to make the assumption that vibrational partition functions are about unity, and rotational partition functions about 10 to 100. Thus it is argued that the "steric factor" for bimolecular reaction between non-linear reactants should be 10^{-5} to 10^{-10}. This argument is a very poor one. Whereas it is true enough that most vibrational partition functions for ordinary molecules at low temperatures are about unity, the five "new" vibrational degrees of freedom of the complex are typically low-frequency functions, free internal rotations, and very "soft" bends (Fig. 1 and 2).

Fig. 12–2. Identification of vibrational degrees of freedom that change in Fig. 1.

Setting the vibrational partition function to unity is usually a good approximation for the $3N - 12$ degrees of freedom canceled in going from Eqs. 1 and 2 to Eq. 3; it is a very poor approximation for the five vibrational partition functions in Eq. 3 or the s vibrational partition functions in Eq. 4. The poorness of this assumption can be seen theoretically by an analysis in terms of "local bond properties" (Chapter 8, Section E), or from a study of experimental data.   For reactions of atoms (H, Cl, or Br) with molecules (H_2, HCl, CH_4, C_2H_6, etc.), a plot is given in Fig. 3 of pre-exponential factor against number of atoms in the activated complex; there is no decrease of Arrhenius A-factor with number of atoms.   Similarly, reactions of methyl radicals with saturated hydrocarbons and with diatomic molecules are also shown; again there is little or no trend for the series.   However, the first

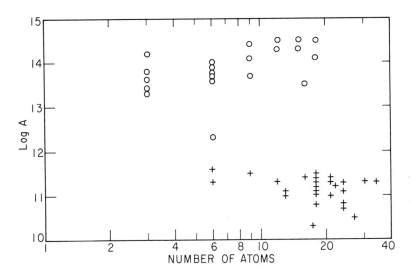

Fig. 12–3. Pre-exponential factor in units of cc/mole-sec as function of number of atoms in activated complex: $\bigcirc$ = Cl + HR; $+$ = CH_3 + HR.   Examples[75] taken from A. F. Trotman-Dickenson, *Gas Kinetics*, Academic Press, Inc., New York (1955).

series and the second series differ from each other by more than two orders of magnitude.   A realistic discussion of the theory of this effect is given in the next section.

B.   MODEL CALCULATIONS AND FORMULAE

In this section, rate expressions for various geometrical models will be derived from Eq. 8–70.   The unknown factors $\langle \kappa \rangle$ and $\langle 1 + \phi \rangle$ are set to unity. The local bond properties that do not change are canceled without being evaluated. The basic rate expression is then

$$k = \frac{\mathbf{B}_e \mathbf{B}_\sigma \mathbf{B}_r}{w} \prod_{\substack{\text{that change}}} \frac{(lJ)_\ddagger}{(lJ)_r} \prod_{\text{new}} l_\ddagger \nu^* \exp\left(-V^*/kT\right) \qquad (12\text{-}5)$$

$$= \frac{\mathbf{B}_e \mathbf{B}_\sigma \mathbf{B}_r}{w} \mathbf{B}' \exp\left(-V^*/kT\right)$$

where r represents reactants and $\ddagger$ the activated complex. If the internal coordinates are valence bonds and angles (Table 6–1) the product of Jacobian factors per unit volume always has the form

$$
\begin{aligned}
J &= 1 \text{ atom} \\
J &= 4\pi R_1^2 R_2^2 \cdots R_N^2 \qquad \text{linear} \\
J &= 8\pi^2 R_1^2 R_2^2 f(\text{angles}) \qquad \text{nonlinear}
\end{aligned}
\qquad (12\text{-}6)
$$

For atom-transfer reactions, there is always one more internal interatomic distance in the complex than in the reactants. Thus the function

$$\mathbf{B}_J = J_\ddagger / J_A J_B \qquad (12\text{-}7)$$

always has the form of a product of ratios $(R_\ddagger/R_r)^2$ and one $R_\ddagger^2$ not in ratio form:

$$\mathbf{B}_J \propto R_\ddagger^2 \prod \left(\frac{R_\ddagger}{R_r}\right)_i^2 \qquad (12\text{-}8)$$

The factors 4π and $8\pi^2$ appear in various places in the rate expression for different types of reaction. These (temperature-independent) factors $\mathbf{B}_J$ are illustrated by these examples:

$(\text{atom})_A + (\text{atom})_B \rightarrow (\text{linear})_\ddagger$	$4\pi R_\ddagger^2$
$(\text{atom})_A + (\text{linear})_B \rightarrow (\text{nonlinear})_\ddagger$	$2\pi \sin\phi R_\ddagger^2 \prod (R_\ddagger/R_A)^2$
$(\text{atom})_A + (\text{linear})_B \rightarrow (\text{linear})_\ddagger$	$R_\ddagger^2 \prod (R_\ddagger/R)^2$
$(\text{linear})_A + (\text{linear})_B \rightarrow (\text{nonlinear})_\ddagger$	$(1/2) R_\ddagger^2 \prod (R_\ddagger/R)^2 f(\Phi)$
$(\text{linear})_A + (\text{linear})_B \rightarrow (\text{linear})_\ddagger$	$(1/4\pi) R_\ddagger^2 \prod (R_\ddagger/R)^2$
$(\text{linear})_A + (\text{nonlinear})_B \rightarrow (\text{nonlinear})_\ddagger$	$(1/4\pi) R_\ddagger^2 \prod (R_\ddagger/R)^2 f(\Phi)$
$(\text{nonlinear})_A + (\text{nonlinear}) \rightarrow (\text{nonlinear})_\ddagger$	$(1/8\pi^2) R_\ddagger^2 \prod (R_\ddagger/R)^2 f(\Phi)$

$$(12\text{-}9)$$

The famous "decreasing pre-exponential factor" with "increasing complexity of reactants" is largely, though not entirely, given by the Jacobian factors 4π and $8\pi^2$ that appear in various combinations in $\mathbf{B}_J$. These factors vary as 4π, 2π, 1, 1/2, $1/4\pi$, $1/8\pi^2$, or a range of 1000, for the cases cited above.

TABLE 12–1

Classical Vibration Amplitudes

T°K	300	400	500	667	1000
A. Stretching Vibrations (amplitudes in angstrom units)					
$10^{-5}F$ dynes/cm					
16	0.04	0.05	0.05	0.06	0.07
4	0.08	0.09	0.10	0.12	0.15
1	0.16	0.18	0.21	0.24	0.29
0.25	0.32	0.37	0.42	0.48	0.59
B. Bending (amplitudes in radians)					
$10^{11}F_\Phi$ ergs/radian²					
0.64	0.2	0.2	0.3	0.3	0.4
0.16	0.4	0.5	0.5	0.6	0.7
0.04	0.8	0.9	1.0	1.2	1.5
0.01	1.6	1.8	2.1	2.4	2.9

Vibrational amplitudes for valence bonds are in units of length, l, and for valence angles in units of radians, l_Φ. The one new bond that gives a factor $R_\ddagger^2$ in $\mathbf{B}_J$ gives a new factor $l_\ddagger$ also. Thus in atom-transfer reactions the free translational volume V of one reactant is reduced to the volume $R_\ddagger^2 l_\ddagger$ of the collision complex. If the reaction volume is taken to be one cubic centimeter, if $l_\ddagger$ and $R_\ddagger$ are expressed in angstrom units, if the "frequency" ν^* in units of sec⁻¹ is converted to ω cm⁻¹, and if the rate is expressed in molar units, the rate factor $\mathbf{B}$ in units of cc/mole-sec becomes

$$\mathbf{B} = \mathbf{B}_e\mathbf{B}_\sigma\mathbf{B}_\Gamma\left[\prod \frac{(R^2 l l_\phi)_\ddagger}{(R^2 l l_\phi)_r}\right](1.81 \times 10^{13}Y)R_\ddagger^2 \prod l_\ddagger\left(\frac{\omega^*}{1000w}\right) \qquad (12\text{--}10)$$

all internal coordinates of *reactants*

where Y is the coefficient of $R_\ddagger^2 \prod (R_\ddagger/R)^2$ in Eq. 9, that is, the product of factors 4π, $8\pi^2$, $f(\Phi)$. Table 1 gives classical vibrational amplitudes as a function of force constant and temperature for both linear and angular coordinates. Table 6–1 gives angular Jacobian factors for simple cases or Eq. 6–47 may be used for more complex cases. With these tables it is extremely easy to formulate the rate factor $\mathbf{B}$ for any model of interest. Such a formulation will be carried through for a few examples, with $\mathbf{B}$ expressed in cc/mole-sec.

(i) Diatomic Molecule Plus Atom To Give Nonlinear Complex

$$\text{O—O} + \text{O} \rightarrow \text{O} \cdot \overset{\displaystyle \cdot \text{O} \cdot}{\underset{R_1 \qquad\quad R_2}{}} \cdot \text{O} \qquad (12\text{--}11)$$

$$\Phi$$

$$\mathbf{B} = \mathbf{B}_e\mathbf{B}_\sigma\mathbf{B}_\Gamma\left[\left(\frac{R_\ddagger}{R}\right)_1^2\left(\frac{F}{F_\ddagger}\right)_1^{1/2}\right]\left(\frac{\omega^*}{1000w}\right)(R_2^2 l_2 \sin\Phi)l_\phi 2\pi \times 1.81 \times 10^{13}$$

To emphasize the features varied in this portion of the problem, a new term is defined:

$$\mathbf{B}' = (\mathbf{B}/\mathbf{B}_e\mathbf{B}_\sigma\mathbf{B}_\Gamma) \text{ cc/mole-sec} \qquad (12\text{-}12)$$

(ii) Diatomic Molecule Plus Atom To Give a Linear Complex

$$
\begin{array}{ccc}
\text{O—O} + \text{O} \rightarrow & \text{O}\cdots\text{O}\cdots\text{O} \\
R_1 & R_1 \quad R_2
\end{array}
$$

$$\Phi,\ \Phi' \qquad (12\text{-}13)$$

$$\mathbf{B}' = \left[\left(\frac{R_{\ddagger}}{R}\right)_1^2 \left(\frac{F}{F_{\ddagger}}\right)_1^{1/2}\right]\left(\frac{\omega^*}{1000w}\right)(R_2^2 l_2)_{\ddagger} l_\Phi^2 1.81 \times 10^{13}$$

with l_1 and R_2 in angstrom units and l_Φ in radians.

(iii) Other Examples

$$
\begin{array}{ccccc}
\text{O} & \text{O} & \text{O} + \text{O} \rightarrow & \text{O} & \text{O}\cdots\text{O}\cdots\text{O} \\
R_3 & R_1 & & R_3 & R_1 \quad R_2
\end{array}
$$

$$\Phi_\beta,\ \Phi'_\beta \qquad\qquad \Phi_\beta,\ \Phi'_\beta \quad \Phi_\alpha,\ \Phi'_\alpha \qquad (12\text{-}14)$$

$$\mathbf{B}' = \left[\left(\frac{R_{\ddagger}}{R}\right)_3^2 \left(\frac{F}{F_{\ddagger}}\right)_3^{1/2}\right]\left[\left(\frac{R_{\ddagger}}{R}\right)_1^2 \left(\frac{F}{F_{\ddagger}}\right)_1^{1/2}\left(\frac{F_\Phi}{F_{\Phi\ddagger}}\right)_\beta\right]\left(\frac{\omega^*}{1080w}\right)(R_2^2 l_2) l_{\Phi\alpha}^2 1.81 \times 10^{13}$$

The first square bracket includes internal coordinates which may not change between reactants and complex (compare Fig. 1), the second square bracket contains terms that certainly change (enclosed by line segments), and "new" coordinates are underlined.

$$
\begin{array}{ccccc}
\text{O—O} + \text{O—O} \rightarrow & \text{O}\cdots\text{O}\cdots\text{O—O} \\
R_1 \qquad R_3 & R_1 \quad R_2 \quad R_3
\end{array}
$$

$$\Phi_\alpha,\ \Phi'_\alpha\ \Phi_\beta,\ \Phi'_\beta \qquad (12\text{-}15)$$

$$\mathbf{B}' = \left[\left(\frac{R_{\ddagger}}{R}\right)_3^2 \left(\frac{F}{F_{\ddagger}}\right)_3^{1/2}\right]\left[\left(\frac{R_{\ddagger}}{R}\right)_1^2 \left(\frac{F}{F_{\ddagger}}\right)_1^{1/2}\right]\left(\frac{\omega^*}{1000w}\right)(R_2^2 l_2)_{\ddagger} l_\alpha^2 l_\beta^2 \frac{1.81}{4\pi} \times 10^{13}$$

$$
\begin{array}{ccccc}
& \text{O} & & \text{O} \quad\quad \text{O} \\
& / \quad \backslash & + \text{O} \rightarrow & / \quad \backslash \quad / \\
\text{O} & & \text{O} & \text{O} \quad\quad \text{O} \\
R_3 & & R_1 & R_3 \quad R_1 \quad R_2 \\
& \Phi_\beta & & \Phi_\beta \quad \Phi_\alpha \\
& & & \tau
\end{array}
$$

Here τ refers to an internal rotation, more or less about the bond R_1. The full rate factor is

$$\mathbf{B'} = \left[\left(\frac{R_\ddagger}{R}\right)^2_3 \left(\frac{F}{F_\ddagger}\right)^{1/2}_3 \left(\frac{\sin \Phi_\ddagger}{\sin \Phi}\right)_\beta\right]\left[\left(\frac{R_\ddagger}{R_A}\right)^2_1 \left(\frac{F}{F_\ddagger}\right)^{1/2}_1 \left(\frac{F_\Phi}{F_{\Phi\ddagger}}\right)^{1/2}_\beta\right] \quad (12\text{–}16)$$

$$\times \quad \left(\frac{\omega^*}{1000w}\right)(l_2 R_2^2 \sin \Phi_\alpha)(l_\alpha l_\tau) \times 1.81 \times 10^{13}$$

For more complex molecules the expression becomes unwieldy. Certain coordinates of the complex are separated by lines and regarded as "unchanged," and "new" internal coordinates are underlined. By simple inspection one may write down the factor $\mathbf{B'}$. For the rest of this section a new factor $\mathbf{B''}$ will be used; $\mathbf{B''}$ is $\mathbf{B'}$ omitting all ratios of similar terms.

$$\text{O—O—O} + \text{O—O} \rightarrow \text{O—O}\cdots\text{O}\cdots\text{O—O}$$

$$\mathbf{B''} = (R_2^2 l_2) l_\alpha^2 l_\gamma^2 \frac{1.81}{4\pi} \times 10^{13} \quad (12\text{–}17)$$

$$\mathbf{B''} = (R_2^2 l_2)(l_\alpha l_\gamma l_{\tau_1} l_{\tau_2}) \frac{1.81}{4\pi} \times 10^{13} \quad (12\text{–}18)$$

$$\mathbf{B''} = (R_2^2 l_2)(l_\alpha l_\beta l_{\tau_1} l_{\tau_2} l_{\tau_3}) \frac{1.81}{8\pi^2} \times 10^{13} \quad (12\text{–}19)$$

For the last three cases, special note should be given to the vibrational amplitude of internal rotations. If the internal rotations are "free" (that is, if reaction is equally probable for all orientations of the collision partners with respect to the angle τ), the vibrational amplitude is 2π. These factors may partially cancel out the 4π and $8\pi^2$ terms in the denominator of these rate expressions.

For infinite zig-zag chain reactants the model of the complex is

$$\mathbf{B}'' = (R_2^2 l_2)(l_\alpha l_\beta l_{\tau_1} l_{\tau_2} l_{\tau_4}) \frac{1.81}{8\pi^2} \times 10^{13} \qquad (12\text{--}20)$$

By expressing the rate in terms of local (bond and angle) coordinates, one has for the cases of Eqs. 19 or 20 a relatively simple relation; the corresponding expressions in normal-mode coordinates are hopelessly complicated. In normal-mode coordinates there is cancellation of terms between the moments of inertia and the mass factors in the bending vibrations and internal rotations. If the overall moment of inertia is used, one must be extremely careful accurately to evaluate partition functions for the low frequency vibrations and internal rotations, in order to cancel out the moment of inertia, molar mass, and other extraneous factors.

C. INTERNAL ROTATIONS

One of the advantages of the "local bond" partition functions over normal coordinate partition functions is the much greater ease of treating internal rotations by the local bond method. In the configuration integral Z, the torsion angle τ contributes an integral of the form

$$l_\tau = \int_0^{2\pi/n} \exp\left[-U(\tau)/kT\right] d\tau \qquad (12\text{--}21)$$

where the barrier repeats with n-fold symmetry about τ. If the internal rotation is strongly restricted, with a high barrier V_0, the force constant is

$$F_\tau = \tfrac{1}{2}n^2 V_0 \qquad (12\text{--}22)$$

and the configuration integral is similar to that for an ordinary vibration:

$$l_\tau = (2\pi kT)^{1/2}/F_\tau^{1/2} \simeq (2\pi/n)(RT/\pi V_0)^{1/2}$$
$$\Gamma_\tau = (u/2)/\sinh(u/2)$$
$$u = (h/2\pi kT)(F_\tau/I_r)^{1/2} \qquad (12\text{--}23)$$

On the other hand, if the internal rotation is free, the distinguishable free angle is simply

$$l_r = 2\pi/n \qquad \Gamma_r = 1 \qquad (12\text{--}24)$$

For the difficult intermediate case the effective vibrational amplitude is

$$l_r = (2\pi/n)\exp\left[-(F - F_f)/RT\right] \qquad (12\text{--}25)$$

where $(F - F_f)$ refers to the increase in free energy over the free rotor case, and it is tabulated under the column $1/Q_f = 0$ by Pitzer and Gwinn.[73]

For all cases except that for free rotation, the value of the reduced moment inertia I_r for the internal rotation is needed. If the internal rotation can be regarded as two colinear spherical tops, CH_3—$C\equiv C$—CF_3 for example, the reduced moment of inertia is simply

$$I_r = I_1 I_2/(I_1 + I_2) \qquad (12\text{--}26)$$

where I_1 is the moment of inertia of one top about the common axis and I_2 is the moment of inertia of the other top about the same axis. For more complicated or less symmetrical situations, Pitzer[21] has analyzed the problem.

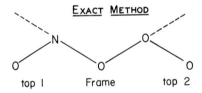

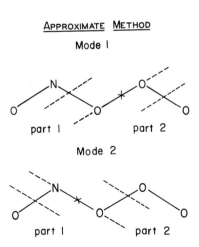

Fig. 12–4. Approximate method to evaluate reduced moments of inertia for internal rotations (Eq. 12–26 and following discussion).

One selects a rigid frame relative to which various "tops" can rotate, and the transformations to uncouple the internal rotations from overall rotations give the reduced moment of inertia—for any particular case the problem may involve numerical evaluation since the algebra becomes quite complicated. Also, Pitzer has suggested a much simpler approximate method[74] useful for certain cases, illustrated here for the reaction: $NO + O_3 \rightarrow$

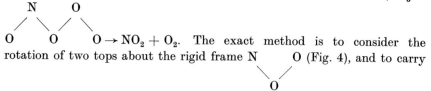

$O \rightarrow NO_2 + O_2$. The exact method is to consider the rotation of two tops about the rigid frame (Fig. 4), and to carry out appropriate coordinate transformations. The approximate method is also indicated by Fig. 4. One imagines a bond about which internal rotation occurs to be cut, X in Fig. 4. The moment of inertia of each separate group is evaluated about a line parallel to the "cut" bond and through the center of mass of the group. The reduced moment of inertia for that mode is then found from Eq. 26, where now I_1 and I_2 refer to the two groups. By this procedure two reduced moments of inertia are to be found for the complex.

13

Kinetic Isotope Effect[70]

According to simple, separable activated-complex theory, the general quantum-mechanical rate constant may be written in two equivalent forms, Eq. 8–69 or Eq. 8–70. These two expressions are written out here, with the terms grouped into "mass-dependent" and "mass-independent" sets. Almost every term in the rate expression with partition functions, Eq. 8–69, involves some dependence on mass, M, I, ν, zero-point energy:

$$\mathbf{k} = \underbrace{\left\{\frac{kT}{h} \exp\left(-V^*/kT\right)\right\}}_{\text{mass-independent}} \underbrace{\left\{\frac{\langle\kappa\rangle^{\mathrm{B}}\langle 1 + \phi\rangle^{T} f'_{\ddagger}\Gamma_{*}}{f^{\alpha}_{\mathrm{A}} f^{\beta}_{\mathrm{B}} f^{\gamma}_{\mathrm{C}}} \exp\left(-ZPE/kT\right)\right\}}_{\text{mass-dependent}}$$

where vibrational partition functions are $(1 - e^{-u})^{-1}$. On the other hand, the rate expression in terms of local properties, Eq. 8–70, gives maximum separation of mass-dependent factors:

$$\mathbf{k} = \underbrace{\left\{\frac{\left(w^{-1} \prod^{N}_{\alpha} J_{\alpha} \prod^{3N-6} l_{s}\right)_{\ddagger} \exp\left(-V^*/kT\right)}{\left(w^{-1} \prod^{N}_{\alpha} J_{\alpha} \prod l_{s}\right)_{\text{reactants}}}\right\}}_{\text{mass-independent}} \underbrace{\left\{\frac{\sigma_{\mathrm{ch}}\langle\kappa\rangle^{\mathrm{B}}\langle 1 + \phi\rangle^{T} \nu_{*} \prod \Gamma_{\ddagger}}{\prod \Gamma_{\text{reactants}}}\right\}}_{\text{mass-dependent}}$$

The term σ_{ch} is the number of equivalent reaction sites, Eq. 8–16, which may awkwardly be computed from a careful counting of rotational and other symmetry numbers of reactants and activated complex; it is mass-dependent in the sense that isotopic substitution breaks this multiplicity. The relative reaction rate by isotopically substituted reactants may be calculated by either one of the two identical equations above; however, it is obvious that the relation in terms of local properties is the simpler for this purpose. The term ϕ is zero for reactions with an equilibrium distribution of reactants, and the term $\langle\kappa\rangle$ is assumed to have the value one. Thus the ratio of rate constants for two different sets of isotopically substituted reactants is

$$\frac{\mathbf{k}_1}{\mathbf{k}_2} = \frac{\nu_1^*}{\nu_2^*} \prod^{3N-6} \left(\frac{\Gamma_1}{\Gamma_2}\right)_{\ddagger} \prod \left(\frac{\Gamma_2}{\Gamma_1}\right)_{\text{reactants}} \left(\frac{\sigma_1}{\sigma_2}\right)_{\mathrm{ch}} \tag{13–1}$$

where Γ of reactants and $3N - 7$ of the $\Gamma_{\ddagger}$ are quantum corrections of the form

$$\Gamma = \frac{u/2}{\sinh u/2} \qquad u = \frac{h\nu}{kT} \qquad (13\text{--}2)$$

and the final Γ is the tunneling correction as discussed in Chapters 2, 8, and 10. The activation energy cancels from the expression, and the entire kinetic isotope effect depends on the frequencies of reactants and complex of both isotopic reactions.

For bimolecular H -transfer one may use either the LEPS surface or the BEBO method to evaluate force constants and then frequencies. For the LEPS method one fits the parameter Δ to the observed activation energy; then the kinetic isotope effect is unambiguously predicted and no further adjustment of parameters is to be tolerated. The most difficult function to evaluate is the tunneling correction, Γ_{*}. It is recommended that one use method a of Table 10–7 for the LEPS potential-energy surface and method c'' of that table for the BEBO function. These methods are used for all cases discussed in this chapter. These examples are chosen to illustrate the magnitude of the kinetic isotope problem, and no effort is made to cover all cases in the literature.

A. $CF_3 + CH_4$ AND LEPS POTENTIAL ENERGY[76,77]

The reaction between tri-fluoro-methyl radical and methane is in one sense of the word a "three-atom" reaction:

$$CF_3 + H - CH_3 \rightarrow CF_3 \cdots H \cdots CH_3 \rightarrow CF_3 - H + CH_3 \quad (13\text{--}3)$$

with a potential-energy surface in terms of two distances R_1 and R_2 and two equal bending-force constants. As such, it can be treated by the semi-empirical method of London-Eyring-Polanyi-Sato or by the bond-energy–bond-order method; it is much too complicated to support a completely theoretical study at the present state of the art. On the other hand, the bimolecular reaction does involve nine atoms. Even assuming the complex to be linear about the atom being transferred, one has a rather complicated structure

$$
\begin{array}{ccc}
F & & H \\
\backslash & & / \\
F\text{---}C \cdots H \cdots C\text{---}H & & (13\text{--}4) \\
/ & & \backslash \\
F & & H
\end{array}
$$

This structure has enough symmetry so that a complete vibrational analysis is feasible, with the aid of an electronic computer. By virtue of its symmetry, substitute models with five, four, or three atoms readily suggest themselves, Eq. 3 above and

$$F—CF_2 \cdots H \cdots CH_2—H$$
$$CF_3 \cdots H \cdots CH_2—H$$

(13–5)

It is very difficult to carry out a complete vibrational analysis on the full nine-atom model. It is desirable to use simpler models, and it is necessary to understand how such a substitute model affects the calculated values of observable quantities, such as the Arrhenius **A**-factor or the kinetic isotope effect.

This reaction has been studied over a wide range of conditions.[76] The kinetic isotope effect has been observed from 300 to 1800°K, and the direct chemical reaction rate has been measured over a moderate range.

The reaction mechanism was worked out by Ayscough, Polanyi, and Steacie.[77] The kinetic isotope effect is conveniently studied by use of CH_2D_2 or CHD_3 as reactant. CF_3 radicals were produced photochemically, at low temperature, 300–700°K, and thermally from the decomposition of hexa-fluoro-azomethane at high temperature, 900–1800°K. The reaction is automatically competitive:

$$CF_3 + HCD_3 \xrightarrow[3k_D]{k_H} \begin{array}{l} CF_3H + CD_3 \\ CF_3D + CHD_2 \end{array}$$

(13–6)

The kinetic isotope effect is

$$\frac{R_{CF_3H}}{R_{CF_3D}} = \frac{k_H}{3k_D}$$

(13–7)

(i) Vibrational Analyses

The full nine-atom model was used for this study. The bond lengths, angles, and force constants were found from the LEPS potential-energy surface. Any bond not directly involved in the reaction was assumed to have the normal bond length and force constant found in a stable molecule. All bond angles about carbon were assumed to be tetrahedral (trial calculations with planar CH_3 groups showed this feature to have only a small effect). The force constant for bending two single bonds was set equal to the stable-molecule value, but a bending-force constant between a single bond and a reacting bond was assigned half the stable-molecule value (compare Eq. 4–56). Free rotation about all bonds was assumed. Except for the strong interaction constant F_{12} between the bonds being broken and formed, a valence-bond force field without interactions was used. Figure 1d gives a diagram of the model. The vibrational analysis was performed by setting up symmetry coordinates and using an **FG**-matrix computer program.

The calculation of vibrational frequencies for the full nine-atom model

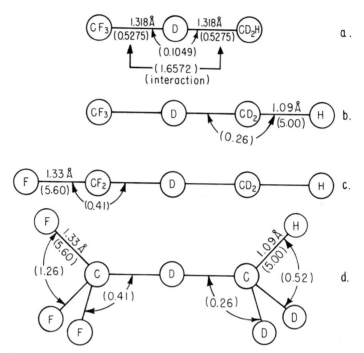

Fig. 13–1. Models of activated complexes (force constants in parentheses).

is a very tedious job. Several simpler models of the activated complex were investigated, a five-atom linear complex, a four-atom linear complex, and a three-atom linear complex. These models are also given by Fig. 1 For the real reaction, the reactants are identical for the two isotopic processes, and this feature is preserved in the nine-, five-, and four-atom models. For the three-atom model it is necessary to consider appropriate models for the reactants; in this case the reactants are diatomic, (CD_3)—H and (CD_2H)—D.

(ii) Tunneling Corrections

The normal mode associated with the negative eigenvalue or imaginary frequency is not necessarily the most efficient path for tunneling. In the case of H or D transfer between heavy end groups, $A - x - B$, the effective mass for a straight-line motion on an R_1–R_2 diagram is given by Eq. 3–23. For light central atom and heavy end groups, the effective mass is a minimum for $dR_2/dR_1 = c = -1$ or a motion of $-45°$ on the $R_1 - R_2$ diagram. The effective mass for such a motion is

$$ m^* = \frac{m_x}{2} \frac{m_A + m_B}{M} \approx \frac{m_x}{2} \qquad (13\text{–}8) $$

In this motion the R_{AB} distance remains constant, the pair AB move just enough to preserve the center of mass, and the principal motion is particle x jumping from A to B. The continuation of a line of $-45°$ slope or $c = -1$ (compare Figs. 10–10 and 10–11) runs into the steeply rising side walls of the potential energy surface, thus giving a potential-energy profile more or less similar to an Eckart function (Fig. 2–3), except the depths ΔV_1^* and ΔV_2^* are much less than the full potential energy of reaction. An Eckart tunneling correction depends on three parameters, ΔV_1^*, ΔV_2^*, and ν^*. Thus for any cut of slope -1 on a potential-energy surface, one can readily calculate a one-dimensional Eckart tunneling correction for a Boltzmann distribution of incident particles. The average of such a series of parallel cuts (compare entry a of Table 10–8) or the value at the most probable tunneling path gives an estimate of tunneling by the Eckart method.

Alternatively, these cuts through the potential-energy surface may be used to construct a truncated, inverted parabola, for which R. P. Bell[24] has evaluated the tunneling correction (Fig. 2–1).

(iii) Arrhenius **A**-factor for the Four Different Models

To compute the Arrhenius A-factor, one needs force constants and vibration frequencies of reactants and activated complex, the tunneling correction, and the temperature coefficient of quantum corrections for all normal-mode coordinates. For each of the four models, these tedious computations were carried out for 400°K, using the Eckart tunneling corrections. The Arrhenius **A**-factor and the experimental **A**-factor for deuterium transfer (chosen to minimize the tunneling correction) are given in Table 1. The **A**-factor is sensitive to the model chosen. The simplified three-atom model differs by almost a factor of 1000 from the value of **A** calculated by the full nine-atom model (compare Eq. 12–9). The nine-atom model gives a value about a factor of 10 lower than that observed, which is not very good agreement, even in this rough-and-tumble game.

TABLE 13–1
Calculation of Pre-Exponential Factors for D Atom Abstraction at 400°K

Number of Mass Points			Pre-Exponential Factor	
Reactants		Complex	log **B**(T)	log **A**
CF$_3$	CHD$_3$			
1	2 (D—CHD$_2$)	3	14.1	13.0
1	3 (D—CD$_2$—H)	4	14.7	13.0
2 (F—CF$_2$)	3 (D—CD$_2$—H)	5	12.9	11.8
4	5	9	11.2	10.2
Experimental				11.3

(iv) Kinetic Isotope Effect

For H transfer or for D transfer the reactants are identical (Eq. 6), and thus the kinetic isotope effect has the unusually simple form

$$\frac{k_H}{k_D} = \frac{(\nu^*\Gamma^*\prod\limits^{3N-7}\Gamma)^{\ddagger}_H}{(\nu^*\Gamma^*\prod\limits^{3N-7}\Gamma)^{\ddagger}_D} \tag{13-9}$$

where $\Gamma = (u/2)/\sinh(u/2)$ and Γ^* is the tunneling correction.

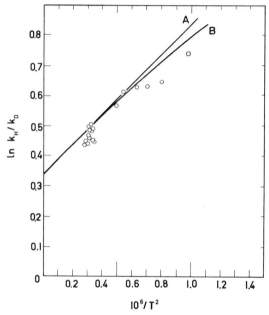

Fig. 13–2. High temperature (1000–1900°K) data for $CF_3 + CHD_3$ plotted against $1/T^2$: A, curve calculated using theoretical coefficient of $1/T^2$. B, full theoretical curve.

At sufficiently high temperature, the de Broglie wavelength of the atom transferred becomes comparable to the quadratic zone of the potential-energy surface, so that the tunneling correction reduces to $\Gamma^* = (|u^*|/2)/\sin(|u^*|/2)$. In this case a straight-forward Taylor series expansion gives

$$\ln\frac{k_H}{k_D} = \ln\frac{\nu^*_H}{\nu^*_D} + \frac{a}{T^2} + \frac{b}{T^4} + \cdots \tag{13-10}$$

$$a = (N/24)(h/2\pi k)^2[\text{Tr}(\mathbf{FG})_H - \text{Tr}(\mathbf{FG})_D]$$

where N is Avogadro's number, k is Boltzmann's constant, h is Planck's constant, and $\text{Tr}(\mathbf{FG})$ is the trace of E. B. Wilson's $\mathbf{FG}$ matrix. In this expression use is made of the relation $\text{Tr}(\mathbf{FG}) = \sum_i \lambda_i = (4\pi^2 c^2/N) \sum_i \omega_i^2$. At very high temperatures the kinetic isotope effect does not follow an Arrhenius relation, but rather the data should give a linear plot in $\ln k_H/k_D$ against $1/T^2$. The intercept should be the ratio of frequencies of the reaction coordinate, to give a specific check on the theory. The slope gives a check on the vibrational analysis as a whole.

Experimental points between 1000 and 1800°K are plotted in Fig. 2 with two lines drawn in: A is the limiting theoretical curve (Eq. 10), and B is the full theoretical curve (Eq. 9). The intercept at infinite temperature is $k_H/k_D = 1.400$, and the ratio of imaginary frequencies from the vibrational analysis is 1.392. The data follow the full theoretical curve quite well, and they are consistent with the $1/T^2$ function at temperatures above 1500°K. This figure provides a direct confirmation of Wigner's analysis of quantum corrections for any sort of barrier: at sufficiently high temperature each normal coordinate has a quantum correction of the form $(1 - u^2/24)$. In view of the generality of Wigner's analysis, the beautiful agreement of experiment and theory shown by Fig. 2 is more nearly confirmation of the data than confirmation of theory. One merit of this study is that it demonstrates how high one must go in temperature to enter Wigner's simple regime, that is, above 1500°K for hydrogen-transfer reactions. Another point of interest is the value of the intercept, 1.40. The antisymmetric, unstable, normal mode is the *only* normal vibration for which the $F_3C{-}H{-}CD_3/F_3C{-}D{-}CD_2H$ ratio is about 1.4, and of course, the reduced mass of the separated reactants from a collision point of view is exactly one. This fact shows that the drastic assumption about one-and-only-one reaction coordinate is an excellent approximation for this particular reaction.

The observed isotope effect over a wide range of temperature is presented by Figs. 3, 4, and 5. Theoretical curves are presented for three-, four-, five-, and nine-atom models; and for each model the ratio k_H/k_D is given for (1) no tunneling, (2) tunneling corrections by Bell's method of truncated parabola, and (3) Eckart corrections averaged over many parallel paths of $-45°$ slope on an R_1-R_2 plot. In Fig. 3 experimental data are compared with the various models with no tunneling correction. The experimental points lie far above the calculated curves, except that the high temperature points approach the calculated curves. In Fig. 4 experimental data are compared with theoretical curves, using Bell's tunneling correction. Most of the discrepancy seen in Fig. 3 between calculated and observed points is removed by the tunneling correction. In Fig. 5 the Eckart tunneling corrections are added to the calculated curves, and again the calculated curves are very close to the experimental points.

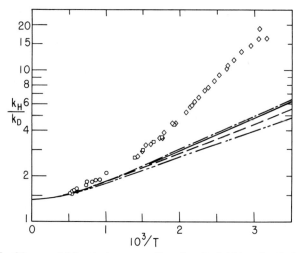

Fig. 13–3. Observed kinetic isotope effect ($\bigcirc$–Ref. 76b; $\Diamond$–Ref. 76a) over a wide range of temperature. Theoretical kinetic isotope effect excluding tunneling for various models of the activated complex: 3 mass points including reactants, – – –; 4 mass points, – · – · – ·; 5 mass points, – · · – · · – · ·; and full 9-atom model, ———.

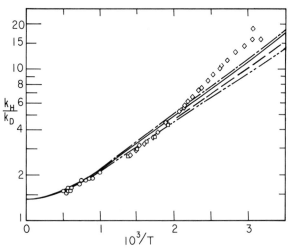

Fig. 13–4. Observed and theoretical isotope effect including Bell's correction for tunneling (symbols as in Fig. 3).

For the kinetic isotope effect, it can be seen that it makes relatively little difference whether one uses a full nine-atom model or the ultrasimple three-atom model; this insensitivity to the model is in strong contrast to the situation for Arrhenius A-factors, Table 1.

The four figures (Figs. 2, 3, 4, and 5) may be evaluated as follows: Fig. 2 gives a surprisingly good confirmation of activated complex theory as applied to the kinetic isotope effect; the theoretically-sound, limiting slope of

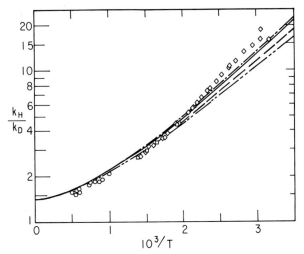

Fig. 13–5. Observed and theoretical isotope effect including Eckart correction for tunneling (symbols as in Fig. 3).

Wigner gives an infinite temperature intercept at the calculated value of ν_H^*/ν_D^*. With confidence in the method based on this result, one sees in Figs. 3, 4, and 5 a convincing demonstration of the presence and importance of quantum-mechanical tunneling in this reaction. Figure 3 without tunneling corrections misses the data by a wide margin. With any reasonable model for tunneling (through truncated, inverted parabola or through an Eckart function of appropriate dimensions), the calculated kinetic isotope effect is in good agreement with experimental data (Figs. 4 and 5).

The experimental points between 300 and 700°K are of unusually high precision. It can be seen that they lie very nearly on a straight line in an Arrhenius plot, log k_H/k_D vs $1/T$, even though large tunneling is known to occur. The calculated curves, which include large tunneling factors, are very nearly straight over moderate ranges of temperature. The literature often expresses a misconception here: it is said occasionally that lack of deviation of the kinetic isotope effect from an Arrhenius plot indicates absence of tunneling or conversely that presence of curvature of an Arrhenius plot is the expected symptom of tunneling. In the first place, the exponential factor $\exp(-V^*/kT)$ cancels out of the expression for the kinetic isotope effect, and one does not especially expect an Arrhenius plot in any case. To be sure, at low temperature the zero-point energy terms are exponential $\exp(-u/2)$, but the general product of terms $(u/2)/\sinh(u/2)$ is not, a priori, of an Arrhenius form. Thus whether the kinetic isotope effect conforms to or departs from an Arrhenius expression is no indication one way or another as to the presence or magnitude of tunneling.

Some authors prefer to plot the kinetic isotope effect according to the Arrhenius method, and to interpret the results in terms of Arrhenius' $\mathbf{A}$ and $\mathbf{E}$. At any one temperature one *can* express the kinetic isotope effect as

$$\mathbf{k_H}/\mathbf{k_D} = \mathbf{A_{HD}} \exp(-\mathbf{E_{HD}}/RT) \qquad (13\text{-}11)$$

where $\mathbf{k_H}/\mathbf{k_D}$ is the value of the isotope effect at the temperature and $\mathbf{E_{HD}}$ is the slope of an Arrhenius plot at the temperature.

$$\mathbf{E_{HD}} = -R \frac{d \ln(\mathbf{k_H}/\mathbf{k_D})}{d(1/T)} \qquad (13\text{-}12)$$

The pre-exponential factor $\mathbf{A_{HD}}$ is thus defined as

$$\mathbf{A_{HD}} = (\mathbf{k_H}/\mathbf{k_D})_T \exp(\mathbf{E_{HD}}/RT) \qquad (13\text{-}13)$$

The nature of $\mathbf{E_{HD}}$ and $\mathbf{A_{HD}}$ can readily be found by differentiation of Eq. 9, for example,

$$-R \frac{d \ln(\mathbf{k_H}/\mathbf{k_D})}{d(1/T)} = RT \left[\Theta_H^* + \sum^{3N-7} \Theta_H - \Theta_D^* - \sum^{3N-7} \Theta_D \right] \qquad (13\text{-}14)$$

where Θ^* is $d \ln \Gamma^*/d \ln T$ and Θ is $d \ln \Gamma/d \ln T$. For further abbreviation one writes

$$\Theta_H = \Theta_H^* + \sum^{3N-7} \Theta_H$$

$$\Theta_D = \Theta_D^* + \sum \Theta_D \qquad (13\text{-}15)$$

so that the $\mathbf{E_{HD}}$ of Eq. 11 or 12 is

$$\mathbf{E_{HD}} = \exp(\Theta_D - \Theta_H) \qquad (13\text{-}16)$$

and the pre-exponential factor is

$$\mathbf{A_{HD}} = \frac{\nu_H^*}{\nu_D^*} \frac{\Gamma_H^*}{\Gamma_D^*} \frac{\sum^{3N-7} \Gamma_H}{\sum^{3N-7} \Gamma_D} \exp(\Theta_H - \Theta_D) \qquad (13\text{-}17)$$

Between 300 and 700°K, the experimental points on an Arrhenius plot (Fig. 3) lie on a line that is almost straight (it takes only a little experimental error to obscure a slight curvature). The value of $\mathbf{A_{HD}}$ is about 0.6. The points between 1000 and 1900°K can be forced to fit an Arrhenius plot with an $\mathbf{A_{HD}}$ of about 1.2. The infinite-temperature intercept is 1.4. It is quite tedious to calculate the temperature derivatives or Θ terms, and no new information is developed over the straightforward calculation of $\mathbf{k_H/k_D}$. It is felt that the forcing of kinetic isotope data to the Arrhenius pattern is to carry a traditional procedure over to a place where it has little or no advantage.

B. $CF_3 + CH_4$ WITH LONDON-EYRING-POLANYI POTENTIAL-ENERGY SURFACE[78]

A portion of the London-Eyring-Polanyi-Sato potential-energy surface with its single saddlepoint is shown in Fig. 6. A portion of the London-Eyring-Polanyi potential-energy surface with its two saddlepoints and

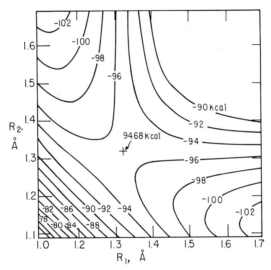

Fig. 13–6. Portion of potential-energy surface near the saddlepoint based on method of London-Eyring-Polanyi-Sato.

"well in the top of the pass" is shown in Fig. 7. This potential-energy surface is calculated from Eqs. 10–47, 4–22, and 4–16, with the parameter f adjusted to fit the observed activation energy at the indicated activated complex, ‡ of Fig. 7. From this point, the kinetic isotope effect is unambiguously predicted, and parameters must not be further adjusted. The calculated kinetic isotope effect for a three-atom model is given by Fig. 8. For comparison the experimental data are shown on the same figure.

The failure of the LEP method is total. This example shows that the kinetic isotope effect is sensitive to the potential-energy surface used. Also, it confirms the recommendation that the LEP method should not be used.

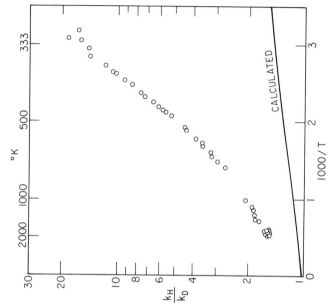

Fig. 13-8. Comparison of experimental data ($\bigcirc$) with London-Eyring-Polanyi prediction based on potential-energy function of Fig. 7.

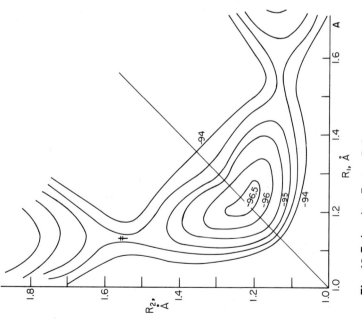

Fig. 13-7. London-Eyring-Polanyi potential-energy surface for the CH_3—H—CF_3 activated complex.

C. $CD_3 + C_2H_6$

The kinetic isotope effect for the reactions

$$CD_3 + C_2H_6 \rightarrow CD_3H + C_2H_5$$
$$CD_3 + C_2D_6 \rightarrow CD_4 + C_2D_5$$

(13–18)

was carefully studied by McNesby.[79]   The experimental points are given by Fig. 9, and curves calculated without and with tunneling are shown.   These curves were calculated by the LEPS method, as discussed in Section A above. For this case, there is excellent agreement between calculated function and observed data.

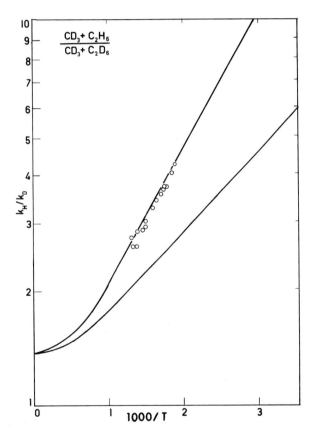

Fig. 13–9. Methyl radical plus ethane kinetic isotope effect.   Lower curve is calculated without correction for tunneling; upper curve is calculated with correction for tunneling (method *a* of Table 10–8)—J. R. McNesby, *J. Phys. Chem.*, **64** (1960).

D. MODEL CALCULATIONS COMPARING LEPS AND BEBO METHODS; TREND OF k_H/k_D

For the "model" reaction

$$-\text{C}-\text{H} + \text{C} \rightarrow -\text{C}\cdots\text{H}\cdots\text{C} \rightarrow -\text{C} + \text{H}-\text{C}- \quad (13\text{--}19)$$

where the dissociation energy of the bond being formed is 100 kcal, and the

TABLE 13–2

Comparison of LEPS and BEBO Methods of Obtaining
Properties of Activated Complex for Three-Atom Models

| | Ref. | Energy of Bond Being Broken, kcal | | | | |
		100	90.9	83.3	76.9	66.7
n_1	b	0.50	0.62	0.72	0.79	0.88
n_2	b	0.50	0.38	0.28	0.21	0.12
R_1 (Å)	a	1.30	1.23	1.19	1.17	1.15
	b	1.27	1.22	1.18	1.15	1.12
R_2 (Å)	a	1.30	1.40	1.51	1.58	1.78
	b	1.27	1.34	1.42	1.49	1.65
V^* (kcal)	a	12.8	8.8	6.4	4.9	3.1
	b	12.8	8.4	5.4	3.6	1.6
$10^{-5}F_{11}$	a	0.52	1.03	1.57	1.81	2.16
	b	0.71	1.75	2.73	3.46	4.25
$10^{-5}F_{22}$	a	0.52	0.025	−0.16	−0.20	−0.19
	b	0.71	0.11	−0.19	−0.15	−0.13
$10^{-5}F_{12}$	a	1.64	1.50	1.17	1.00	0.66
	b	1.79	1.64	1.38	1.05	0.59
$10^{11}F_\Phi$	a	0.103	0.096	0.082	0.072	0.052
	b	0.125	0.118	0.102	0.084	0.052
$(\omega^*/i)_H$	a	1958	1827	1303	951	377
	b	1946	1524	938	402	197
$(\omega, \text{str})_H$	a	382	397	478	591	1177
	b	415	481	816	1566	2320
$(\omega, \text{bend})_H$	a	648	620	565	523	433
	b	736	707	657	581	453
$(\omega^*/i)_D$	a	1398	1307	950	731	352
	b	1391	1148	746	380	194
$(\omega, \text{str})_D$	a	382	392	463	555	898
	b	415	478	733	1184	1687
$(\omega, \text{bend})_D$	a	462	444	403	374	310
	b	527	506	469	417	324
$(\omega_r)_H$	a	2959	2823	2696	2597	2404
$(\omega_r)_D$	a	2133	2035	1945	1870	1733
k_H/k_D at 400°K	a	9.2	5.5	3.6	3.0	1.7
	b	8.8	4.4	3.2	1.9	1.3

a. London-Eyring-Polanyi-Sato method.
b. Bond-energy–bond-order method. D_1 in kcal/mole; D_2 is 100 kcal/mole; force constants are in cgs units; vibration frequencies are in cm^{-1}.

dissociation energy of the bond being broken varies from 100 to 66.7 kcal, the properties of the activated complex was calculated by the LEPS method using the same value of Δ throughout and by the BEBO method using the same value of p throughout.   This model represents abstraction of a hydrogen atom from a hydrocarbon by a hydrocarbon free radical.   The two methods are compared in Table 2.   The "properties of the activated complex" are

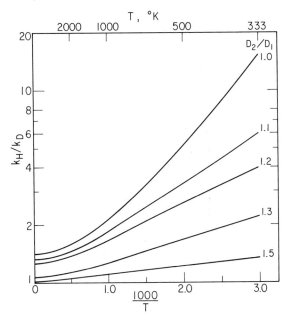

Fig. 13–10. Hydrocarbon radical plus hydrocarbon kinetic isotope effect.   All curves calculated by BEBO method, with corrections for tunneling.   The curves differ as to dissociation energy D, of bond being broken.   The calculations are based on $D_2 = 100$ kcal/mole.

very nearly the same by the two methods, over most of this wide range of conditions; however the methods begin to diverge somewhat for highly exothermic reactions.   The kinetic isotope effect at 400°K, including tunneling corrections, is also included in the table.   The two methods give very nearly the same predictions for the kinetic isotope effect.

The properties of the activated complex and the kinetic isotope effect (Fig. 10) change markedly with dissociation energy of the bond being broken.   For thermoneutral reactions, the bond orders of the complex are 0.5–0.5, the imaginary frequency is a maximum, the total zero-point energy in other coordinates is a minimum, and the kinetic isotope effect is a maximum.   For highly exothermic reactions, the activated complex has orders such as 0.88–0.12, that is, it closely resembles reactants. For strongly endothermic reactions, the activated complex resembles the product. For highly exothermic reactions, the bending force constant decreases and the bending vibrational amplitude increases; this feature leads to the total breakdown of the assumption of small vibrations (Eqs. 4–35 and 4–36), separable coordinates (Eqs. 6–13 and 6–14), and the usual expression for activated-complex theory (Eq. 8–32) and kinetic isotope effect (Eq. 13–1). Specifically, for a bending force constant of 0.025×10^{-11} ergs/radian^2 at room temperature, the classical vibrational amplitude is one radian (compare Table 12–1); this is *not* an infinitesimal displacement from the reference structure. Either in the theory of chemical equilibrium or in kinetics, one should realize that bending force constants of the order of magnitude of 0.01×10^{-11} ergs/radian^2 signal the collapse of the basis of simple, separable partition-function theory.

E. $CH_3 + H_2$, D_2, HD

The relative rate of reaction between methyl radicals and hydrogen isotopes has been studied by Steacie and co-workers (references are given in Ref. 41b):

$$CH_3 + H_2 \xrightarrow{2k_{HH}} CH_4 + H \qquad (13\text{–}20)$$

$$CH_3 + D_2 \xrightarrow{2k_{DD}} CH_3D + D \qquad (13\text{–}21)$$

$$CH_3 + HD \xrightarrow{k_{HD}} CH_4 + D \qquad (13\text{–}22)$$

$$CH_3 + HD \xrightarrow{k_{DH}} CH_3D + H \qquad (13\text{–}23)$$

These results were analyzed in great detail by the BEBO method.[41b]   The experimental error is larger for these reactions than for the other examples in this chapter, and thus only one case will be discussed in detail here.

Students often ask the following question: "The duration of a collision is about 10^{-13} to 10^{-12} second; the period of a vibration is of the same order of magnitude; how does an activated complex have time to explore all phases and states of vibration to justify use of the partition function in the rate expression?"   The answer to this question has already been given in Chapter 8: one activated complex lives but 10^{-13} or so second; and while the reaction coordinate progresses, the other normal modes (vibrations, rotations, or translations) have some one structure and momentum.   For a large number of reaction events, the values possessed by the other co-ordinates are distributed uniformly over available phase space; the partition function is the enumeration of these parallel paths.   For example, the symmetric stretch vibration of the complex does not "have time to be quantized" during a single reaction event; but it acts as a "narrow slit" and causes diffraction effects for low-energy, long-wavelength incident particles, that is, it demands zero-point-energy.   One kinetic isotope effect,

$$H_3C—D—H/H_3C—D—D \qquad\qquad (13\text{-}24)$$

provides a direct experimental demonstration that the "vibrations" of the activated complex are indeed quantized.   For this case the imaginary frequencies are the same, the tunnel effect is the same, and the only effects

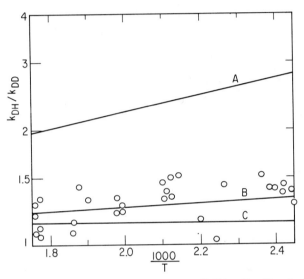

Fig. 13–11. Kinetic isotope effect CH_3—D—H/CH_3—D—D calculated from: A, vibration of reactants only (Eq. 25); B, reactants and stretch of complex (Eq. 26); C, reactants and stretch, bends, and wags of complex (Eq. 27).

contributing to the kinetic isotope effect are the (a) zero-point-energy difference of the reactants D—H and D—D, (b) the zero-point-energy difference of the symmetrical stretch of the complex, and (c) the zero-point-energy difference of the bending and wagging modes.   The observed kinetic isotope effect is shown in Fig. 11 with three calculated curves.   Curve A is based solely on the reactants:

$$\frac{k_{DH}}{k_{DD}} = \frac{\Gamma_{DD}}{\Gamma_{DH}} \qquad\qquad (13\text{-}25)$$

This curve lies far above the experimental points; and since the reactants are certainly quantized, this curve is an unambiguous starting point.   The only way to lower the calculated curve is to acknowledge that the activated complex has zero-point energy.   Curve B adds the consideration of quantized stretching vibrations of the complex:

$$\frac{k_{DH}}{k_{DD}} = \frac{\Gamma_{DD}}{\Gamma_{DH}}\left(\frac{\Gamma_{me-D-H}}{\Gamma_{me-D-D}}\right)^{\ddagger} \tag{13-26}$$

Curve C quantizes the bending and wagging vibrations in addition to the factors of Eq. 26:

$$\frac{k_{DH}}{k_{DD}} = \frac{\Gamma_{DD}}{\Gamma_{DH}}\frac{(\Gamma_{str}\Gamma_b^2\Gamma_{wag}^2)_{DH}^{\ddagger}}{(\Gamma_{str}\Gamma_b^2\Gamma_{wag}^2)_{DD}^{\ddagger}} \tag{13-27}$$

The experimental error is such that no choice can be made between Eqs. 26 and 27. However, the discrepancy between Eq. 25 and the data is so large that it is clearly demonstrated that the activated complex does possess a substantial amount of zero-point energy in its transient coordinates.

F.   Cl + H₂, D₂, HD, HT

The kinetic isotope effects of chlorine atoms plus various isotopes of hydrogen have been studied by several workers; references are given to previous investigators in the article by Goldfinger and co-workers[80] and by

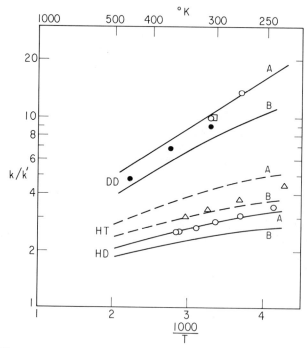

Fig. 13–12. Kinetic isotope effect between chlorine atoms and various isotopes of hydrogen: curves B, without tunneling correction; curves A, with tunneling correction. Experimental points: ●–Ref. 80; other points –Ref. 81 and references cited there.

Bigeleisen and co-workers.[81] The observed kinetic isotope effects are not always simple ratios of rate constants because of the nature of the chain reaction. Thus the term $\mathbf{k}/\mathbf{k}'$ has the following meanings:

$$\mathbf{k}_{HH}/\mathbf{k}_{DD} \qquad \text{for DD}$$

$$\frac{2\mathbf{k}_{HH}}{\mathbf{k}_{HD} + \mathbf{k}_{DH}} \qquad \text{for HD} \qquad (13\text{--}28)$$

$$\frac{2\mathbf{k}_{HH}}{\mathbf{k}_{HT} + \mathbf{k}_{TH}} \qquad \text{for HT}$$

The theoretical analysis is based on the LEPS potential-energy surface and method a for tunneling.

A comparison is given in Fig. 12 between observed isotope effects and those calculated: B, without correction for tunneling; A, with correction for tunneling. The agreement between theory and experiment is only fair. The experimental points for the HT series and the HD series lie much closer to each other than indicated by the calculation.

These reactions are almost thermoneutral, but even so the bond orders of the complex are about 1/3, 2/3. The relationship between potential-energy barrier and zero-point energies, is given by an energy profile, Fig. 13 (compare Fig. 10–2 and 10–3).

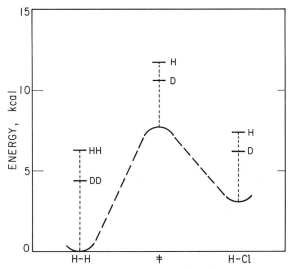

Fig. 13–13. Energy profile for the reaction between chlorine atoms and H_2 and D_2.

G. CHLORINE ATOMS PLUS HYDROCARBONS[80]

The two reactions

$$Cl + CH_4 \rightarrow HCl + CH_3 \qquad (13\text{--}29)$$

$$Cl + C_2H_6 \rightarrow HCl + C_2H_5 \qquad (13\text{--}30)$$

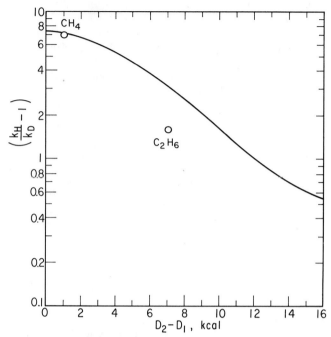

Fig. 13–14. Kinetic isotope effect as a function of dissociation energy of hydrocarbon-bond being broken for reactions with chlorine atoms: calculated curve, observed points for methane and ethane.

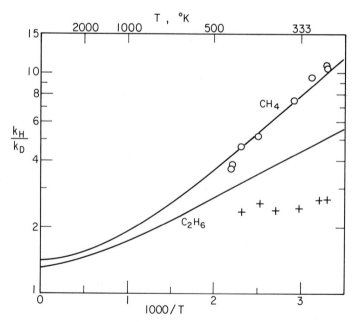

Fig. 13–15. Kinetic isotope effect as a function of temperature for $Cl + CH_4$ and $Cl + C_2H_6$: calculated lines and experimental points, Ref. 80.

have been studied relative to the completely deuterated species. Reaction 29 is almost thermoneutral, that is, $D_{HCl} - D_{CH_3-H}$ is 1.1 kcal; reaction 30 is exothermic by 7 kcal. Since the activation energy of the thermoneutral reaction is low (3.9 kcal), one expects (Chapter 11) this system to change very rapidly with dissociation energy of the bond being broken. For this reason, an extensive set of model calculations was made by the BEBO method, and these reactions were studied experimentally. The calculated isotope effect at 333°K is plotted in Fig. 14 as a function of decreasing dissociation energy of bond being broken. The point for methane lies very close to the calculated curve, but the point for ethane lies far below the calculated curve. (This calculation is based on a three-atom model.) A further comparison of experimental data at various temperatures and calculated curves is given by Fig. 15. Over a moderate range of temperature, the calculated curve (with a small correction for tunneling) shows good agreement for the methane case. However, the calculated curve for ethane (tunneling correction is zero) is in strong disagreement with the data.

H. COMPARISON OF CASES

In the examples cited above there are some reactions for which agreement between theory and experiment is excellent:

$$CF_3 + CH_4/CD_4 \qquad (13\text{-}31)$$

$$CD_3 + C_2H_6/C_2D_6 \qquad (13\text{-}32)$$

$$Cl + CH_4/CD_4 \qquad (13\text{-}33)$$

There are some cases where agreement between theory and experiment is only fairly good:

$$CH_3 + H_2/D_2,\ HD,\ DH \qquad (13\text{-}34)$$

$$Cl + H_2/D_2,\ HD + DH,\ HT + TH \qquad (13\text{-}35)$$

And for at least one case, experimental results are in strong disagreement with theory:

$$Cl + C_2H_6/C_2D_6 \qquad (13\text{-}36)$$

One naturally asks whether there is any basis for understanding why the theory works in some cases and fails in others. To explore this question, one may examine energy profiles (Figs. 10–2 and 10–3) for reactions 31, 33, 35, and 36, with three-atom models in all cases. Such a profile has already been given for reaction 35 as Fig. 13. The full detailed components of all energy terms for reaction 31 are given in Table 3, where the base of the potential energy curve for product, CF_3—H, is taken as zero. Quantities listed are potential energy minimum for reactant and potential energy maximum for the activated complex. The zero-point energies of reactant, product, and each normal mode of the complex are included. Except for the reaction coordinate, these zero-point energies are positive and temperature-independent; the negative, temperature-dependent effective tunneling depth ($RT\, d \ln \Gamma^*/d \ln T$) is interpreted as the zero-point energy of the reaction coordinate. The term Θ for vibrational modes in Table 3 is not the temperature coefficient of $\Gamma = (u/2)/\sinh u/2$, because the zero-point energy has already been considered separately. Rather it is $d \ln (1 - e^{-u})^{-1}/d \ln T$, and it is the average thermal energy of the oscillator

TABLE 13–3

Detailed Analysis of the Various Energies That
Contribute to the Activation Energy of the Reaction: *

$$CF_3 + H\!-\!CH_3 \rightarrow CH_3 + H\!-\!CF_3$$

		Reactant		Complex		Product	
		CH	CD	H	D	CH	CD
V		1.8	1.8	14.7	14.7	0	0
ZPE	str	4.16	2.98	0.55	0.52	4.33	3.08
	b(2)	—	—	1.68	1.22	—	—
	r.c.	—	—	−1.2	−0.90	—	—
ΘRT	str	~0	~0	0.54	0.57	~0	~0
	b(2)	—	—	0.76	1.02	—	—
	int. tr.	1.50	1.50	—	—	1.50	1.50
	rot.	1.00	1.00	1.00	1.00	1.00	1.00
	r.c.	—	—	1.00	1.00	—	—
$E_Z = \Sigma\, ZPE$		4.16	2.98	1.03	0.84	4.33	3.08
$H = \Sigma\, \Theta RT$		2.50	2.50	3.30	3.59	2.50	2.50
$V + E_Z$		6.0	4.8	15.7	15.5	4.3	3.1
$V + E_Z + H$		8.5	7.3	19.0	19.1	6.8	5.6
$\mathbf{E}_{act}$				10.5	11.8	—	—

* Based on a three-atom model; 500°K. All energies are given in kcal/mol.

above the zero-point energy. The thermal energy $(3/2)RT$ of the center of mass is omitted from the table, but the three components of relative velocity of reactants is considered as the internal translational energy of the collision complex. These detailed contributions to the energy of activated complex for both H and D reactions are given in Table 3. Similarly, for reactions 33 and 36, the detailed energies of the H-transfer process are given in Table 4.

Potential-energy profiles (Figs. 10–2 and 10–3), with zero-point energy indicated by a bar and with internal thermal energy indicated by a circle, are shown in Fig. 16. For the reaction of CF_3 with CH_4, the zero-point energy of reactant or product is far below the barrier height. For the reaction of Cl with CH_4, the zero-point energy of reactant is about two-thirds as high as the barrier, and the zero-point energy of product is only about

TABLE 13–4

Detailed Analysis of the Various Energies That Contribute to
Activation Energy of Reactions:
I. $Cl + CH_4$; II. $Cl + C_2H_6$

	C—H I	C—H—Cl‡ I	C—H II	C—H—Cl‡ II	HCl
V (HCl $= 0$)	1.1	7.5	7.0	10.6	0
ZPE str	4.25	0.71	4.25	1.40	4.21
b(2)	—	2.03	—	1.89	—
r.c.	—	−1.25	—	−0.28	—
ΘRT str.	0.001	0.45	0.001	0.18	0.001
b(2)	—	0.61	—	0.66	—
int. tr.	1.50	—	1.50	—	1.50
rot.	1.00	1.00	1.00	1.00	1.00
r.c.	—	1.00	—	1.00	—
$E_z = \Sigma\,ZPE$	4.25	1.49	4.25	3.01	4.21
$H = \Sigma\,\Theta RT$	2.50	3.06	2.50	2.84	2.50
$V + E_z$	5.4	9.0	11.2	13.6	4.2
$V + E_z + H$	7.9	12.1	13.7	16.4	6.7
E_{act}		4.2		2.7	

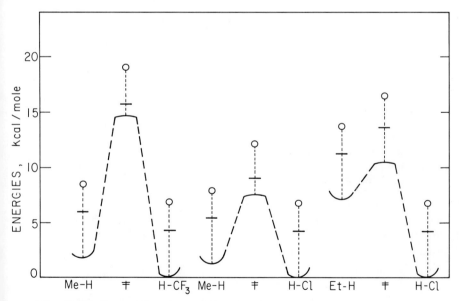

Fig. 13–16. Potential-energy profiles for three reactions: $CF_3 + H—CH_3 \rightarrow$ $CF_3—H + CH_3$; $Cl + H—CH_3 \rightarrow HCl + CH_3$; $Cl + H—C_2H_5 \rightarrow HCl + C_2H_5$. All cases are based on a 3-atom model. Zero-point energies are shown as a bar; thermal excitation of internal degrees of freedom are shown as circles.

half as high as the barrier.   For these two cases, theory and experiment are in good agreement.

From Fig. 13 for the reaction of Cl with hydrogen, one sees that the zero-point energies of H_2 on one side and HCl on the other are very nearly equal to the barrier height.   Here agreement between experiment and theory is neither very good nor very bad.

The reaction of Cl with C_2H_6 provides a strong example where zero-point energy of reactant is *higher* than the potential-energy barrier, and the average internal energy of the colliding pair is far above the barrier height.   Consider Fig. 4–6 and the ice-skater analogy discussed in Chapter 4.   The lowest plane of constant energy along which reactants approach the complex is higher than the barrier, and the average thermal plane of approach is high above the barrier.   The average "frozen lake" lies at about -2 in Fig. 4–6, that is, twice the barrier height.   The rate will be determined by the dynamics and quantum-mechanical effects over the broad potential-energy gap between -2 on one side and -2 on the other.   It seems incredible that the reaction rate in this case is determined by small-vibration theory, by the second derivatives of the saddlepoint, which is buried so deeply below.   As can be seen from Fig. 2–5 in comparison with Fig. 16, the hydrogen isotope (which must hit above the barrier) reacts slower than classically, while the deuterium isotope (which may hit below the barrier) may react faster than classically.   It should be strongly emphasized that the usual formulations of activated-complex theory (including its version of the kinetic isotope effect) is based on small-vibration theory, on neglect of terms beyond the quadratic in a Taylor series expansion.   When these clearly stated assumptions of the theory are violated strongly enough, the predictions of the theory fail.   One can readily spot two situations where such a failure is to be expected, and it can probably be demonstrated in one case.   The theory will fail if:

1. Vibrational amplitudes are too large, and specifically if bending force constants are much below 10^{-12} ergs/radian^2.
2. Zero-point energy of the bond being broken exceeds potential energy of activation.

Considerable further research is recommended to delimit the region wherein activated complex theory of the kinetic isotope effect breaks down; the converse of this study would be to clarify wherein the theory may be used confidently to make predictions.

14

Termolecular Reactions; Recombination of Iodine Atoms

A. EXPERIMENTAL RESULTS

By illuminating iodine vapor, I_2, in the presence of an inert gas M, Rabinowitch and Wood[82a] achieved a measurable (though small) reduction in I_2 concentration as a stationary state was achieved between light absorption,

$$I_2 + h\nu \rightarrow I(^2P_{3/2}) + I(^2P_{1/2}) \tag{14–1}$$

homogeneous recombination,

$$I + I + M \xrightarrow{k_R} I_2 + M \tag{14–2}$$

and heterogeneous recombination on the walls. From a knowledge of the rate of light absorption and the steady-state concentration of iodine atoms, it was possible to measure third-order recombination rate constants for several different foreign gases M.

Following the introduction of flash spectroscopy,[82b] several laboratories[82c–g] were able to follow reaction 2 directly, by means of light absorption by I_2, with data photographed on the face of a cathode ray tube; total reaction times were about 1 millisecond. Over a narrow range of temperature, the rate of reaction (2) decreased with temperature.[82f,g]

By use of a shock tube[82h] the rate of thermal dissociation of iodine

$$I_2 + M \xrightarrow{k_D} 2I + M \tag{14–3}$$

was followed between 1000 and 1600°K. By means of the equilibrium constant for the reaction

$$I_2 = 2I \qquad K = k_D/k_R \tag{14–4}$$

TABLE 14–1

Effect of Temperature on Rate Constant for Iodine
Atom Recombination

Catalyst	$T°K$	$10^{33}k$ cc² sec⁻¹
Ar	300	8.3
	1300	1.3
I_2	300	5200
	1300	36

TABLE 14–2

Third-Order Rate Constants by Russell and Simons for
Recombination of Iodine Atoms at Room Temperature as a
Function of Foreign Gas

Catalyst	$10^{33}k$ (cm^6 sec⁻¹)	Boiling Point of Catalyst (°K)
He	4.7	4
Ne	5.0	27
Ar	10.0	87
H_2	13.1	20
N_2	12.5	77
O_2	18.4	90
CO_2	37.2	194
CH_4	24.5	111
Propane	83	231
Cyclopropane	109	239
n-Pentane	130	237
2-2-Dimethyl Propane	120	263
Cyclohexane	150	354
Ethylene	47	169
Tetrafluoro-ethylene	58	195
Benzene	240	353
Toluene	580	383
p-Xylene	915	411
Mesitylene	1120	438
Water	137	373
Methanol	179	338
Dimethyl ether	170	308
Methylene dichloride	131	313
Carbon tetrachloride	140	250
Ethyl chloride	131	313
Ethyl bromide	221	311
Ethyl iodide	690	345

$$\frac{d[I_2]}{dt} = k[I]^2[M]$$

the rate of the recombination can be found: $k_R = k_D/K$. Comparing the rate of recombination at high temperature with that at room temperature, one sees a strong decrease of rate with increase of temperature (Table 1).

Russell and Simons[82d] made a wide study of the effect of identity of foreign gas on the recombination rate constant. Their data plus a few

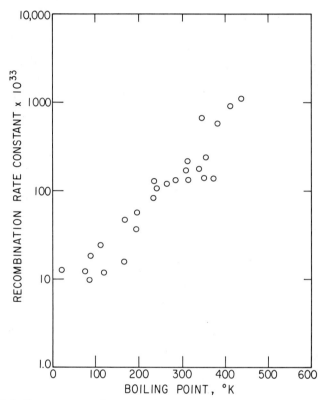

Fig. 14–1. Rate constant for recombination of iodine atoms as a function of the boiling point of the energy-transfer catalyst.

other examples are given in Table 2. A remarkable, empirical correlation was discovered by Russell and Simons. If the logarithm of the rate constant k_{RM} is plotted against the boiling point of the catalyst M, one sees a strong correlation (Table 2 and Fig. 1). The relative efficiency of different gases covers a range of 240. This range is far greater than that of hard-sphere collision diameter. This correlation suggest that the forces that bind a molecule M to itself to form a liquid state are similar to the forces that bind M to I to form an intermediate complex MI. The boiling point is a measure of M·M attractions and thus correlates with the rate constant.

B. MECHANISM

For a long time the "termolecular" recombination of iodine atoms,

$$I + I + M \xrightarrow{k} I_2 + M \tag{14-5}$$

has been discussed in terms of two mechanisms. On the one hand, there is the energy-transfer mechanism:

$$I + I \underset{b}{\overset{a}{\rightleftharpoons}} I_2* \tag{14-6}$$

$$I_2* + M \xrightarrow{c} I_2 + M \tag{14-7}$$

On the other hand, there is the intermediate-complex theory:

$$I + M + M \underset{e}{\overset{d}{\rightleftharpoons}} IM + M \tag{14-8}$$

$$IM + I \xrightarrow{g} I_2 + M \tag{14-9}$$

It is worthwhile to examine a three-atom potential-energy function for a clue as to which "mechanisms" are important. A potential-energy contour for atom recombination was presented as Fig. 4–7, and this figure is given again as Fig. 2 with the "surface of separation" indicated. The reactants are $I + I + M$ with zero energy in the upper-right-hand corner; the products are I_2 with negative energy, parting from the catalyst M. The shaded area of Fig. 2 defines a plane with total energy about kT below zero. In the energy-transfer mechanism, the iodine atoms pass through this plane in a negative direction, but of course the total energy for catalyst plus molecule remains constant. This mechanism includes as a special case the simultaneous collision of three atoms, a trajectory of $-45°$ from $I + I + M$ to $M \cdot I_2$ and then a trajectory moving off to the right. Many other trajectories can be visualized where $I + I + M$ starts with zero or positive energy; a collision trajectory on Fig. 2 may cross the dashed line and hit the repulsive wall; and the products may separate with I_2 moving to the right. However, on the potential-energy surface the pair $M \cdot I$ can have a negative energy. These pairs can be produced by IMI energy-transfer collisions, or more importantly by the separate mechanism

$$M + I \rightleftharpoons MI* \tag{14-10}$$

$$MI* + M \rightarrow MI + M \tag{14-11}$$

A second surface of separation drops from the dashed line down to the potential-energy surface. If the stabilized complexes MI are produced exclusively by the MMI mechanism, then the distribution of particles incident on the dividing surface at negative energies is a projection of the distribution of MI at large separations R_{II}. The phase integral of the Lennard-Jones complex MI from zero energy down to the potential-energy curve gives the partition function for the species MI. The contribution of this mechanism to the reaction is the collision of MI with I, a reaction analogous to atom-transfer reactions considered in previous chapters. Thus one sees that a sensible dividing surface between reactants and products consists of two orthogonal surfaces. The passing of I_2* down through the horizontal surface constitutes the energy-transfer mechanism; the passing

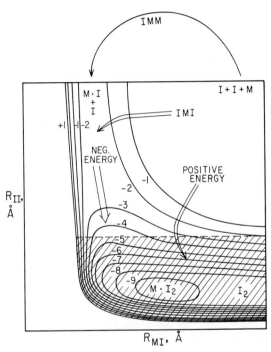

Fig. 14–2. Qualitative potential-energy function for iodine atom recombination in presence of energy-transfer catalyst, M. Horizontal surface-of-separation just below zero energy identifies the energy-transfer mechanism, I_2* + M. Vertical surface-of-separation identifies the "bound-complex" mechanism, IM + I.

of bound MI complexes with negative energy through the vertical surface below the dashed line of Fig. 2 constitutes Bunker and Davidson's bound-complex mechanism; and there are no other trajectories between reactants and products.

There is considerable debate in the literature as to which mechanism is important, energy transfer or bound complex. From Fig. 2 one sees that, of course, they must both be operative. There is not some one "activated complex" for this reaction, but two separate physical processes. It is necessary to estimate the order of magnitude contributed by each mechanism to see if one or the other is dominant.

C. THEORIES

(i) Energy-Transfer Mechanism

An ultrasimple energy-transfer theory was proposed by E. Rabinowitch.[83] Bunker and Davidson[84] developed a simple theory of the bound intermediate complex. Serious theories have been proposed by Wigner,[85] by Keck,[86] and by Light.[87] An extensive numerical research with fast computers was carried out by Bunker,[88] and several other discussions and theories have also been given from time to time. In this chapter, the ultrasimple theories will be presented and tested against experimental data.

Rabinowitch's energy-transfer theory identifies: the rate constant a of Eq. 6 as the collision-rate constant between I and I, the rate constant c as the collision-rate constant between I_2 and M, and the rate constant b as $1/\tau$, the reciprocal period of vibration of an I_2 molecule.

$$\mathbf{R}/P = c[I_2^*][M] = \frac{ac}{b}[I]^2[M] \tag{14-12}$$

$$= Z_{I \cdot I} Z_{II \cdot M} \tau \tag{14-13}$$

where P is the "steric factor," assigned as 1/2 depending on whether the collision is exciting by about kT or de-exciting by about kT and also a factor for electronic multiplicity (discussed below). One gets a slightly different result depending on whether one uses the hard-sphere model for collision rate (Eq. 9–20) or the rate constant for "close collision" for molecules that attract at large distances by the London dispersion force (Table 9–1 for $s = 6$). The second method acknowledges effects due to angular momentum and non-head-on collisions. If the attractive potential is taken to be the empirical Lennard-Jones term

$$V = -4\varepsilon\sigma^6/R^6 \tag{14-14}$$

then the ratio of the two methods of calculating collision rate is

$$\frac{\mathbf{R}_{LJ}}{\mathbf{R}_{hard-sphere}} = 2.71\left(\frac{\varepsilon}{kT}\right)^{1/3} \tag{14-15}$$

(ii) Electronic Multiplicity

As noted in Eq. 1, the iodine molecule dissociates into a ground state $^2P_{3/2}$ atom and an excited $^2P_{1/2}$ atom, of multiplicities 4 and 2 respectively. It is presumed that the $^2P_{1/2}$ atoms are converted to ground state $^2P_{3/2}$ atoms by collision with I_2, although its natural lifetime with respect to spontaneous emission of radiation is greater than 0.1 sec.[5] The combined electronic degeneracy of two $^2P_{3/2}$ atoms is 16; the electronic multiplicity of molecular I_2 ($^1\Sigma$) is one. Thus, at first sight, it appears that the electronic function $\mathbf{B}_e$ is 1/16. However, this discussion is based on Russell-Saunders coupling, which is obeyed only by light elements. Heavy atoms[31] such as iodine follow "jj coupling rules." In addition to the ground state of molecular iodine, four other states are mildly attractive, and the rest are repulsive.[88] For heavy atoms such as iodine the attractive states can mix readily by allowed "spin flipping," but repulsive states including two units of orbital angular momentum cannot mix with the state of zero orbital angular momentum. Bunker concluded that the electronic function should be between 1/16 and 5/16 with 1/8 as the best estimate. The value 1/8 is used in the present calculations.

(iii) Bound-Complex Model

The bound-complex theory considers the equilibrium constant for reaction 8:

$$K = \frac{[MI]}{[M][I]} = \frac{f_{MI}}{f_M f_I} \exp(\varepsilon/kT) \tag{14-16}$$

Since the reactants M and I have energy greater than the intermediate MI by the amount of the Lennard-Jones energy ε, the exponential factor in Eq. 9 is positive. The translational partition function of MI is simple and straightforward, Eq. 6-19. The rotational partition function is adequately given by Eq. 6-20 where $I = \mu R_0^2 = 2^{1/3}\mu\sigma^2$. The vibrational partition function is not given by the harmonic oscillator function but rather by a direct evaluation of the phase integral. As a good approximation for heavy atoms and molecules (He and H_2 excluded), Bunker and Davidson give the number of vibrational states in a Lennard-Jones "bound" cluster as

$$f_{LJ} = 0.056(\sigma^2 \mu\varepsilon/k)^{1/2} \tag{14-17}$$

For light atoms, numerical evaluation of the phase integral was carried out. As a good numerical approximation to the equilibrium constant, Bunker and Davidson give

$$\frac{K}{(\sigma_{MI})^3} = \pi^{1/2}\left(\frac{\varepsilon_{MI}}{kT}\right)^{3/2}\left[\frac{8}{3} + \frac{32}{45}\frac{\varepsilon_{MI}}{kT}\right] \tag{14-18}$$

The rate of reaction is given in terms of Eq. 9:

$$R/P = g[IM][I] = Kg[I]^2[M] \tag{14-19}$$

The rate constant g is the collision-rate constant, and the steric factor P depends on the electronic multiplicities.

According to the discussions given above, the rate is the sum of the energy-transfer process and the bound-complex term:

$$R/P = \tfrac{1}{2}Z_{I \cdot I}Z_{II \cdot M}\tau + KZ_{MI \cdot I} \tag{14-20}$$

The relative values of these two terms for several different foreign gases at 300°K is given in Table 3. For argon and butane these two terms are shown at 300°K and 1200°K. These calculations indicate that the energy-transfer mechanism is negligible compared to the bound-complex mechanism for

TABLE 14-3

Relative Contribution to Rate by the Two "Mechanisms"*

T	M	Energy-Transfer	Bound-Complex	Total
300	Ar	1.0	5.7	6.7
1200	Ar	1.5	0.8	2.3
300	Butane	1.8	38	40
1200	Butane	2.7	5	7.7
300	He	1.0	0.4	1.4
300	Ne	0.8	1.4	2.2
300	Kr	0.8	7.8	8.6
300	Xe	0.8	13.4	14.2
300	H_2	2.2	1.6	3.8
300	N_2	0.7	5.7	6.4
300	O_2	1.1	6.3	7.4
300	CH_4	1.4	9.0	10.4
300	CCl_4	1.4	37	38.4
300	C_6H_6	1.7	45.3	47.0

* Units of 10^{-33} cm^6 sec^{-1}.

TABLE 14-4

Relative Rate Constants for Different Gases as Catalysts in the Recombination of Iodine Atoms:

k_M/k_{Ar}

M	a	b	c	Calc. Eq. 20
He	0.50	0.47	0.37	0.2
Ne	—	0.50	0.53	0.3
Ar	1.00	1.00	1.00	1.0
Kr	—	—	1.25	1.3
Xe	—	—	1.71	2.1
H_2	1.11	1.32	—	0.6
N_2	1.83	1.24	—	1.0
O_2	2.91	1.84	—	1.1
CO_2	5.0	3.72	—	2.5
CH_4	3.3	2.45	—	1.6
C_3H_8	—	8.3	—	3.1
n-C_5H_{12}	—	12.9	—	7.0
cyclo-C_6H_{12}	—	15.0	—	7.5
C_2H_4	—	4.72	—	2.7
C_6H_6	28	24	—	7.0
CCl_4	—	14.0	—	5.8
I_2	—	—	650	7.0

a. E. Rabinowitch and W. C. Wood, *J. Chem. Phys.*, **4**, 497 (1936).
b. K. E. Russell and J. Simons, *Proc. Roy. Soc.* (London), **A217**, 271 (1953).
c. M. I. Christie, *J. Am. Chem. Soc.*, **84**, 4066 (1962).
d. The absolute values of these rate constants are distorted by the large contribution of I_2 to the rate.

highly polarizable gases at low temperature. However, for He and H_2 at 300° and for Ar at 1200°, the case is reversed: the energy-transfer rate is slightly larger than that for the bound complex. Thus in general neither mechanism may be neglected, although the bound-complex mechanism is usually the more important of the two.

The observed relative efficiencies of a number of different foreign gases are compared with calculated values in Table 4. All data are normalized to

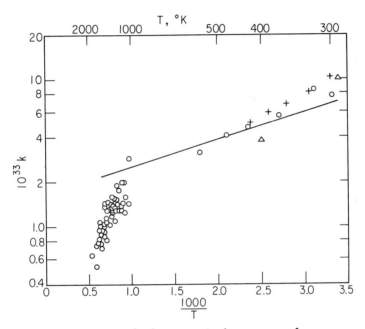

Fig. 14–3. Recombination of iodine atoms in the presence of argon, over a wide range of temperature. Line calculated from simple Rabinowitch-Davidson theory (Eq. 20): ○ — Davidson's laboratory; + —Willard *et al.*; △ — Russell and Simons.

the value observed with argon as catalyst. This simple theory follows most of the major trends in these data, except that in some cases the efficiency of a catalyst gas is considerably greater than that calculated, especially benzene and molecular iodine. These cases are regarded as forming much more stable intermediates than the Lennard-Jones cluster, the I_3 molecule and a "charge-transfer" complex to benzene. Similarly nitric oxide was found to be extraordinarily effective as a recombination catalyst, and the spectrum of the transient species ONI was actually observed.[89]

The rate of recombination of iodine atoms in the presence of argon has been repeatedly studied, in different laboratories, and over a wide range of temperature. These data are plotted in Fig. 3, and the line calculated by the simple theory of Eq. 20 is drawn on the figure.   Again the simple theory with no adjustable parameter agrees with the data within a factor of 2 or so.   It will be noted that the data themselves show considerable scatter, especially at high temperature.   The electronic multiplicity factor is uncertain by a factor of 2 or more.

There are much more elaborate theories, but they agree with experiment no better than the ultrasimple theory given above.   The theories of Wigner,[85] of Keck,[86] and of Light[87] are much more dignified in derivation than that of Rabinowitch, Bunker, and Davidson.   However, when one reaches the level where numbers are inserted, approximations are made, Lennard-Jones or other empirical functions are used, and the final result is essentially a "chemists' theory" after all.   Wigner's theory and Keck's theory disagree with experiment much more than the simple theory.   The theory of Light gives results comparable to that of Bunker and Davidson, but there is no real improvement.   These examples illustrate a fairly general effect not otherwise emphasized in this book: simple "chemical" theories (compare Debye-Hückel theory) give results almost as good as or perhaps better than much more elaborate "chemical" theories.   The simple theory is only semi-quantitative, it tantalizingly follows some trends, but it never really fits precisely.   In an effort to improve the simple theory, one is likely to build up elaborate extensions which often fit the data worse rather than better than the simple theory.   (This discussion excludes theories that drag in adjustable constants.)

PROBLEMS

(1) From the literature, find the rate of recombination of some atoms other than iodine.

(2) For some noble gas M, evaluate the relative contribution of the two simple mechanisms discussed in this chapter.   Compare the calculated rate constant with observed rate constant.

15

Unimolecular Reactions

A. GENERAL LINDEMANN-HINSHELWOOD MECHANISM[90,91]

Unimolecular isomerizations and decompositions have been discussed in a preliminary way in Chapters 1 and 4. A somewhat more detailed discussion of the nature of molecular processes in a unimolecular decomposition is given here with Fig. 4–3 as a highly simplified model. Three different types of processes and three different functions are involved: excitation of the reactant molecule A by collision with an energy-transfer agent M; deactivation of vibrationally excited A by M; and decomposition of molecules A* that have internal energy equal to or greater than the critical energy. For an unrealistically simplified model consisting of a seven-level molecule with critical energy between the third and fourth, all such processes are indicated by vectors in Fig. 1. Quantities of interest are the concentration of reactants in various quantum states i, $[A_i^*]$, and the molecular rate constants c_i for decomposition of activated molecules. The rate of reaction is then

$$\mathbf{R} = \sum_{i=0}^{\infty} c_i [A_i^*] \tag{15-1}$$

where the summation is over all states with non-zero rate constant c_i. The molecular rate constant c_i is a mechanical property of an excited molecule; the interesting "fall-off" with pressure shown by Fig. 1–12, for example, all depends on change of the distribution function for excited molecules. This distribution, on the other hand, may depend on the complete spectrum of activation and de-activation illustrated by Fig. 1.

For the overall chemical reaction, A → products, a general form of the Lindemann mechanism is

$$A_j + M_k \xrightarrow{a_{jkil}} A_i^* + M_l$$

$$A_i^* + M_l \xrightarrow{b_{iljk}} A_j + M_k \tag{15-2}$$

$$A_i^* \xrightarrow{c_i} \text{products}$$

M is an inert gas in great excess, or the pure reactant A for the initial reaction. The subscript j represents completely the internal quantum state of A from zero energy to infinity, and the subscript i represents the same thing for molecules with energy above the critical energy. The subscript k or l refers to relative motion of A and M (Eq. 9–36, for example) and to the internal state of M. The first step in the mechanism represents the completely

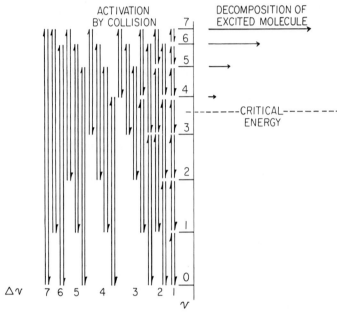

Fig. 15–1. Vector diagram illustrating activation by collision, deactivation by collision, and unimolecular decomposition of activated molecules for an ultrasimple molecular model.

general case of a collision between A and M, such that A is left in the quantum state i, and the second step is the exact reverse of the first. If the first step includes all processes forming the given state A_i, and if the second step includes the reverse of each, no detailed processes are omitted. In the third step of Eq. 2 and in Eq. 1, the rate constants c_i have already been implicitly summed over all allowed states of the products. Since the sum of a set of constants is a constant, one may further abbreviate:

$$\sum_l a_{jkil} = a_{jki}$$

$$\sum_j \sum_k b_{iljk} = b_{il}$$

$$(15\text{--}3)$$

The differential equation for formation of excited molecules in the state i is

$$\frac{d[A_i^*]}{dt} = \sum_j \sum_k a_{jki}[A_j][M_k] - \sum_l b_{il}[A_i^*][M_l] - c_i[A_i^*] \qquad (15\text{--}4)$$

In principle, the problem is solved by evaluating $[A_i^*]$ from the set of simultaneous differential equations represented by Eq. 4 and substituting the values into Eq. 1 to get the rate. With this approach one has as unknown the vast spectrum of transition probabilities and the concentrations of species in all detailed states. These detailed molecular quantities are, however, readily interpreted in terms of averages by use of the following definitions of probability:

$$P_j^A = [A_j]/[A] \qquad (15\text{--}5)$$

$$P_l^M = [M_l]/[M] \qquad (15\text{--}6)$$

and by use of the general definition of an average (Eq. 6–6). The second summation in Eq. 4 is multiplied in numerator and denominator by the sum over all states of M:

$$\sum_l b_{il}[A_i^*][M_l] = \sum_l [M_l] \frac{\sum_l b_{il}[A_i^*][M_l]}{\sum_l [M_l]} \qquad (15\text{--}7)$$

$$= [M]\langle b_i \rangle_{av}^M [A_i^*] \qquad (15\text{--}8)$$

where the summation over all microscopic states of M is just the macroscopic concentration of M. The first summation in Eq. 4 is similarly seen to be

$$\sum_j \sum_k a_{jki}[A_j][M_k] = [A][M] \sum_j \sum_k a_{jki} P_j^A P_k^M \qquad (15\text{--}9)$$

$$= [A][M] \sum_{j \& k} a_{jki} P_{j \& k}^{A,M} \qquad (15\text{--}10)$$

$$= [A][M]\langle a_i \rangle_{av}^{A,M} \qquad (15\text{--}11)$$

where Eq. 10 follows from the law of combining of probabilities, and Eq. 11 follows from the general definition of an average.

When M is a foreign gas in great excess (note: it is not lost by reaction), it is highly plausible that the foreign gas has an equilibrium distribution over all its states and at one temperature the average $\langle b_i \rangle_{av}^M$ is constant, that is, it does not depend implicitly on concentration of M. Thus the following assumption is regarded as a very good one for isothermal reaction systems:

$$\langle b_i \rangle_{av}^M = b_i \qquad (15\text{--}12)$$

The constancy of the average function in Eq. 11 is much more dubious, however. It is easily demonstrated (see Fig. 1–12, for example) that unimolecular reaction readily depletes the equilibrium distribution of states above the critical energy. Consider vibrational state 5 of Fig. 1. Molecules are brought into this state from three different sources: (1) activation from reactant states, 3, 2, 1, and 0, below the critical energy by "strong collisions"; (2) activation from the neighboring excited state 4 by a one-quantum process; and (3) deactivation from higher excited states, 6, 7, etc. These three processes may be written out as

$$\langle a_i \rangle_{av}^{A,M} = \sum_{j,k=0}^{E_c} a_{jki} P_{j\,\&\,k}^{\circ} + \sum_{E_c}^{\infty} a_{jki} P_{j\,\&\,k}^{*} \tag{15-13}$$

$$= \underset{\substack{\text{average over}\\ \text{non-reacting states}}}{\langle a_i \rangle_{av}^{\circ}} + \underset{\substack{\text{average over}\\ \text{states that react}}}{\langle a_i^{*}(M) \rangle_{av}} \tag{15-14}$$

The second term on the right-hand side of Eq. 13 certainly involves a strongly non-equilibrium distribution function and has implicit dependence on concentration of M; the first term is certainly less distorted, and it is reasonable to assume it not to depend on [M]. The average excitation function may thus be assumed to have the following dependence on foreign gas:

$$\langle a_i \rangle_{av}^{A,M} = a_i^{\circ} + a_i^{*}(M) \tag{15-15}$$

where the functional dependence on M is unknown.

With these interpretations and reasonable assumptions, one may re-express Eq. 4 as

$$\frac{d[A_i^{*}]}{dt} = \{a_i^{\circ} + a_i^{*}(M)\} \, [A][M] - b_i[M][A_i^{*}] - c_i[A_i^{*}] \tag{15-16}$$

If one makes the steady-state assumption for the excited-state species, the value is

$$\frac{[A_i^{*}]}{[A]} = \frac{[a_i^{\circ} + a_i^{*}(M)][M]}{b_i[M] + c_i} \tag{15-17}$$

and the rate is (Eq. 1):

$$R = [A] \sum_i \frac{c_i[a_i^{\circ} + a_i^{*}(M)][M]}{b_i[M] + c_i} \tag{15-18}$$

To evaluate rates by means of Eq. 18, one must use a complete theory of vibrational-translational energy transfer, and analyze the full set of simultaneous equations (like Eq. 16) to solve for the actual distribution over all states. For an attack on this very difficult problem, see Ref. 92.

B. STRONG-COLLISION ASSUMPTION

The well-known theories of unimolecular reactions[62,93] make the strong-collision assumption, namely, that activation from the bulk of reactant states below the critical energy is much more important than adjacent excited states in populating a given activated state. In terms of Eq. 13 the assumption is that

$$\langle a_i \rangle_{av}^{\circ} \gg \langle a_i^*(M) \rangle_{av} \tag{15-19}$$

In this case the average excitation rate function is a second-order rate constant

$$\langle a_i \rangle_{av}^{A,M} = a_i \tag{15-20}$$

The actual distribution function for activated reactant is

$$Q_i = \frac{[A_i^*]}{[A]} = \frac{a_i[M]}{b_i[M] + c_i} \tag{15-21}$$

The distribution function for molecules that react per unit time, Tolman's distribution function,[94] is

$$T_i = \frac{a_i c_i[M]}{b_i[M] + c_i} \tag{15-22}$$

The rate expression is

$$\mathbf{R} = [A] \sum_i Q_i c_i = [A] \sum_i T_i \tag{15-23}$$

$$= [A] \sum_i \frac{a_i c_i[M]}{b_i[M] + c_i} = \mathbf{k}[A] \tag{15-24}$$

The high-pressure limit is

$$\mathbf{R}_\infty = [A] \, \Sigma \, a_i c_i / b_i = \mathbf{k}_\infty[A] \tag{15-25}$$

The low-pressure limit is

$$\mathbf{R}_0 = [A][M] \, \Sigma \, a_i = \mathbf{k}_0'[A][M] \tag{15-26}$$

With this "strong-collision" model, one may state many simple general conclusions.[91] Derivatives of $\mathbf{k}$ with respect to [M] have alternating signs:

$$\frac{d\mathbf{k}}{d[M]} = \sum_i \frac{a_i c_i^2}{(b_i[M] + c_i)^2} \tag{15-27}$$

$$\frac{d^2\mathbf{k}}{d[M]^2} = -\sum_i \frac{2a_i b_i c_i^2}{(b_i[M] + c_i)^3} \tag{15-28}$$

One sees from these simple considerations that a plot of $\mathbf{k}$ vs [M] (compare Fig. 1–12) has positive slope and negative curvature everywhere; there can be no inflection points. These theorems may be used as consistency tests for experimental data. One may rewrite Eq. 24 with 1/[M] as independent variable or it may be expressed as $\mathbf{k}/[M]$. By simple formulation of first and second derivatives in terms of these variables, one can readily show that a plot of $\mathbf{k}$ vs 1/[M] has negative slope and positive curvature everywhere, and it has a finite intercept $\mathbf{k}_\infty$ at zero 1/[M]. A plot of 1/$\mathbf{k}$ vs 1/[M] has positive slope and negative curvature. A plot of $\mathbf{k}'$ or $\mathbf{k}/[M]$ has negative slope and positive curvature everywhere, and it has a finite intercept k_0' at $[M] = 0$. Also a plot of $\log k$ vs $\log [M]$ has positive slope varying from one to zero.

The rate constant k_∞ at infinite pressure is given by Eq. 25 and the rate constant k_0' at zero pressure is given by Eq. 26. The rate constant function $(k_\infty - k)/k$ is thus

$$\frac{k_\infty - k}{k} = \frac{\sum \left(\dfrac{a_i c_i}{b_i} - \dfrac{a_i c_i [M]}{b_i [M] + c_i} \right)}{\sum \dfrac{a_i c_i [M]}{b_i [M] + c_i}} \tag{15-29}$$

$$= \frac{\sum \dfrac{c_i}{b_i [M]} \dfrac{a_i c_i [M]}{b_i [M] + c_i}}{\sum \dfrac{a_i c_i [M]}{b_i [M] + c_i}} = \left\langle \frac{c}{b[M]} \right\rangle^T \tag{15-30}$$

where Eq. 29 is simply the statement of k_∞ and k in terms of Eqs. 24 and 25, and the interpretation of Eq. 30 as the average of $c_i/b_i[M]$ over Tolman's distribution function is an example of Eq. 6-6. Similarly, the rate constant function $(k_0' - k')/k'$ is interpreted as

$$\frac{k_0' - k'}{k'} = \frac{\sum \left(\dfrac{b_i [M]}{c_i} \right) \dfrac{a_i c_i [M]}{b_i [M] + c_i}}{\sum \dfrac{a_i c_i [M]}{b_i [M] + c_i}} = \left\langle \frac{b[M]}{c} \right\rangle^T \tag{15-31}$$

By virtue of Schwarz's inequality, the product of Eqs. 30 and 31 is equal to or greater than one:

$$\left\langle \frac{b[M]}{c} \right\rangle^T \left\langle \frac{c}{b[M]} \right\rangle^T \geq 1 \tag{15-32}$$

Thus the observable function of rate constants, defined as $\mathbf{J}$, must be equal to or greater than one:

$$\mathbf{J} = \left(\frac{k_\infty - k}{k} \right) \left(\frac{k_0' - k'}{k'} \right) \geq 1 \tag{15-33}$$

In the limit of $\mathbf{J} = 1$, Eq. 33 reduces to

$$\frac{1}{k} = \frac{1}{k_\infty} + \frac{1}{k_0'[M]} \tag{15-34}$$

which is the case of only one term in the summation of Eq. 24.

Perhaps the most carefully and extensively studied unimolecular reaction is B. S. Rabinovitch's investigation of the isomerization of methyl isocyanide:[7]

$$CH_3NC \rightarrow CH_3CN$$

This reaction will be used to illustrate several general features of unimolecular reaction-rate theory. The rate constants at one temperature are plotted as a function of pressure in Fig. 1–4, and an extensive "fall-off" with pressure is seen. The evaluation of rate constant at infinite pressure k_∞ is given by a plot of $1/k$ against $1/P$ in Fig. 2; the curvature of this plot proves that there is a spread in the molecular rate function, c_i, that is, all values of c_i are not

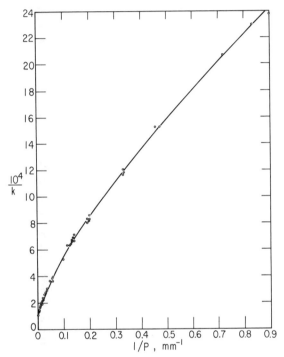

Fig. 15–2. Evaluation of k_∞ for thermal isomerization of methyl isocyanide. (Compare Fig. 1–2.)

the same. The quantity J from Eq. 33 was evaluated for the data for the thermal isomerization of methyl isocyanide at 503°K (Fig. 3). The quantity varies from about 30 at low pressures to about 6 at high pressures. This large spread in J confirms the conclusion drawn from Fig. 2, namely, a wide range of states contributes noticeably to the rate.

The following argument relates the activation function a_i to the deactivation function b_i. Consider two states of different energy A_i and A_j. At equilibrium these two states are related by a Boltzmann factor P_{ij},

$$\{[A_i]/[A_j]\}_{eq} = P_{ij} \qquad (15\text{--}35)$$

At equilibrium, the average rate of transition from j to i is equal to the average rate of transition from i to j:

$$a_{ij}[A_j]_{eq}[M] = b_{ij}[A_i]_{eq}[M] \qquad (15\text{–}36)$$

Thus by considering the situation in the special case of equilibrium, one discovers a general relation between constants

$$a_{ij}/b_{ij} = P_{ij} \qquad (15\text{–}37)$$

For the "strong-collision" mechanism, this detailed relation leads to the averaged relation

$$a_i/b_i = P_i = [A_i^*]_{eq}/[A] \qquad (15\text{–}38)$$

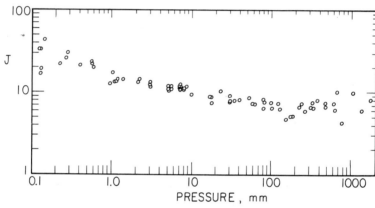

Fig. 15–3. The function $J = \langle c/b[M]\rangle\langle b[M]/c\rangle$ for the isomerization of methyl isocyanide illustrating the wide spread of states that contribute to the rate. Data observed at 503°K.

Thus the rate equation may be written as Eq. 23 with three functions a_i, b_i, and c_i, or as

$$\mathbf{k} = \sum \frac{b_i c_i P_i[M]}{b_i[M] + c_i} \qquad (15\text{–}39)$$

with three functions b_i, c_i, and P_i.

C.   THREE INDEPENDENT MOLECULAR FUNCTIONS

The expression for the unimolecular rate constant as given by Eq. 39 involves three physically different, independent functions: P_i, the equilibrium fraction of molecules in the general quantum state i; b_{Mi} the second-order rate constant (depending on the identity of the collision partner M and the reactant state i) for *deactivation* of the excited reactant; and c_i, the first-order rate constant for decomposition of an excited reactant molecule. These three functions and certain simple models for them are discussed in this section.

(i) Equilibrium Probability Distribution Function P_i

The general solution for the probability distribution function has been given by Eqs. 6–3 and 6–4, but a more specific formulation is also needed. For a molecule of N atoms, one must have $3N$ coordinates. The three translations of center of mass may be separated (Eqs. 7–13 and 7–14, for example), and one has $3N - 3$ internal coordinates including 2 or 3 rotational coordinates, bond stretches, bends, and internal rotations. For a system of mass points constrained to move in only one cartesian dimension, any extension of the $(N - 1)$ internal coordinates may be represented by an equal number of separable normal coordinates (Chapter 5), provided that the potential-energy function obeys Hooke's law (Eq. 4–18). For systems of nonlinear geometrical structure or that undergo nonlinear bending vibrations the normal coordinates are independent only if one considers infinitesimal displacement from a point of extremum. This second restriction arises from R in expressions for bending normal coordinates (compare Eq. 3–33). About an extremum point, very small displacements assure the adequacy of Hooke's law (Eq. 4–35) and bond distances R are effectively constant. One can then separate the Schroedinger equation into $3N - 6$ equations of one dimensional harmonic oscillators, and one can speak of having m quanta of energy $h\nu$ in a particular oscillator. The total wave function is the product of these $3N - 6$ one-dimensional wave functions. The harmonic-oscillator approximation is a good one at low energies familiar to infrared spectroscopists, but a poor one at the high energies required for chemical decomposition. The potential-energy function can no longer be approximated by a quadratic function, and finite increments to the bond lengths render non-quadratic the kinetic energy of bending modes. Schroedinger's equation is not separable into $3N - 6$ one-dimensional equations, and the number of quanta in a given mode is not a good quantum number. In other words, "energy flows" from one normal coordinate to another.

For the case of separable normal modes, the meaning of P_i in Eq. 38 can be readily stated: a given value of i corresponds to a specification of the quantum number of each normal coordinate; $v_1, v_2, v_3 \cdots v_{3N-6}$. A change of any one of these quantum numbers gives a new value to i. For $3N - 6$ different frequencies the problem of P_i is straightforward (Eqs. 6–3 and 6–4) and tedious. For $3N - 6$ normal modes all of the same frequency, simple, illustrative relations may be written down. The following model calculation, discussed fully by Kassel,[62] is designed to give certain important aspects of the distribution function for any molecule, although it is realistic for no molecule.

The model is s identical harmonic oscillators, all of frequency ν. The energy level (less definite than the quantum state) is specified by stating the total number j of quanta in the molecule. The multiplicity of the energy state is simply the number of ways of distributing j identical balls in

s distinguishable boxes, and it is

$$\omega_j = \frac{(j + s - 1)!}{j! \, (s - 1)!} \tag{15-40}$$

The partition function is the sum of $\omega_j \exp\left(-jh\nu/kT\right)$ over all states (Eq. 6-4):

$$f = \sum_{j=0}^{\infty} \frac{(j + s - 1)!}{j! \, (s - 1)!} \exp\left(-jh\nu/kT\right) \tag{15-41}$$

$$= \left(\frac{1}{1 - \exp\left(-h\nu/kT\right)}\right)^{s} \tag{15-42}$$

Thus the equilibrium fraction P_j of molecules in state j is

$$P_j = \frac{N_j}{N} = [1 - \exp\left(-h\nu/kT\right)]^s \frac{(j + s - 1)!}{j! \, (s - 1)!} \exp\left(-jh\nu/kT\right) \tag{15-43}$$

In the limit of classical mechanics, that is, large quantum numbers, the model of s coupled oscillators of frequency ν is expressed in terms of the vibrational energy E; but one is careful to normalize by the factor $h\nu$ to guarantee that any energy under discussion is indeed much larger than one quantum (compare Eq. 6-33). The total number of vibrational states for s oscillators for all permutations of energy between oscillators and for all energies between zero and E is (Ref. 44, p. 492):

$$G(E) = \frac{(E)^s}{s! \, (h\nu)^s} \tag{15-44}$$

For s non-identical oscillators of frequencies ν_i $(i = 1, \cdots s)$, the total number of quantum states between zero and E is

$$G(E) = \frac{(E)^s}{s! \displaystyle\prod_{i=1}^{s} (h\nu_i)} \tag{15-45}$$

For degenerate oscillators one has

$$\rho(E) = \frac{dG(E)}{dE} = \frac{E^{s-1}}{(s - 1)! \, (h\nu)^s} \tag{15-46a}$$

$$\omega(E) = \rho(E) \, dE \tag{15-46b}$$

while for non-degenerate oscillators, the expression is

$$\rho(E) = \frac{dG(E)}{dE} = \frac{E^{s-1}}{(s - 1)! \displaystyle\prod_{i=1}^{s-1} (h\nu_i)} \tag{15-47a}$$

$$\omega(E) = \rho(E) \, dE \tag{15-47b}$$

Provided dE is equal to or greater than one quantum of vibrational energy, $h\nu$, the expressions $\omega(E)$ are the classical-mechanical limits of the multiplicity of the quantum model, Eq. 40. The partition function is the integral of the density of states times the Boltzmann factor:

$$f = (kT/h\nu)^s \qquad \text{degenerate oscillators} \qquad (15\text{--}48)$$

$$f = \prod_{i=1}^{s} \frac{kT}{h\nu_i} \qquad \text{non-degenerate oscillators} \qquad (15\text{--}49)$$

Thus the equilibrium fraction of molecules with vibrational energy between E and $E + dE$ is (compare Eq. 43)

$$P(E)\, dE = \frac{N(E \text{ to } E + dE)}{N} = \frac{E^{s-1}\, dE \exp{(-E/kT)}}{(s-1)!\, (kT)^s} \qquad (15\text{--}50)$$

As noted above, this classical expression must not be extended to energies below $h\nu_i$ for any oscillator. It is not obvious what is the minimum energy that can be treated for the system of s oscillators. Clearly, some cut-off point of the order of magnitude of $\Sigma h\nu_i$ is required. The total zero-point energy

$$E_Z = \tfrac{1}{2} \Sigma\, h\nu_i \qquad (15\text{--}51)$$

has been suggested as the cut-off energy. Whitten and Rabinovitch[95] solved this problem "experimentally." They devised a computer program for the number of states. $G(E)$, and they calculated this quantity for a large number of molecules. They replace Eq. 45 by

$$G(E) = \frac{(E + aE_Z)^s}{s! \displaystyle\prod_{i=1}^{s} (h\nu_i)} \qquad (15\text{--}52)$$

where values of a for any molecule are readily found in terms of the spread in the frequencies $\langle \nu_i^2 \rangle / \langle \nu_i \rangle^2$ and other parameters given by Whitten and Rabinovitch. This approximate method gives results agreeing within 1 or 2 percent of those found by actual count for a large family of molecules. Similarly, one readily finds the density of states (Eq. 47), and the Boltzmann factor (Eq. 50).

A closely related method for obtaining these quantities (based on a slightly different manipulation of Eq. 45) has been proposed by Wahrhaftig et al.[96] This method is somewhat simpler than that of Whitten and Rabinovitch[95] for very small molecules (less than five atoms), but it becomes much more complicated for larger molecules. The results of this method agree very well with those of Whitten and Rabinovitch. Several other methods have been discussed for this problem; generally speaking, these methods are either less accurate or more laborious to apply than that of Whitten and Rabinovitch, whose method is recommended for general use.

For some purposes (Sections F and G below) it is convenient to use Kassel's degenerate oscillator model, even for a real molecule with a spread of frequencies. In this case one sees, by comparing Eqs. 48 and 49, that the appropriate frequency is the geometric mean:

$$\nu = \left(\prod_i^s \nu_i\right)^{1/s} \tag{15-53}$$

The classical-mechanical functions, Eqs. 44 through 50, fail very seriously for low energies. The physical nature of the failure is readily found. Equation 40 gives the number of ways to distribute $j\,h\nu$ energy among s identical oscillators; Eq. 47 gives the number of ways of distributing energy between E and $E + dE$ among s non-identical oscillators. If the energy specified is less than the smallest quantum, $h\nu_1$, there are zero ways for the molecule to accept this energy. If the energy specified is between the lowest frequency $h\nu_1$ and the next highest frequency $h\nu_2$, the number of oscillators that can accept the energy is not s but rather one. So long as the total energy is less than that of the highest-frequency oscillator, $h\nu_s$, then the total number of oscillators that can share the energy is less than s. If one uses Eqs. 44 or 47 as an approximation, then the parameter s is not a constant but a rapidly increasing function of energy, at low energies. Finally, as the total energy becomes very large compared to the high-frequency $h\nu_s$, then the classical relations, Eqs. 44 to 50, become good approximations. Molecules containing hydrogen typically have fundamental frequencies around 3000 cm^{-1} or around 9 kcal/mole. Thus one expects the classical relations to fail very seriously at chemically interesting energies.

(ii) Energy-Transfer Function b_i[97]

The simplest case of energy transfer is that for two free particles of mass m_1 and m_2 constrained to move in one dimension. Before collision the velocities are v_{10} and v_{20}, and after collision the velocities are v_{11} and v_{21}. Conservation of energy and conservation of momentum give the relations:

$$\tfrac{1}{2}m_1v_{10}^2 + \tfrac{1}{2}m_2v_{20}^2 = \tfrac{1}{2}m_1v_{11}^2 + \tfrac{1}{2}m_2v_{21}^2$$
$$m_1v_{10} + m_2v_{20} = m_1v_{11} + m_2v_{21}$$

For the special case of particle 1 initially at rest, the final velocities in terms of initial velocity of particle 2 are

$$v_2 = \frac{m_2 - m_1}{m_2 + m_1}v_{20} \qquad v_1 = \frac{2m_2}{m_2 + m_1}v_{20} \tag{15-54}$$

The energy transferred in this simple two-atom example depends only on the masses of the particles and not on the mechanism of the collision.

For the head-on collision of an atom with a diatomic molecule (a three-particle one-dimensional problem) the amount of energy transferred depends

on the mechanism of the collision process.   The model is given by Fig. 4.
The interaction of atom A with atom B is given by a potential-energy
function $V(R)$, and thus the force is

$$f = -\partial V/\partial R$$

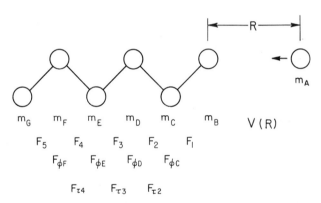

Fig. 15–4. Models for translational-vibrational energy transfer. Collinear
collision of an atom and diatomic molecule; collision of atom and polyatomic
molecule.   From the arguments of Landau and Teller, one sees from these models
that translational-vibrational energy transfer is much more probable for polyatomic molecules than for diatomic molecules.

The force exerted on atom C by atom B is Fr, where r is the distortion of the
bond length from its equilibrium value.   If the collision is "soft," that is,
if the force exerted by A on B is very slowly applied, then an infinitesimal
distortion of the bond length communicates the interaction from B to C.
The force of the collision is exerted almost equally on atom B and atom C,
and the molecule in this case rebounds very much the same way as did the
atom in the first example, Eq. 54, with no excitation of the oscillator.   On
the other hand, consider the case of a "hard collision"; that is, the duration

of collision and rebound of atom A on atom B is very short compared to the period of vibration of the molecule.   In this case, atom B is displaced, and the spring is compressed before atom C has had time to respond to the collision; maximum translational-vibrational energy transfer has occurred. These qualitative ideas of Landau and Teller[97] have been developed as a three-particle, three-dimensional, quantum-mechanical theory by Herzfeld[98] and co-workers.   This theory leads to the prediction that, for diatomic molecules such as N_2 at room temperature, it requires approximately 10^9

TABLE 15–1
Number of Collisions Z to Deactivate Molecule from Vibrational State $v = 1$ to $v = 0$

Gas	$T°K$	Z (calc.)	Z (obs.)
O_2	288	7.3×10^7	2.1×10^7
	1372	2.06×10^4	3.6×10^4
	1953	6400	12000
	2912	1900	1800
N_2	550	7.61×10^8	1.1×10^8
	778	7.30×10^7	6.5×10^6
	1020	1.22×10^7	4.5×10^6
	1168	3.03×10^6	2.3×10^6
	3640	23000	24000
	4630	8400	8000
Cl_2	288	1.8×10^5	3.4×10^4
	1000	2100	550
	1372	780	200

Data from K. F. Herzfeld and T. A. Litovitz, *Absorption and Dispersion of Ultrasonic Waves*, Academic Press, Inc., New York (1959), p. 324.

collisions to deactivate the molecule from the first excited vibrational state to the ground state.   Sample values of the $1 \rightarrow 0$ vibrational deactivation rate constants are given in Table 1, with a comparison of theoretical and experimental values.   Thus for diatomic molecules the qualitative discussion of vibrational-translational energy transfer as presented by Landau and Teller is confirmed by the somewhat complicated theory of Herzfeld, and for low-lying levels of diatomic molecules such energy transfer is an improbable process, requiring 10^6 or so collisions.

For polyatomic molecules the Landau-Teller argument can be extended—with different results.   One example is illustrated by Fig. 4.   For atom A to undergo a "soft" collision with the entire molecule, the "duration of collision" must be long enough for the impulse to be communicated through four angles, three internal rotations, and five bonds to atom G.   This requirement is far more restrictive than for the diatomic molecule.   A collision, "soft" with respect to atoms B and C, might still be very "hard" indeed with respect to atoms F and G. Thus one expects translational-vibrational energy transfer to be much more probable for polyatomic molecules than for diatomic molecules, although a detailed theoretical treatment is not available.

The best information available concerning vibrational energy transfer from polyatomic molecules comes from quenching of fluorescence[99] and from experiments with chemical activation.[100] "Given a polyatomic molecule A with a large excess of vibrational energy ΔE over the thermal mean value, what quantity E of this excess ΔE can be transferred on the average by a collision with a foreign molecule M?"[99] The stabilization of photo-excited β-naphthylamine by collision with foreign gases showed that the average amount of vibrational energy in kcal/mole removed per collision was [99]

$$\text{He, 0.2; } H_2, 0.2; \text{ } D_2, 0.14; \text{ } N_2, 0.5; \text{ } CO_2, 1.5; \text{ } NH_3, 3.0; \text{ } n\text{-}C_5H_{12}, 4.7;$$

$$CHCl_3, 3.5. \qquad \Delta E = 28 \text{ kcal/mole}$$

In an ingenious series of experiments involving chemical activation B. S. Rabinovitch and co-workers have illuminated every aspect of unimolecular reaction-rate theory. The chemical addition of a hydrogen atom to cis-butene-2 yields sec-butyl radicals[100] having excess vibrational energy of 40 kcal per mole. These chemically activated radicals could be stabilized by energy-transfer collisions (to react further in a known manner to produce observable stable products) or they could decompose with carbon-carbon bond rupture with a critical energy of 33 kcal per mole. Thus these experiments give the average number of collisions required to remove 7 kilocalories of vibrational energy. The interpretation of data is not completely free of ambiguities since highly excited molecules decompose faster than molecules with energy just above the threshhold, but even so the data are much more direct than either the fluorescence studies or regular kinetic studies. The average energy (kcal/mole) removed per collision in this case according to the "stepladder" model is[100]

$$\text{He, 2.5} \pm 0.5; \text{ Ne, 2.5; Ar, 3; Kr, 3.5; } H_2, D_2, N_2, 2.5; \text{ } CD_3F, CH_3Cl,$$

$$SF_6, C_4H_8, \geqslant 9. \qquad \Delta E = 40 \text{ kcal/mole.}$$

For the example of the isomerization of methyl isocyanide,[3] the average energy (Tolman's distribution) of molecules that react with an equilibrium distribution of excited reactants is only 2 to 2.5 kcal/mole above the critical energy, that is, the difference in activation energy between high-pressure and low-pressure limits. The critical energy itself is about 36 kcal/mole.

Thus one sees that the average collision of almost any foreign gas will de-activate an excited reactant by a sufficient amount to count as a "strong collision." To be sure, some reaction still occurs at energies above the high-pressure average value, and deactivation by He would still leave it above the critical energy. However the value of c_i at this lower energy is so much less than that of the higher energy that even this case is effectively "complete deactivation." Thus the traditional assumption of "strong collision" or "deactivation upon every collision" appears to be an excellent approximation for thermal, unimolecular reactions.

The conclusion is that the function b_i of Eq. 24 or 39 should be replaced by a collision-rate constant, perhaps the hard-sphere collision-rate constant or one based on close collisions subject to a realistic potential-energy function. As a newly justified simple expression, one writes the hard-sphere expression

$$b_i = b = \pi d^2 \left(\frac{8kT}{\pi \mu}\right)^{1/2} n_A \text{ cc/mole-sec} \qquad (15\text{-}55a)$$

or one should also consider the inverse sixth power of attraction (compare Eq. 14–15):

$$b_i = b = 2.71 b_{HS} (\varepsilon/kT)^{1/3} \qquad (15\text{-}55b)$$

The rate equation in this case is

$$\mathbf{R} = [A] \sum \frac{b P_i c_i [M]}{b[M] + c_i} \qquad (15\text{-}56)$$

One can interpret the high- and low-pressure rate constants as

$$\mathbf{k}_\infty = \sum P_i c_i \qquad (15\text{-}57)$$

$$\mathbf{k}_0' = b \sum P_i \qquad (15\text{-}58)$$

and one can evaluate the average molecular rate constant and average lifetime of excited molecules from experimental data:

$$\left(\frac{\mathbf{k}_\infty - \mathbf{k}}{\mathbf{k}}\right) b[M] = \langle c \rangle^T \qquad \text{average rate constant} \qquad (15\text{-}59)$$

$$\frac{\mathbf{k}_0' - \mathbf{k}'}{\mathbf{k}'} \frac{1}{b[M]} = \left\langle \frac{1}{c} \right\rangle^T \qquad \text{average lifetime} \qquad (15\text{-}60)$$

$$\mathbf{J} = \langle c \rangle^T \left\langle \frac{1}{c} \right\rangle^T \qquad (15\text{-}61)$$

Since the collision constant is known, these very definite interpretations of

TABLE 15–2

Average Rate Constants for Molecules That React at High Pressures

Molecule	Atoms in Molecule	$T°K$	E/RT	$\langle c \rangle_{av, \ sec^{-1}}$
N_2O	3	888	35	2.0×10^{10}
NO_2Cl	4	420	34	3.5×10^{10}
CH_3NC	6	504	38	2.0×10^{9}
N_2O_5	7	300	37	1.4×10^{9}
Cyclopropane	9	773	42	6.0×10^{7}
Cyclobutane	12	722	43	3.0×10^{6}

experimental data can be made. Values of the average molecular rate constant (hard-sphere model) for several molecules (Eq. 59) are given by Table 2. These interpretations are more general than and independent of the model or theory one uses to evaluate the functions P_i or c_i. The average lifetime for excited methyl isocyanide molecules at different pressures and temperatures are given by Fig. 5. At high pressures the equilibrium distribution over states is effectively maintained in spite of reaction, and the average lifetime of the molecules that react is 2×10^{-8} seconds or about 10^5 vibrational periods. At low pressures, reaction depletes the equilibrum distribution, and the steady-state distribution function between excitation and molecular isomerization is approached. The average lifetime (in the excited states) of the molecules that react is about 10^{-6} seconds, a very long time on the scale of molecular vibrations.

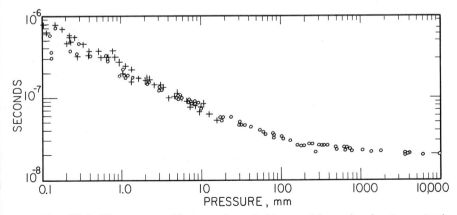

Fig. 15–5. The average lifetime of methyl isocyanide molecules in excited states: $\bigcirc = 503°K$; $+ = 533°K$.

(iii) Microscopic or Molecular Rate Constant c_i

The manner with which the decomposition rate of a polyatomic molecule increases with energy above the critical energy is one of the most interesting problems in the field of gas-phase kinetics. The theoretical approaches to this problem have been along two different lines: on the one hand, the problem is expressed in terms of transition probability and the density of vibrational quantum states; and on the other hand, the problem has been treated as one of molecular dynamics. A brief outline of these developments is given here, and the outline will be followed by a brief discussion of the simpler models.

Statistical models	References
Rice, Ramsperger, Kassel, 1928–32	62
Rice, Marcus, 1950–52	101
Rosenstock, Wallenstein, Wahrhaftig, Eyring, 1952	102
Rabinovitch, 1955–63	7, 95
Vestal, Wahrhaftig, Johnston, 1962	96

Dynamical models	
Polyani, Wigner, 1928	103
Slater, 1939–59	93

It is well known that statistical problems are much simpler than dynamical problems. Thus the models for which statistical treatments can be carried through are much more nearly realistic than the models used in dynamical theories.

(a) Rice-Ramsperger-Kassel Model.[62] Kassel's model is that of s oscillators all of the same frequency, ν (compare Eqs. 40 to 43). The oscillators are assumed to be coupled so that the state of the system is adequately given by the total vibrational energy, and its actual distribution over the oscillators is unimportant. The mechanism of this coupling is anharmonicity in the potential-energy function and finite displacements of bond lengths which then interact with the bending modes. The theory is a zero-order approximation: the energy is expressed in terms of the harmonic oscillator basis functions and the contribution of the coupling-perturbations is neglected.

Reaction cannot occur unless the molecule has m quanta of vibrational energy, that is, the critical energy is $mh\nu$. It is sometimes stated that the condition for reaction is m quanta in one bond; rather the condition is m quanta in some one fixed distribution. The condition could be in terms of a fixed combination of normal coordinates. Kassel presents physical arguments to the effect that for a given molecule, the molecular reaction rate is proportional to the probability that the molecule has m quanta out of

$m + i$ in one specified state and thus i quanta anywhere is s modes.

$$\begin{bmatrix} \text{specific molecular} \\ \text{reaction rate for} \\ \text{molecule with } m + i \\ \text{quanta} \end{bmatrix} \propto \frac{\begin{bmatrix} \text{number of ways to distri-} \\ \text{bute } m + i \text{ quanta over } s \\ \text{oscillators with } m \text{ locked in} \\ \text{one configuration} \end{bmatrix}}{\begin{bmatrix} \text{number of ways to distri-} \\ \text{bute } m + i \text{ quanta over } s \\ \text{oscillators} \end{bmatrix}} \quad (15\text{–}62)$$

$$c_i = D \frac{\dfrac{(i + s - 1)!}{i!\,(s - 1)!}}{\dfrac{(m + i + s - 1)!}{(m + i)!\,(s - 1)!}}$$

$$= D \frac{(m + i)!\,(i + s - 1)!}{i!\,(m + i + s - 1)!} \quad (15\text{–}63)$$

where D is the proportionality constant. By this assumption the quantum-state rate function c_i is separated into a constant with dimensions of sec^{-1} and a universal probability factor. The rate constant D is a mechanical property of the individual molecule. In the limit of classical mechanics, Eq. 63 becomes

$$c_i = D\left(\frac{E - E_c}{E}\right)^{s-1} \quad (15\text{–}64)$$

Use of Eqs. 44 and 64 leads to very serious errors, and Eqs. 43 and 63 are to be preferred.

The rate is thus given by

$$k = Db[\text{M}] \sum_{i=0}^{\infty} \frac{(1 - e^{-x})^s \dfrac{(i + s - 1)!}{i!\,(s - 1)!} \exp\left[-(m + i)x\right]}{b[\text{M}] + \dfrac{D(m + i)!\,(i + s - 1)!}{i!\,(m + i + s - 1)!}} \quad (15\text{–}65)$$

where x is $h\nu/kT$. The high-pressure limit is

$$k_\infty = De^{-mx} \sum_{i=0}^{\infty} (1 - e^{-x})^s \frac{(i + s - 1)!}{i!\,(s - 1)!} e^{-ix}$$

$$= De^{-mx} \quad (15\text{–}66)$$

The low-pressure limit is

$$\left(\frac{k}{[\text{M}]}\right)_0 = k_0' = b \sum_{i=0}^{\infty} (1 - e^{-x})^s \frac{(m + i + s - 1)!}{(m + i)!\,(s - 1)!} \exp\left[-(m + i)x\right]$$

$$\approx \frac{b(m + s - 1)!}{m!\,(s - 1)!} \frac{(1 - e^{-x})^s e^{-mx}}{\left(1 - \dfrac{m + s}{m + 1} e^{-x}\right)} \quad (15\text{–}67)$$

Experimental data can be interpreted by these relations with D found empirically as the "pre-exponential factor" at high pressures, m can be fitted empirically to the activation energy and s is taken to be the full $3N - 6$ oscillators.

(b) Evaluation of RRK Constant D.   In Rice-Ramsperger-Kassel theory the constant D in Eqs. 63 or 64 is an empirical factor to be determined from the rate constant at high pressure (Eq. 66).   By use of the same model as RRK, one can evaluate the constant D by means of activated-complex theory.[101,102]   The argument is most clearly presented for the case of identical quantized oscillators.   For a given energy $(m + i)h\nu$ above the zero-point energy of the reactant molecule, one may compare the multiplicity of the reactant with s oscillators,

$$\omega_{m+i} = \frac{(m + i + s - 1)!}{(m + i)! \, (s - 1)!} \tag{15-68}$$

with that for the activated complex with $s - 1$ oscillators and one reaction coordinate, an internal translation.   If the reaction coordinate has zero energy, the $s - 1$ oscillators have i quanta (since $mh\nu$ is the critical energy) and the multiplicity is

$$(\omega_i')^{\ddagger} = \frac{(i + s - 2)!}{i! \, (s - 2)!} \tag{15-69}$$

However, if the reaction coordinate has kinetic energy E_t^* equivalent to j quanta, the total number of states is (compare Eq. 44)

$$G^* = \frac{\delta}{\Lambda} = \frac{\delta p^*}{h} = \frac{\delta(2\mu E_t^*)^{1/2}}{h} \tag{15-70}$$

where δ is the arbitrarily defined "width" of the reaction coordinate and Λ is the de Broglie wavelength associated with translational momentum p^* or energy E_t^* (Chapter 2).   The density of translational states is (compare Eq. 46)

$$\rho^* = \frac{dG^*}{dE_t^*} = \frac{\delta}{2h} \left(\frac{2\mu}{E_t^*}\right)^{1/2} \tag{15-71}$$

and the multiplicity of the reaction coordinate with energy between E_t^* and $E_t^* + dE_t^*$ is

$$\omega^* = \frac{\delta}{2h} \left(\frac{2\mu}{E_t^*}\right)^{1/2} dE_t^* \tag{15-72}$$

For a complex with translational energy of magnitude $jh\nu$ directed from complex to reactant, the rate of crossing the dividing surface of width δ is (compare Eq. 8-27)

$$\mathbf{k}_{ij\ddagger} = \frac{p}{m\delta} = \frac{1}{\delta} \left(\frac{2E_t^*}{\mu}\right)^{1/2} \tag{15-73}$$

At complete chemical equilibrium (between reactants and products and over all quantum states), every molecular process and its exact reverse occur at the same average rate:

$$c_i[A(m + i)] = \sum_{k=0}^{i} k_{ij\ddagger}[X_{ij\ddagger}] \qquad (15\text{--}74)$$

Since each excited reactant $A(m + i)$ and each activated complex X_{ij} have the same total energy, their Boltzmann factor or equilibrium statistical ratio is simply the ratio of multiplicities (Eq. 6–2):

$$\frac{[X_{ij\ddagger}]}{[A(m + i)]} = \frac{\omega_{ij\ddagger}}{\omega_{m+i}} = \frac{(\omega_j^* \omega_k')_\ddagger}{\omega_{m+i}} \qquad (15\text{--}75)$$

where $k = i - j'$. When terms are collected, it is seen that there is extensive cancellation:

$$k_{ij\ddagger}\omega_j^* = \frac{dE_t^*}{h} = \nu_\ddagger \qquad (15\text{--}76)$$

The general expression for the molecular rate constant c_i is

$$c_i = \frac{\nu_\ddagger}{\omega_A} \sum_{k=0}^{i} \omega_{k\ddagger}' \qquad (15\text{--}77)$$

The summation in Eq. 77 is the total number of ways of distributing up to $ih\nu$ of energy in $s - 1$ oscillators, and it thus has the same physical interpretation as $G(E)$ in Eq. 44. The density of states of reactant is the multiplicity ω_A divided by the smallest definable interval $dE = h\nu$:

$$\rho = \omega/h\nu \qquad (15\text{--}78)$$

If the reactant and complex have the same frequency ν, then Eq. 77 takes the semiclassical form[102]

$$c(E) = \frac{G_\ddagger'(E - E_c)}{h\rho_A(E)} \qquad (15\text{--}79)$$

If the quantum, degenerate-frequency model is used throughout, the molecular rate constant is

$$c_i = \frac{\nu(s - 1)! \, (m + i)!}{(m + i + s - 1)!} \sum_{k=0}^{i} \frac{(k + s - 2)!}{k! \, (s - 2)!} \qquad (15\text{--}80)$$

Upon passing to the classical-mechanical limit, this expression becomes

$$c(E) = \nu \left(\frac{E - E_c}{E}\right)^{s-1} \qquad (15\text{--}81)$$

Comparison of Eq. 81 and Eq. 64 identifies the coefficient D of classical RRK theory with the oscillator frequency:

$$D = \nu \text{ (degenerate oscillator model)} \qquad (15\text{--}82)$$

If classical mechanics is used throughout (however, normalized by $h\nu$), this derivation can be carried through for a group of oscillators of different frequencies: $\nu_1, \nu_2 \cdots \nu_s$ for reactant; $\nu_{\ddagger 1}, \nu_{\ddagger 2} \cdots \nu_{\ddagger s-1}$ for activated complex.[102] The rate constant for reactants with energy E is

$$c(E) = \frac{\prod\limits^{s} \nu_i}{\prod\limits_{s-1} \nu_{j\ddagger}} \left(\frac{E - E_c}{E}\right)^{s-1} \tag{15-83}$$

In this case, Kassel's D is identified as the ratio of the product of $3N - 6$ frequencies of reactant to the product of $3N - 7$ frequencies of the activated complex:

$$D = \frac{\prod\limits^{s} \nu_i}{\prod\limits_{s-1} \nu_{j\ddagger}} \tag{15-84}$$

The expressions above for the molecular rate constant c (Eqs. 77, 79, 80, 81) were derived by use of the assumption of chemical equilibrium. However, this assumption is no restriction whatsoever on their validity. The constant c_i is the transition probability per unit time for a molecule A in a single internal-energy state i. The basic assumption is that energy is exchanged between internal degrees of freedom so rapidly that an energy specification is sufficient (rather than a detailed list of quantum numbers for each degree of freedom). Nothing in the derivation concerns the distribution of molecules over energy levels, and thus the mechanical rate constant c_i is the same whether molecules are distributed over energies according to an equilibrium or non-equilibrium distribution. This question leads to endless debates, and it will be stated in yet other words: Back at Eq. 63 there was a term c_i known to be a *constant* for the energy level i, but the value of the constant was unknown. Between Eqs. 73 and 75 it was shown that the value of this constant could be discovered, under conditions of chemical equilibrium (Eq. 77). However, this relation between constants is valid under all conditions (I discovered on Tuesday that $12/4 = 3$; I am not assuming it to be Tuesday upon any day I use this relation).

The values of the molecular rate function $c(E)$ for Kassel's quantized, degenerate oscillator model for nitryl chloride are given as a broad step function in Fig. 6, and the classical mechanical function is shown also. Nitryl chloride is a simple enough molecule that its vibrational[105] energy levels above the critical energy (taken as 29.8 kcal) can be counted to give $G^{\ddagger}(E - E_c)$ of Eq. 79, and the density of states for the reactant molecule $\omega(E)$ can readily be found by use of the convenient computer program (available upon request from B. S. Rabinovitch). In this way, the density of states was evaluated exactly, and the molecular rate function $c(E)$ as computed by Eq. 79 is plotted in Fig. 6 as the relatively irregular step function. At energy $E/E_c = 1.13$, this method is discontinued, since at higher energies the curve calculated by the approximate method of Whitten and Rabinovitch agrees with the "exact" curve within about one percent. The continuous approximation method of Whitten and Rabinovitch is in excellent agreement with that of Vestal, Wahrhaftig, and Johnston, and each

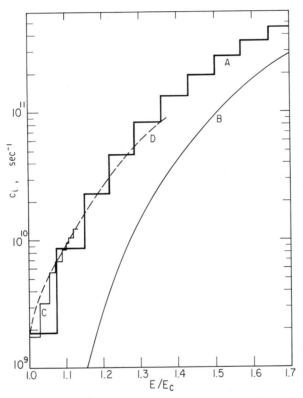

Fig. 15–6. Comparison of various methods of calculating how molecular rate constant for NO_2Cl varies with energy above the critical energy: A. Kassel's quantum model, degenerate oscillators; B. Rice-Ramsperger-Kassel classical model; C. Exact sum over states as evaluated by computer; D. Whitten and Rabinovitch's continuous approximation to exact sum over states.

of these is close to the "exact" step function shown in Fig. 6—with about the same intercept at the critical energy. Furthermore, these four methods, Kassel, exact count of states, Rabinovitch's method, and Wahrhaftig's method, give very similar plots of rate constant **k** against total pressure or [M].

(c) **Extensions of RRK Theory.** The derivation given above assumes that the activated complex is similar to the reactant in all internal degrees of freedom except one. An inspection of simple potential-energy surfaces shows this assumption to be a reasonable hope for certain isomerizations (Fig. 4–4), or for exothermic decompositions (Fig. 4–5). However, for breaking off of an atom or radical (Fig. 4–3), the activated complex is the same as that for recombination of radicals (Chapter 9) and is very far removed from the reactant. Considerations of this sort led Marcus and Rice[101] to distinguish between "rigid complexes" and "loose complexes." The derivations given above all refer to rigid complexes. The principles involved in going to "loose complexes" will be illustrated by one example below.

Consider the reaction to be the breaking of one bond:

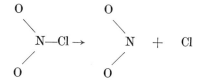

In this reactant, there are 4 atoms and 12 coordinates:

3 center of mass: X, Y, Z
3 rotations with principal axes I_1, I_2, I_3
6 vibrations

The activated complexes for this decomposition are the same as those for the recombination of NO_2 and Cl, and they can be found as the maximum in the effective potential energy (Chapters 7 and 9). The distribution of activated complexes as a function of angular momentum gives a fairly concentrated grouping about the most probable case. Thus the unimolecular decomposition problem can be treated as if there is but one activated complex. In the case here, separation of NO_2 and Cl at this most probable value is 4.5 Å, at which point the bending-force constant (Eq. 4–56) is essentially zero and the vibrational amplitude for the bending mode (Eq. 6–23 and Table 12–1) is far greater than 2π. Thus the degrees of freedom of the complex are

$$
\begin{array}{c}
O \\
\backslash \\
N\text{------------------------------}Cl \\
/ \\
O
\end{array}
$$

3 center of mass
3 rotations: I_1, I_2, I_3, of NO_2Cl
1 reaction coordinate
2 free rotations of NO_2: I_A, I_B
3 vibrations of NO_2

One rotation of NO_2 is identical with one rotation of NO_2Cl (on the long axis), and this rotation could be assigned to either. With this model, the internal energy of the reactant is specified as $(m + i)h\nu_A$; and the internal energy of the complex is:

$kh\nu$ vibrational quanta in NO_2

$jh\nu$ equivalents of rotational energy in I_A and I_B

$(i - j - k)h\nu$ equivalents of translational energy in the reaction coordinate

The equilibrium rate of forming the complex from reactant equals the reverse rate:

$$c_i[A(m + i)] = k_i[X_i] = \sum_{k=0}^{i} \sum_{j=0}^{i-k} k_{ijk}[X_{ijk}] \tag{15-85}$$

Solving for c_i, one finds

$$c_i = \sum_{k=0}^{i} \sum_{j=0}^{i-k} k_{ijk}\omega * \frac{(\omega_k \omega_j)_\pm}{(\omega_{m+i})_A} \tag{15-86}$$

Equation 76 is valid here also, so one has

$$c_i = \frac{\nu_+}{(\omega_{m+i})_A} \sum_{k=0}^{i} \sum_{j=0}^{i-k} (\omega_k \omega_j)^\dagger \tag{15-87}$$

The rotational energy levels are treated by classical mechanics; the multiplicity is

$$\omega_j = \frac{8\pi^2 (I_A I_B)^{1/2}}{\sigma h^2} dE_r \tag{15-88}$$

and the molecular rate constant is

$$c_i = \frac{\nu_+}{(\omega_{m+1})_A} \sum_{k=0}^{i} \omega_k \int_0^{(i-k)h\nu} \frac{8\pi^2 (I_A I_B)^{1/2}}{\sigma h^2} dE_r \tag{15-89}$$

$$= \frac{8\pi^2 (I_A I_B)^{1/2} h\nu}{\sigma h^2} \frac{\nu_+}{\omega_{m+i}} \sum_{k=0}^{i} (i - k)\omega_k$$

By use of the degenerate oscillator model, this expression takes the explicit form

$$c_i = \frac{8\pi^2 (I_A I_B)^{1/2} \nu^2}{\sigma h} \frac{(m + i)! \, (s - 1)!}{(m + i + s - 1)!} \sum_{k=0}^{i} (i - k) \frac{(k + s - 4)!}{k! \, (s - 4)!} \tag{15-90}$$

In the limit of classical mechanics, the summation becomes $i^{s-2}/(s - 2)!$ and the molecular rate constant is

$$c(E) = \frac{8\pi^2 (I_A I_B)^{1/2} \nu^3 (s - 1)}{\sigma} \frac{(E - E_c)^{s-2}}{E^{s-1}} \tag{15-91}$$

(d) Theory of N. B. Slater.[93] The RRK theory and its extensions are deliberately vague about the mechanism whereby an excited reactant molecule passes to the "activated complex" or to the products. These theories relate molecular rate constants c_i to relative density of vibrational states. If this relation is a valid one, then it is not necessary to specify the mechanism whereby excited molecules move on a constant-energy surface to become products. To judge the degree of validity of the RRK assumption, one needs to understand the dynamics of the process, at least for certain cases. It is here that N. B. Slater has made an elegant contribution to chemical kinetics. Starting with a clearly stated, artificial model, Slater has solved the dynamical problem (classical mechanics) of how fast excited molecules become activated complexes. The model used is unrealistic, and thus one should never expect Slater theory exactly to fit experimental data.

Slater expresses all motions of the excited molecule in terms of the normal coordinates of the molecule. The reaction coordinate is defined as a linear combination of normal coordinates. For a simple three-atom molecule, the reaction coordinate is the breaking of one bond and would be given by an appropriate superposition of symmetric and antisymmetric stretching normal modes. The condition for reaction is that the reaction coordinate attain a certain critical extension (contrast this clear-cut physical statement with the vague statement of RRK theory about m quanta of energy constrained in an unspecified, unique way). The molecule is regarded as purely harmonic up to the breaking point, and then the molecule is regarded as having reacted. Figure 7 shows both a one-dimensional and a two-dimensional expression of this reaction condition; the dotted lines show the continuation of the quadratic potential-energy functions.

The mathematical calculations are carried out using the full quadratic potential-energy functions, that is, including the dotted line portions in Fig. 7, and regarding the critical extension of the reacting bond R_c as a hypothetical "dividing surface" (Chapter 8). At the end of one collision, the molecule as a whole has some fixed internal energy, and according to Slater's model each normal mode has a certain constant energy and phase. At the end of another collision, the state of the molecule and its normal modes are changed. Between two collisions, the total energy of the excited molecule can be visualized as a "frozen lake" including a full ellipse (solid and dotted, in Fig. 7). The vibrations of the molecule are represented by a "skater" on the surface of the constant-energy ellipse. The trajectory of the "skater" is given by the sum of the two normal coordinates, each of fixed energy and with initial phases set by the collision. With this model, the representative point would eventually cross in the positive direction, the line representing the critically extended bond R_1^* and then later cross it again in the negative direction. Over a long period of time the representative point would cross the dividing line R_1^* a large number of times, and one can evaluate the average frequency of crossing the line. One-half this average frequency of crossing the line can be identified with average frequency with which the excited molecule decomposes.

The mathematical problem is set up as follows: the extension of the reaction coordinate R^* is expressed as a linear combination of normal coordinates, that is, as a sum of weighted sine functions. The difference $R^* - R_c^*$ is formulated. This function is negative for the molecule, zero when the reaction coordinate attains its critical value, and positive when the reaction coordinate is in the hypothetical region shown dotted in Fig. 6.

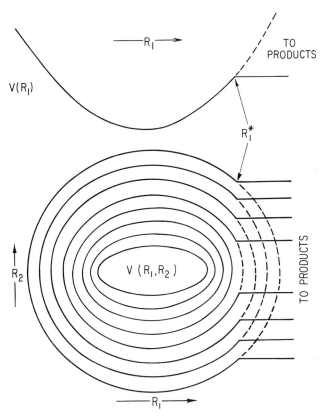

Fig. 15–7. One-dimensional model of N. B. Slater's reaction coordinate, which is quadratic up to the point of dissociation. Two-dimensional potential-energy surface illustrating Slater's model, which is quadratic (concentric-ellipse potential-energy contours) up to critical extension of one bond.

The function $R^* - R_c^*$ will be zero both for upward-directed crossings of the critical surface and for downward-directed crossings. Slater used a general mathematical result due to Kac, wherein he evaluated the number of zeros of this function over a long period of time. The average frequency of zeros of the function is the limit of the total number divided by the time as the time becomes very large. One-half this frequency of zeros is the average rate of decomposition of the molecule, with the specified initial state. To get the rate constant for a specified energy, one must average over all ways the normal modes can give the energy. Slater found

$$c(E) = \langle v \rangle \left(\frac{E - E_c}{E} \right)^{n-1} \qquad \text{if } E > E_c$$
$$= 0 \qquad \qquad \qquad \text{if } E < E_c$$

$$(15\text{--}92)$$

The form is the same as in RRK theory. The frequency in Slater's theory is an average over the normal modes that contribute to the reaction coordinate, where the weighting factors of the average frequency are related to the weighting factors of the normal modes in their contribution to the reaction coordinate. The number n is the number of normal coordinates that contribute to the reaction coordinate.

Slater's result Eq. 92 is to be compared with the Rice-Ramsperger-Kassel-Marcus-Rosenstock expression, Eq. 83. Each considers the molecule to have a spread of normal-mode frequencies and each is classical-mechanical. The average frequencies differ somewhat, and the dependence on energy is not identical if the number of oscillators differs. By virtue of interchange of energy among the normal-mode coordinates, RRK theory calls for all oscillators of the molecule. By virtue of his (unrealistic) assumption about independent normal modes, Slater's effective number of oscillators may be less than the total number. The important point is that Slater's theory of molecular dynamics gives essentially the same form of $c(E)$ as RRK theory based on molecular statistics.

In his book[93] and numerous papers, Slater gives details of his theory (actually, he has several different theories) with extensive model calculations. The physical model behind the mathematical theory, taken literally, asserts that no interchange of energy takes place between normal coordinates of highly excited, widely vibrating molecules. The literal aspects of this model are not to be taken seriously; but one should not judge the theory on this ground. One should study this theory of the frequency and distribution of zeros of $R^* - R_c^*$ not so much to calculate rate constants as to educate oneself concerning molecular dynamics (as noted in the Preface, chemists are determined to understand the molecular dynamics of chemical change).

D.   HIGH-PRESSURE LIMIT OF UNIMOLECULAR REACTION RATES

At the high-pressure limit of a unimolecular reaction, the distribution of excited molecules over the states responsible for the observable reaction is essentially the equilibrium distribution function. With respect to Eq. 24, for example, the condition is stated as

$$b_i[\text{M}] \gg c_i \qquad (15\text{--}93)$$

This inequality must be true for all states for which the contribution to the reaction is observable. The increasing function c_i (Eq. 63) is multiplied by the exponentially decreasing function P_i (Eq. 43) to give Tolman's distribution of molecules that react T_i. For very high energies, T_i may be negligible at low temperatures, and thus Eq. 93 is for all states that count, at some moderate pressure. At high temperatures, the distribution function is broadened, and high values of c_i now contribute measurably to the population that reacts. For this condition, Eq. 93 will demand a higher gas density [M] than at lower temperatures. Thus the pressure that gives Eq. 93 as a good approximation must increase with increasing temperature; and at any temperature the existence of a high-pressure limit is a good approximation, not the literal satisfaction of Eq. 93 for all states.

The high-pressure rate constant can be expressed in the form

$$\mathbf{k} = \mathbf{B} \exp{(-W/RT)} \qquad (15\text{--}94)$$

where $\mathbf{B}$ is not necessarily temperature-independent. Within the framework of classical mechanics, N. B. Slater has shown by a rigorous mathematical analysis that, if $\mathbf{B}$ is literally temperature-independent, then the molecular rate function must be of the form

$$c(E) = \mathbf{B}\left(\frac{E - W}{E}\right)^{s-1} \qquad (15\text{--}95)$$

Thus one can immediately write down the high-pressure limit for all classical-mechanical cases discussed above. To summarize examples already considered, one notes:

$\mathbf{B} = D$, empirical, RRK, quantum (Eq. 66)

$\mathbf{B} = \nu$, RRKM, quantum theory, all ν's equal (Eq. 81)

$\mathbf{B} = \prod\limits^{s} \nu / \prod\limits^{s-1} \nu^{\ddagger}$, Rosenstock et al., classical (Eq. 83)

$\mathbf{B} = \langle \nu \rangle$, Slater, classical (Eq. 92)

One need not go by way of an analysis of the three functions, P_i, c_i, and b_i, to evaluate the high-pressure rate constant by means of activated-complex theory. The rate constant as an example of the ultrasimple Eq. 8–29 is

$$\mathbf{k}_{\infty} = \frac{kT}{h}\frac{f'_{\ddagger}}{f} \exp{(-E_c/kT)} \qquad (15\text{--}96)$$

As discussed in Chapter 8, this theory asserts that one and only one normal mode of the complex determines the molecular rate constant, and the partition functions of all other normal modes merely measure parallel paths of reaction or "density of states with equal transition probability." If all normal modes of the complex contribute to the molecular rate function, then the rate expression as an example of Eq. 8–35 is

$$\mathbf{k}_{\infty} = \langle \kappa \nu \rangle_{\ddagger} \frac{f_{\ddagger}}{f} \exp{(-E_c/kT)} \qquad (15\text{--}97)$$

that is, the frequency factor is an average over all normal modes.   Clearly, the latter (Eq. 97) is more general than the former (Eq. 96).   N. B. Slater's dynamical, high-pressure theory is an elegant, easily understood example of how all normal-mode frequencies may enter the rate expression in a general theory.

In all cases cited above, except Eqs. 96 and 97, the pre-exponential factor is of the order of magnitude of the vibration frequencies of the reactant molecule.   In Eq. 96 this factor is kT/h, itself the order of magnitude of vibrational frequencies, multiplied by the ratio of partition functions

TABLE 15–3

The Number of Examples of Various Values of Frequency Factor or Pre-Exponential Factor for Unimolecular Gas-Phase Decompositions

log A, sec⁻¹	Molecular Products, Number of Reactions*	Radical Products, Number of Reactions
9.5 to 10.4	3	
10.5 to 11.4	3	
11.5 to 12.4	4	1
12.5 to 13.4	19	15
13.5 to 14.4	6	7
14.5 to 15.4	5	5
15.5 to 16.4	4	1
16.5 to 17.5		1

* This distribution is based on Table XI.4 and XI.5 in S. W. Benson's *Foundations of Chemical Kinetics*, McGraw-Hill Book Company, New York (1960).

between complex and reactant.   S. W. Benson[104] tabulated the frequency factor for forty-four unimolecular decompositions that lead to stable molecular products; the distribution for frequency factors is given by Table 3.   Nineteen cases out of forty-four are between $10^{12.5}$ to $10^{13.5}$, and twenty-nine cases out of forty-four are between $10^{11.5}$ to $10^{14.5}$, which fairly well covers the range of vibrational frequencies.   Thus the predictions of simple RRK or Slater treatment are confirmed for a large majority of cases.   However, six cases occur at low frequencies, $10^{9.5}$ to $10^{11.5}$, and nine cases occur at high frequencies, $10^{14.5}$ to $10^{16.5}$.   In terms of activated-complex theory, the high-frequency factors are explained in terms of "looser" activated complexes than reactants, for example, torsional oscillations of the reactant become free internal rotations of the complex or the reactant is ring compound and the complex is a chain.   Low-frequency factors are usually explained in terms of reactant as a chain compound with the complex as a ring.   Table 3 also gives a list of cases where the reaction products are free radicals.   Most frequency factors are near that of molecular vibration frequencies, but some factors are high.

The source of "high-frequency factors" for a unimolecular reaction is readily seen from the example of an endothermic decomposition. For the example discussed above, the reactant is the rigid-framework molecule $ClNO_2$ whereas the complex involves the NO_2 radical rotating freely in three dimensions. The classical expression for the molecular rate constant has been given by Eq. 91. The probability function is given by Eq. 50; or, if one acknowledges the difference in moments of inertia for the molecule $ClNO_2$ and the complex $Cl \cdots\cdots NO_2$, the expression is

$$P(E)\, dE = \left[\frac{(I_1 I_2 I_3)_{\ddagger}}{(I_1 I_2 I_3)_A}\right]^{1/2} \frac{E^{s-1} \exp{(-E/kT)}}{(s-1)!\,(kT)^s}\, dE \qquad (15\text{--}98)$$

The classical-mechanical rate constant at the high-pressure limit is

$$
\begin{aligned}
k_\infty &= \int_{E_c}^{\infty} c(E) P(E)\, dE \\
&= \frac{8\pi^2 (I_A I_B)^{1/2} \nu^3}{\sigma k T}\left[\frac{(I_1 I_2 I_3)_{\ddagger}}{(I_1 I_2 I_3)_A}\right]^{1/2} \exp{(-E_c/kT)} \qquad (15\text{--}99)
\end{aligned}
$$

This classical-mechanical expression, of course, does not contain Planck's constant h. However, one can multiply and divide by h^{s+6} to convert mechanical quantities ν, I, I/I, M/M to partition functions or partition-function ratios:

$$k_\infty = \frac{kT}{h}\frac{(f_t^3 f_r^3 f_{\text{int rot}}^2 f_v^{s-3})_{\ddagger}}{(f_t^3 f_r^3 f_v^s)_A}\exp{(-E_c/kT)} \qquad (15\text{--}100)$$

For the NO_2Cl example, the ratio $[(I_1 I_2 I_3)^{\ddagger}/(I_1 I_2 I_3)_A]^{1/2}$ gives a factor of 4.2; and the ratio $(f_{\text{int rot}}^2 f_v^{s-3})_{\ddagger}/(f_v^s)_A$ gives a factor about 10^2 at $500°K$. Thus for this case, a frequency factor of about 10^{15} to 10^{16} sec^{-1} is to be expected.

E. LOW-PRESSURE LIMIT OF UNIMOLECULAR REACTIONS

At the low-pressure limit of a unimolecular reaction, the distribution of excited molecules over the states responsible for observable reaction is a steady-state function. The rate of activation to a given state is $a_i[A][M]$, and the rate of reaction is $c_i[A_i^*]$. The distribution function is thus

$$Q_i = [A_i^*]/[A] = a_i[M]/c_i \qquad (15\text{--}101)$$

The condition for the low-pressure limit is

$$b_i[M] \ll c_i \qquad (15\text{--}102)$$

This inequality must be true for all states for which the contribution to the reaction is observable. If some state has a rate constant c_i that is vanishingly small, it will not conform to Eq. 102, but it will also give a vanishingly small contribution to the observed rate. If the pressure were reduced much more, this vanishingly small contribution would be added to the finite value of k_0', making no difference to its observed value. Thus the low-pressure limit can be realized in practice, even though Eq. 102 may not be literally valid for all quantum states.

Under any conditions, the rate is the sum of $c_i[A_i^*]$ over all states, and at the low-pressure limit this is simply

$$k_0 = \frac{R}{[A]} = [M] \sum a_i \qquad (15\text{--}103)$$

The observed rate at low pressures is the rate of activation, that is, purely energy-transfer rate. The molecular rate constant function c_i or $c(E)$ drops completely out of the rate expression. It must be recalled that the energy-transfer rate constants depend on identity of energy-transfer catalyst. If the reaction is being studied with only pure reactant present, the initial rate is $[A]^2 \sum_i a_{iA}$. If a foreign gas M is present, the initial rate is

$$R = [A]\left\{[A] \sum_i a_{iA} + [M] \sum_i a_{iM}\right\}$$
$$= [A]\{a_A[A] + a_M[M]\} \qquad (15\text{--}104)$$

If the rate is studied as a function of total concentration C with constant mole fractions of A and M, the initial rate is

$$R = [A]\{a_A X_A + a_M(1 - X_A)\}C \qquad (15\text{--}105)$$

With pure reactant, the low-pressure limit is

$$a_A = \lim_{[A] \to 0} (R/[A]^2) \qquad (15\text{--}106)$$

With A and M, the low-pressure limit is

$$a_A X + a_M(1 - X) = \lim_{C \to 0} (R/[A]C) \qquad (15\text{--}107)$$

From two separate series of experiments one can obtain both a_A and a_M (compare Fig. 1–14). The relative energy-transfer efficiency a_M/a_A is thus obtainable. Values of this relative efficiency is given for three representative unimolecular decompositions in Table 4.

The rate at the low-pressure limit is the rate of activation of a polyatomic molecule by collision. The nature of this process is totally different from that measured at the high pressure limit. To date, no serious theory has been put forward to explain this excitation of polyatomic molecules. Wigner's discussion of recombination of iodine atoms[85] suggests the general viewpoint: one wants to discuss the complete Hamiltonian function of the reactant molecule A inside the complete Hamiltonian of the collision pair A·M. As the collision pair moves on a constant-energy surface during a collision, the rate process of interest is the changing Hamiltonian of the reactant. This multidimensional process involves the potential of interaction of A with M for many angles of approach as well as the potential-energy functions of the isolated molecules.

TABLE 15–4

Relative Efficiency of Various Foreign Gases in Energy Transfer as Measured at Low-Pressure Limit of Unimolecular Reactions

NO_2Cl		N_2O_5		N_2O	
M	a_M/a_A	M	a_M/a_A	M	a_M/a_A
NO_2Cl[a]	1.00	N_2O_5[b]	1.00	N_2O[c]	1.00
He	0.25	He	0.12	He	0.66
Ne	0.18	Ne	0.09	Ne	0.47
Ar	0.21	Ar	0.14	Ar	0.20
Kr	0.21	Kr	0.16	Kr	0.18
Xe	0.26	Xe	0.15		
H_2	0.34				
N_2	0.29	N_2	0.23	N_2	0.24
O_2	0.26	NO	0.30	O_2	0.23
Cl_2	0.34				
HCl	0.51			H_2O	1.5
CO_2	0.39	CO_2	0.40	CO_2	1.3
N_2O	0.41				
NO_2	1.24				
SiF_4	0.46				
SF_6	0.36	SF_6	0.32		
CCl_2F_2	0.49	CCl_4	0.55		

a. Milton Volpe and H. S. Johnston, *J. Am. Chem. Soc.* **78**, 3903 (1956).

b. D. J. Wilson and H. S. Johnston, *J. Am. Chem. Soc.* **75**, 5673 (1953); H. S. Johnston, *J. Am. Chem. Soc.* **75**, 1567 (1953).

c. M. Volmer and M. Bogdan, *Z. Phys. Chem.* **21***B*, 257 (1933); M. Volmer and H. Froechlich, *Z. Phys. Chem.* **19***B*, 89 (1932).

Specifically, it should be noted that there is no activated-complex theory for this process of excitation of a polyatomic molecule. Indeed the whole concept of an activated complex or any configurational criterion for reaction seems to be completely empty. This is one of many examples wherein the activated-complex theory is not the absolute theory of reaction rates. Overinflated claims for activated-complex theory have caused many serious chemists to reject the whole method, whereas actually, activated-complex theory is a simple, useful computational device that should take its place along with other methods in every kineticist's "bag of tricks."

F.   FALL-OFF REGION OF A UNIMOLECULAR REACTION

One may write Eq. 8–69 for a unimolecular rate constant:

$$\mathbf{k} = \frac{f'_{\ddagger} \, \Gamma^*}{f} \frac{kT}{h} \exp\left(-E_0/kT\right) \qquad \langle \kappa \rangle^B \qquad \langle 1 + \phi \rangle^T \qquad (15\text{–}108)$$

rate of crossing the flat-top dividing surface between reactants and products for an equilibrium distribution of reactants	average fraction of systems that cross the dividing surface and become products without recrossing the surface	Tolman-average departure from an equilibrium distribution on the reactant side of the dividing surface

In Chapter 8 it was proposed to take this equation fairly seriously, so long as quantum corrections were not too large.   In particular, this formulation gives a very precise definition to the average value of κ.   Activated-complex theory as usually used does not calculate the rate of reaction, but rather the rate of crossing a saddlepoint or other flat dividing surface.   For every crossing, the system may or may not become a product, depending on all of the potential-energy surface between activated complex and products. The molecular state function κ_i for a given crossing is either zero or one, but the average of these factors over a Boltzmann distribution of incident systems for all crossings is the term $\langle \kappa \rangle^B$.   As further discussed in Chapter 8, the reactant side of the dividing surface may or may not have an equilibrium distribution over states.   The departure from equilibrium may come about from depletion of a state of the reactant by chemical reaction, by failure to dissipate the heat of reaction, or by the "shadow effect" of portions of the potential-energy surface between reactant and complex.   The molecular rate constants c_i in Kassel's theory are mechanical functions of isolated molecules.   In terms of Eq. 8–69 or 108, the "fall-off" all resides in the term $\langle 1 + \phi \rangle^T$ and not at all in the term $\langle \kappa \rangle^B$.   The fall-off with pressure is a consequence of the changing distribution function of excited molecules from the equilibrium value of a_i/b_i to the steady-state value $a_i[M]/c_i$.

Suppose one had a unimolecular reaction at total chemical equilibrium between reactants and products—but at a low total pressure such that Eq. 102 is valid.   At complete chemical equilibrium, all excited states of reactants, products, and activated complexes would have the equilibrium distribution over states.   In this case, the rate of crossing the transition state is the average of $c(E)$ over the equilibrium distribution function, that is, the same as at the high-pressure limit.   Suppose one hypothetically removed all products in this situation.   The rate of reaction $c_i[A_i]$ is, by postulate, much faster than the rate of activation $a_i[A][M]$, and thus reaction would rapidly deplete the excited states.   The distribution function for excited reactants would collapse from the equilibrium function P_i to the non-equilibrium, steady-state function $a_i[M]/c_i$.   For typical well-studied cases, such as N_2O_5 or CH_3NC, this hypothetical truncation of products would cause a decrease in rate constant by about a factor of 10^3 or 10^4. In this case, it is usually not profitable to apply activated-complex theory to the entire macroscopic rate constant (Eq. 108). However, it is useful to follow Henry Eyring's rule of regarding each non-equilibrium state i as a "separate species"; and as noted in connection with Eqs. 80 and 90, this use of activated-complex theory gives expressions for the microscopic, molecular rate constants c_i, which must then be summed over the actual, non-equilibrium distribution function.

PROBLEM

Assume that a nonlinear triatomic molecule ion is produced in the mass spectrometer with vibrational energy of 5.20 electron volts. Assume the molecule ion and the decomposition fragments have the following properties

	(A———B———C)$^+$		(A—B)$^+$	(A—B)	(B—C)$^+$	(B—C)
R, Å	1.4	1.2	1.2	1.3	1.2	1.2
$10^{-5}F$, dyne/cm	5.0	4.5	6.0	5.5	4.5	4.5
$10^{11}F_\theta$, erg/rad^2	0.40 $\times$ 10^{-11}					
M, amu	15	14	16			

Assume the energies of the following reactions to be:

$$(A—B—C)^+ \rightarrow (A—B)^+ + C \qquad 4.0 \text{ ev}$$
$$\rightarrow A—B + C^+ \qquad 4.8 \text{ ev}$$
$$\rightarrow A + (B—C)^+ \qquad 3.6 \text{ ev}$$
$$\rightarrow A^+ + B—C \qquad 4.6 \text{ ev}$$

Calculate the expected mass spectrum for this case.

16
Theory of Complex Reactions

From Chapters 2 through 15, the theories of reaction rates concerned the theory of elementary chemical reactions. The derivations in Chapter 8 are concerned with phase-space trajectory during a single collision, averaged over all such trajectories. In the interpretation of kinetic data for representative systems (in Chapter 10, for example), considerable effort was involved in showing that the observed rates were the rates of elementary reactions. Most chemical processes are complex reactions. This viewpoint was emphasized in Chapter 1. The treatment of multistep reactions systems is discussed in Appendix A from three points of view relative to the species intermediate between laboratory reactants and products: (1) intermediates described by simultaneous, multivariable, differential equations; (2) the steady-state assumption is made for the intermediates; and (3) the intermediates are assumed to be in chemical equilibrium with reactants. The method of simultaneous differential equations is rigorous, but exceedingly complex in most situations. The third method or equilibrium assumption for intermediates is very simple, but often grossly incorrect. The steady-state method occupies an important intermediate position. It is simple enough to be applied to many practical situations, and it provides criteria to determine when the simpler equilibrium assumption may be used. If one makes model calculations by the first method, one can know when the steady-state method is a good approximation.

When the steady-state treatment is applied to a complex reaction, the resulting rate expression may appear as a complex function of elementary rate constants, for example, Eq. 1–77. The theory of reaction rates applies to the rate constants of the elementary reactions, and each elementary rate constant in the complex rate expression may be replaced by its theoretical form. With confidence, one can proceed in this direction: $12 + 4 - 7 = x$; what is x? On the other hand, various attempts have been made to bypass resolution of the complex reaction into its steps, to apply theory directly to complex reactions, and there is a theorem about *the* reaction with the highest potential-energy barrier being *the* rate-determining step. Direct application of theory to complex reaction systems sometimes leads one to self-deception and false conclusions: $x \pm y \pm z = 57$; what are x, y, and z? In this chapter, activated-complex theory is applied to the elementary rate constants in known complex mechanisms in order to evaluate the applicability of activated-complex theory to complex reactions as a whole.

There is another way in which the difficult molecular details of reactions are replaced by thermodynamic quantities: the evaluation of entropies of activation, enthalpies of activation, and free energies of activation. When applied to elementary reactions, these variables make some sense. The enthalpy of activation is the average energy (above reactants) of the molecules that react, and the entropy of activation is a measure of the number of "parallel" reaction paths or "density of states" that have equal molecular transition probabilities. This formalism is reviewed in this chapter. However, when complex reactions are treated by thermodynamic methods, without resolution of mechanism by the steady-state analysis, confusion may be brought into the picture.

A. COMPLEX MECHANISMS AND PARTITION-FUNCTION RATE EXPRESSIONS

(i) Nitrogen Pentoxide

In Chapter 1, four complex reactions involving N_2O_5 (**1**, **2**, **3**, **4**), were expressed in terms of six elementary steps, (A, B, e, f, g, h). The mechanisms in the sense of steps are

$$
\begin{array}{l}
\textbf{1.}\ A, B, e, f \text{ with steady-state NO, } NO_3 \\
\textbf{2.}\ A, B, f \text{ with steady-state } NO_3 \\
\textbf{3.}\ h, B \text{ with steady-state } NO_3 \\
\textbf{4.}\ A, B, g, h \text{ with steady-state } NO_2, NO_3
\end{array}
\qquad (16\text{-}1)
$$

From a steady-state analysis of the mechanism the rate of the laboratory reaction **3** is that of the elementary reaction, h, Eq. 1–96. Thus one is able at this point to write the laboratory reaction **3** in terms of the ultrasimple theory, Eq. 8–29:

$$
\mathbf{R}_3 = \frac{kT}{h} \frac{f^{\ddagger}_{NO_2 \cdot O_3}}{f_{NO_2} f_{O_3}} \exp\left(-\varepsilon_h / kT\right)[NO_2][O_3]
\qquad (16\text{-}2)
$$

The steady-state analysis of the complex rate expression for reaction **2** gives the rate expression (Eq. 1–80):

$$
\mathbf{R}_2 = \frac{Af[NO][N_2O_5]}{B[NO_2] + f[NO]}
\qquad (16\text{-}3)
$$

Each of the three elementary rate constants A, B, and f may be expressed in terms of Eq. 8–29 and substituted in Eq. 3. For this one case the full substitution and resulting cancellations will be analyzed in detail:

$$\mathbf{R_2} = \frac{\dfrac{kT}{h}\dfrac{f^{\ddagger}_{N_2O_5}}{f_{N_2O_5}}\exp\left(-\varepsilon_A/kT\right)\dfrac{kT}{h}\dfrac{f^{\ddagger}_{NO\cdot NO_3}}{f_{NO}f_{NO_3}}\exp\left(-\varepsilon_f/kT\right)[NO][N_2O_5]}{\dfrac{kT}{h}\dfrac{f^{\ddagger}_{N_2O_5}}{f_{NO_2}f_{NO_3}}\exp\left(-\varepsilon_B/kT\right)[NO_2]+\dfrac{kT}{h}\dfrac{f^{\ddagger}_{NO\cdot NO_3}}{f_{NO}f_{NO_3}}\exp\left(-\varepsilon_f/kT\right)[NO]} \tag{16–4}$$

The partition function for the free-radical intermediate cancels, one power of kT/h cancels, and every observed concentration term takes on a corresponding partition function to give the "absolute activity" $[A]/f_A$:

$$\mathbf{R_2} = \frac{\dfrac{kT}{h}\dfrac{[N_2O_5]}{f_{N_2O_5}}\dfrac{[NO]}{f_{NO}}f^{\ddagger}_{N_2O_5}f^{\ddagger}_{NO\cdot NO_3}\exp\left[-(\varepsilon_A+\varepsilon_f)/kT\right]}{\dfrac{[NO_2]}{f_{NO_2}}f^{\ddagger}_{N_2O_5}\exp\left(-\varepsilon_B/kT\right)+\dfrac{[NO]}{f_{NO}}f^{\ddagger}_{NO\cdot NO_3}\exp\left(-\varepsilon_f/kT\right)} \tag{16–5}$$

In the final complex rate expression, the partition functions of two different activated complexes occur. By "flooding" with nitrogen dioxide the rate of reaction **2** becomes

$$\mathbf{R_2} = \frac{kT}{h}\frac{\dfrac{[N_2O_5]}{f_{N_2O_5}}\dfrac{[NO]}{f_{NO}}}{\dfrac{[NO_2]}{f_{NO_2}}}f^{\ddagger}_{NO\cdot NO_3}\exp\left[-(\varepsilon_A+\varepsilon_f-\varepsilon_B)/kT\right] \tag{16–6}$$

For this special, flooded situation there is only one activated complex, $NO\cdot NO_3$ for reaction f, for which the empirical formula is N_2O_4. The sum and difference of atoms in the observed rate law is

$$2N + 5O + N + O - N - 2O = 2N + 4O \tag{16–7}$$

which gives the empirical formula of the activated complex in step f. The complex rate expression has the form

$$\mathbf{R_2} = \frac{fA}{B}\frac{[N_2O_5][NO]}{[NO_2]} = Kf\frac{[N_2O_5][NO]}{[NO_2]} \tag{16–8}$$
$$= f[NO_3][NO]$$

For this case, the observed rate law gives the empirical formula of the activated complex in the "rate-determining step"; the mechanism is reduced to a pre-equilibrium and a rate-determining step. By flooding with nitric oxide the rate of reaction **2** becomes A, an elementary reaction:

$$\mathbf{R_2} = \frac{kT}{h}\frac{[N_2O_5]}{f_{N_2O_5}}f^{\ddagger}_{N_2O_5}\exp\left(-\varepsilon_A/kT\right) \tag{16–9}$$

The steady-state analysis of reaction **1** gives the rate expression (Eq. 1–79)

$$\mathbf{R_1} = \frac{Ae}{B + 2e} [\mathrm{N_2O_5}] \tag{16-10}$$

Substitution of partition functions for the elementary rate constants gives

$$\mathbf{R_1} = \frac{kT}{h} \frac{[\mathrm{N_2O_5}]}{f_{\mathrm{N_2O_5}}} \frac{f^{\ddagger}_{\mathrm{N_2O_5}} f^{\ddagger}_{\mathrm{NO_2 \cdot NO_3}} \exp\left[-(\varepsilon_A + \varepsilon_e)/kT\right]}{f^{\ddagger}_{\mathrm{N_2O_5}} \exp\left(-\varepsilon_B/kT\right) + 2f^{\ddagger}_{\mathrm{NO_2 \cdot NO_3}} \exp\left(-\varepsilon_e/kT\right)} \tag{16-11}$$

In this case no flooding is possible. The mechanistic rate-constant expression is a complex, unresolvable function of three rate constants (Eq. 10); and the theoretical rate function (Eq. 11) contains partition functions for two different activated complexes:

$$
\begin{array}{ccc}
\mathrm{O} & \mathrm{O} \qquad \mathrm{O} & \mathrm{O} \\
\diagdown & \diagup \qquad \diagdown & \diagup \\
\mathrm{N-O \cdots N} \quad \text{and} \quad & \mathrm{N \cdots O \cdots O \cdots N} & \tag{16-12} \\
\diagup & \diagdown \qquad \diagup & \\
\mathrm{O} & \mathrm{O} \qquad \mathrm{O} &
\end{array}
$$

It happens that these two complexes have the same empirical formula, $\mathrm{N_2O_5}$, which is the stoichiometry observed in the rate expression. If one adopted a thermodynamic approach to this problem, one would have regarded it as an elementary unimolecular reaction.

The steady-state analysis of reaction **4** gives the complex rate expression (Eq. 1–106)

$$\mathbf{R_4} = (Kh)^{2/3}(2g)^{1/3}[\mathrm{N_2O_5}]^{2/3}[\mathrm{O_3}]^{2/3} \tag{16-13}$$

K is the equilibrium constant for the reaction $\mathrm{N_2O_5} = \mathrm{NO_2} + \mathrm{NO_3}$:

$$K = \frac{f_{\mathrm{NO_2}} f_{\mathrm{NO_3}}}{f_{\mathrm{N_2O_5}}} \exp\left(-\Delta H/kT\right) \tag{16-14}$$

In terms of activated-complex theory, the rate expression is

$$\mathbf{R_4} = \frac{kT}{h} \left(\frac{[\mathrm{N_2O_5}]}{f_{\mathrm{N_2O_5}}}\right)^{2/3} \left(\frac{[\mathrm{O_3}]}{f_{\mathrm{O_3}}}\right)^{2/3} (f^{\ddagger}_{\mathrm{NO_2 \cdot O_3}})^{2/3}(2f^{\ddagger}_{\mathrm{NO_3 \cdot NO_3}})^{1/3}$$
$$\times \exp\left\{-\left[(2/3)(\Delta H + \varepsilon_h) + (1/3)\varepsilon_g\right]/kT\right\} \tag{16-15}$$

As usual, only one power of kT/h appears in the final expression, the absolute activities appear as usual even if raised to fractional powers, and partition functions for the steady-state intermediates ($\mathrm{NO_2}$ and $\mathrm{NO_3}$) cancel from the rate expression. However, partition functions for two activated complexes remain in the rate expression, and the stoichiometry of the observed rate expression is the complicated expression

$$(\tfrac{4}{3})\mathrm{N} + (\tfrac{16}{3})\mathrm{O}$$

(ii) Chain Reactions[106]

Chain reactions of halogen atoms X on hydrocarbons are given by these different mechanisms:

$$
\begin{aligned}
\text{Initiation:} \qquad & X_2 + M \xrightarrow{k_1} 2X + M \\
\text{Propagation:} \qquad & X + RH \xrightarrow{k_2} R + HX \\
& R + X_2 \xrightarrow{k_3} RX + X \qquad\qquad (16\text{-}16) \\
\text{Termination:} \quad & X + X + M \xrightarrow{k_6} X_2 + M \\
\text{or} \qquad\quad & X + R \xrightarrow{k_7} RX \\
\text{or} \qquad\quad & R + R \xrightarrow{k_8} R_2
\end{aligned}
$$

In general, termination might occur by way of two or even three different reactions, and in this case the rate has a very complex form. However, it often happens that termination occurs exclusively by some one step out of k_6, k_7, or k_8. For termination by step 6 the rate law is

$$
\begin{aligned}
R &= k_2 \left(\frac{k_1}{k_6} \right)^{1/2} [X_2]^{1/2}[RH] \\
&= \frac{kT}{h} \left(\frac{[X_2]}{f_{X_2}} \right)^{1/2} \left(\frac{[RH]}{f_{RH}} \right) f^{\ddagger}_{RH \cdot X} \exp\left[-(\varepsilon_2 + \tfrac{1}{2}\Delta H)/kT \right] \quad (16\text{-}17)
\end{aligned}
$$

Here, where the termination reaction is the reverse of the initiation reaction, the partition function of only one activated complex appears in the rate expression, and its empirical formula is given by the observed rate law, $\tfrac{1}{2}X_2 + RH$. For termination by step 7 the rate expression is

$$
\begin{aligned}
R &= \left(\frac{k_1 k_2 k_3}{k_7} \right)^{1/2} [X_2][RH]^{1/2}[M]^{1/2} \\
&= \frac{kT}{h} \frac{[X_2]}{f_{X_2}} \left(\frac{[RH]}{f_{RH}} \frac{[M]}{f_M} \right)^{1/2} \left(\frac{f^{\ddagger}_{M \cdot X_2} f^{\ddagger}_{RH \cdot X} f^{\ddagger}_{R \cdot X_2}}{f^{\ddagger}_{R \cdot X}} \right)^{1/2} \\
&\quad \times \exp\left[-\tfrac{1}{2}(\varepsilon_1 + \varepsilon_2 + \varepsilon_3 - \varepsilon_7)/kT \right]
\end{aligned}
\qquad (16\text{-}18)
$$

This rate expression involves partition functions for four different activated complexes, and the observed rate law is not very meaningful. Finally, for termination by process 8, the rate expression is

$$
\begin{aligned}
R &= k_3 \left(\frac{k_1}{k_8} \right)^{1/2} [X_2]^{3/2}[M]^{1/2} \\
&= \frac{kT}{h} \left(\frac{[X_2]}{f_{X_2}} \right)^{3/2} \left(\frac{[M]}{f_M} \right)^{1/2} f^{\ddagger}_{R \cdot X_2} \left(\frac{f^{\ddagger}_{X_2 \cdot M}}{f^{\ddagger}_{R \cdot R}} \right)^{1/2} \exp\left[-(\varepsilon_3 + \tfrac{1}{2}\varepsilon_1 - \tfrac{1}{2}\varepsilon_8)/kT \right]
\end{aligned}
$$

$$(16\text{-}19)$$

This rate expression is a function of the partition function of three different activated complexes. The observed rate law has the stoichiometry of $3X + \frac{1}{2}M$, and as such it is not very diagnostic as to the mechanism.

(iii) Decomposition of Nitric Acid Vapor[110]

The thermal decomposition of nitric acid vapor gives another interesting example of this method. The laboratory reaction is

$$4HNO_3 = 4NO_2 + 2H_2O + O_2 \tag{16-20}$$

The mechanism has several steps in common with that for the decomposition of N_2O_5:

$$HNO_3 \xrightarrow{k} HO + NO_2$$
$$HO + NO_2 \xrightarrow{j} HNO_3$$
$$HO + HNO_3 \xrightarrow{m} H_2O + NO_3 \tag{16-21}$$
$$NO_3 + NO_2 \xrightarrow{e} NO_2 + O_2 + NO$$
$$NO_3 + NO \xrightarrow{f} NO_2 + NO_2$$

where the steady-state intermediates are NO, HO, and NO_3. The rate expression for the formation of oxygen is

$$R = \frac{\frac{1}{2}km[HNO_3]^2}{j[NO_2] + m[HNO_3]} \tag{16-22}$$

The initial rate, where $[NO_2]$ is small, is that for the elementary reaction, and this condition is readily realized in practice:

$$R = \frac{1}{2}k[HNO_3]$$

By flooding the system with nitrogen dioxide, the rate expression becomes

$$R = \frac{1}{2}\frac{km}{j}\frac{[HNO_3]^2}{[NO_2]} \tag{16-23}$$

This extreme, also, can easily be set up in the laboratory. For the flooded case, the rate expression in terms of partition function is

$$R = \frac{1}{2}\frac{kT}{h}\left(\frac{[HNO_3]}{f_{HNO_3}}\right)^2\left(\frac{f_{NO_2}}{[NO_2]}\right)f_{HO \cdot HNO_3}^{\ddagger} \exp[-(\varepsilon_k + \varepsilon_m - \varepsilon_j)/kT] \tag{16-24}$$

The stoichiometry of the observed rate law is $2H + 2N + 6O - N - 2O = 2H + N + 4O$. The rate expression contains the partition function for only one activated complex, and its empirical formula is indeed H_2NO_4. Even without the mechanism one might have deduced from this result that the activated complex involved the hydroxyl-radical attack on nitric acid $H—O \cdots H \cdots ONO_2$. It will be noted that this case involved

1. A pre-equilibrium, k and j.
2. One rate-determining step, m.
3. Two fast follow-up reactions, e and f.

In this case the rate expression is given entirely by step m, and the stoichiometry of the rate law gives the stoichiometry of this step. The fast follow-up reactions e and f do not enter the rate expression. The exponential factor involves the enthalpy of the pre-equilibrium step as well as the activation energy for the rate determining step.

The mechanism of a reaction can often be determined in this way by inspection if it involves

1. Any number of pre-equilibria.
2. One and only one rate-determining step.
3. Any number of fast follow-up reactions.

However, one is by no means guaranteed that these conditions will be met, even with flooding, as the cases cited above have illustrated.

(iv) Postulate of the Rate-Determining Step

An activation energy of 1.3 kcal/mole gives a factor of 0.1 to the rate at room temperature. Activation energies of chemical reactions vary from 0 to 100 or more kcal/mole. A reaction with 65-kcal activation energy is about 50 powers of 10 slower than one with zero activation energy at room temperature, other things being equal. If elementary reactions are randomly distributed over activation energy, then out of a set of five or ten steps of a complex mechanism one would expect some one step to be far slower than all the rest. This argument is the basis for the postulate of "*the* rate-determining step." However, if substance A reacts with substance B with about zero activation energy, then it is highly probable that there are other substances C, D, etc., in the system that also react with A with no activation energy. Examples have already been cited in Chapter 9. If A is a molecule ion, it reacts upon "every collision" with molecules with which it can undergo exothermic charge exchange. If A is a free radical, it can recombine or disproportionate with about equal rate with many other free radicals in the system. There is a reason for reactions clustering about one rate, and in a number of systems the product distribution is determined by fractionation among competing fast "follow" reactions. When the family of competing fast reactions precedes the rate-determining step, the rate expression does not (usually) have any "order" but rather it has a sum of terms in the denominator (compare reaction **2** of Chapter 1). In steady chain reactions there is no "rate-determining step"; rather there are two pairs of equal rates: initiation rate equals termination rate; one propagation rate equals the other propagation rate. Thus one elementary chemical reaction is the rate-determining step in a complex reaction only for certain special situations, not as a general rule.

B. STANDARD-STATE THERMODYNAMIC PROPERTIES OF ACTIVATED COMPLEXES

(i) Entropy of Activation

In Chapter 8 two equations were derived expressing rate constants as a function of standard-state thermodynamic properties of the activated complex. The general theory (subject only to the assumption that the *reactants* are at thermal equilibrium) that permits the molecular transition probabilities or microscopic rate to depend on all coordinates and moments may be written (Eq. 8–41)

$$\mathbf{k} = \langle \kappa \nu \rangle_{\ddagger}^{\mathrm{B}} \exp\left(\Delta S_{\ddagger}^{\circ}/R\right) \exp\left(-\Delta H_{\ddagger}^{\circ}/RT\right) \qquad (16\text{–}25)$$

Here the average product of molecular rate constants is unspecified, and it could be a very complicated quantity. However, the thermodynamic functions factor out even in this very general theory. In the ultrasimple activated-complex theory (Eq. 8–29), the rate can also be cast into thermodynamic form. This model assumes that every rate process goes by way of a one-dimensional reaction coordinate that is separable and essentially flat for one or more de Broglie wavelength; thus according to this theory every process has the same frequency factor, kT/h:

$$\mathbf{k} = \frac{kT}{h} \exp\left(\Delta S_{\ddagger}^{\circ}/R\right) \exp\left(-\Delta H_{\ddagger}^{\circ}/RT\right) \qquad (16\text{–}26)$$

The evaluation of the entropy of activation from rate data is given in connection with Eq. 8–44.

The meaning of the entropy of activation is the difference in entropy of one mole of activated complex (a hypothetical situation) at one atmosphere pressure and at the standard temperature and the molar entropy of reactants under the same conditions:

$$\Delta S_{\ddagger}^{\circ} = S_{\ddagger}^{\circ} - \sum_{\text{reactants}} S^{\circ} \qquad (16\text{–}27)$$

The entropy of reactants is based on the third law of thermodynamics, and the values are listed in tables of thermodynamic data. For gases the standard state is usually one atmosphere total pressure, but in some cases the standard state is in units of moles/liter. The relation of entropy of one mole of ideal gas to pressure and to atmosphere standard-state value S_{A}° is

$$S = S_{\mathrm{A}}^{\circ} - R \ln P/P^{\circ} \qquad (16\text{–}28)$$

If one wishes to change the standard-state to moles/liter, S_c°, the relation is simply

$$S_c^\circ = S_A^\circ - R \ln RT = S_A^\circ - 6.35 \text{ cal/mole-deg for } 298°K \quad (16\text{--}29)$$

since $P^\circ = 1$ atmosphere and P for one mole/liter is RT atmospheres. The value of the standard-state molar entropy of a few molecules[108] is given in Table 1.

Before looking at the magnitudes of the entropy of activation for kinetic systems, it is well to review the magnitude of entropy changes for a few

TABLE 16–1
Standard-State Entropy for Molecules at 298°K *

Molecule	S_A°	Molecule	S_A°
H	27.39	CH_4	44.50
C	37.76	C_2H_6	54.85
O	38.47	C_3H_8	64.51
N	36.61	C_4H_{10} (n)	74.10
F	37.92	C_5H_{12} (n)	83.27
Ne	34.95	C_6H_{14} (n)	92.45
Cl	39.46	C_7H_{16} (n)	101.64
H_2	31.21	C_2H_4	52.54
CO	47.30	C_3H_6	63.80
NO	50.34	C_4H_8 (1-ene)	73.48
O_2	49.00	C_5H_{10} (1-ene)	83.08
N_2	45.77	C_6H_{12} (1-ene)	92.25
F_2	53.29		
CO_2	51.06	C_4H_8 (cyclo)	63.16
N_2O	52.58	C_5H_{10} (cyclo)	70.00
NO_2	57.47	C_6H_{12} (cyclo)	71.28
O_3	56.8	C_7H_{14} (cyclo)	81.25

* Calories/mole-degree.

typical chemical reactions, as is illustrated by Table 2. For chemical reactions with no change of mole number, the entropy change is usually small and is all within the range of -3.3 to $+3.7$ for the examples given in Table 2. If there is no change in mole number for a chemical reaction, then the change in molar entropy for the reaction is the same, regardless of standard state. For chemical reactions in which the mole number decreases by one, there is a large decrease in entropy, which for the examples in Table 2 is between -23 to -36 entropy units if the standard state is one atmosphere and between -17 and -30 if the standard state is one mole/liter. For reactions in which the mole number decreases by two, the decrease in entropy is about twice as great as that for a decrease of one. Although the entropy change for reaction with no change of mole number is usually small, it is quite substantial if the reaction takes a ring compound to a chain compound, as can be seen from Table 2. The opening of a ring gives an increase of entropy of from 10 to 20 calories/mole-degree.

TABLE 16-2

Change in Standard-State Entropy for a Few Chemical Reactions at 298°K*

	Standard State	
	1 atm.	1 mole/liter
No change in mole number		
$C + O_2 = CO + O$	−0.99	−0.99
$O + N_2 = NO + O$	2.71	2.71
$N_2O + O = N_2 + O_2$	3.72	3.72
$NO_2 + CO = NO + CO_2$	−3.30	−3.30
$C_2H_4 + C_3H_8 = C_2H_6 + C_3H_6$	1.60	1.60
$C_4H_8 + C_6H_{14} = C_4H_{10} + C_6H_{12}$	0.42	0.42
Mole number decreases by one		
$H + H = H_2$	−23.57	−17.22
$N + N = N_2$	−27.45	−21.10
$Cl + Cl = Cl_2$	−25.63	−19.28
$N + O_2 = NO_2$	−28.14	−21.79
$H_2 + C_2H_4 = C_2H_6$	−28.90	−22.55
$CH_4 + C_2H_4 = C_3H_8$	−32.53	−26.18
$C_3H_6 + C_3H_8 = C_6H_{14}$ (n)	−35.86	−29.51
Mole number decreases by two		
$C + O + O \rightarrow CO_2$	−63.64	−50.94
$N + N + O \rightarrow N_2O$	−59.11	−49.41
$H_2 + H_2 + C \rightarrow CH_4$	−49.12	−36.42
$H_2 + C_2H_4 + C_2H_4 \rightarrow C_4H_{10}$ (n)	−62.19	−49.49
$CH_4 + C_2H_4 + C_3H_6 \rightarrow C_6H_{12}$ (n)	−68.39	−55.69
Normal chain (1-ene) forms ring		
$C_4H_8 = C_4H_8$ (cyclo)	−10.32	−10.32
$C_5H_{10} = C_5H_{10}$ (cyclo)	−13.08	−13.08
$C_6H_{12} = C_6H_{12}$ (cyclo)	−20.97	−20.97
$C_7H_{14} = C_7H_{14}$ (cyclo)	−20.18	−20.18

* Calories/mole-degree.

By means of observed rate constants and activation energies, values of entropies of activation and enthalpies of activation for a series of bimolecular reactions are evaluated and listed in Table 3. The entropy of activation for the first four cases varies from −26 to −23 entropy units, which is typical for the magnitude of entropy change for chemical reactions involving reactants of about the same mass, Table 2, where the mole number decreases by one. By examples like these, one establishes that entropies of activation are about the same as entropies of reaction for similar overall

reactions.   Once this baseline is established, one may argue that the fifth
and sixth reactions in Table 3 do not go by way of a cyclic activated complex, and that the seventh reaction does involve a four-numbered ring as
activated complex.   Detailed calculations using reasonable molecular
models and partition functions[74] confirm these rather vague conclusions
based on total entropy changes.   In the hands of experts in the field,
certain limited deductions can be drawn from entropies of activation.

TABLE 16–3

Entropies of Activation for a Few Bimolecular Reactions

Reaction	$T°K$	$\Delta H_{\ddagger}^{\circ}$ (kcal/mole)	$\Delta S_{\ddagger}^{\circ}$ (a) (cal/mole-degree)
$NO + O_3 = NO_2 + O_2$	300	2.5	-26
$NO_2 + O_3 = NO_3 + O_2$	300	7.0	-23
$NO_2 + F_2 = NO_2F + F$	300	10.4	-25
$NO_2 + CO = NO + CO_2$	700	31.6	-26
$2NO_2 = 2NO + O_2$	500	26.6	-28
$2NOCl = 2NO + Cl_2$	500	24.5	-25
$2ClO = Cl_2 + O_2$	400	0	-35

(a) Standard state one atmosphere.

However, deductions from molecular models are always to be preferred if
enough data are available.

(ii) Standard-State Thermodynamic Properties of Activated Complexes

Tables of thermodynamic data[111] for chemical substances typically give:

$\Delta_f H°$, enthalpy of formation of one mole of substance from elements, all in
standard state.   This quantity does not change with standard state for
ideal gases.

$S°$, entropy of one mole of substance in its standard state.   This quantity is
very sensitive to standard state, Eq. 28.

$\Delta_f G°$, free energy of formation of one mole of substance from elements, all in
standard state.   This quantity is very sensitive to standard state, $\Delta_f G = \Delta G° + RT \ln P/P°$.

For reactants, products, and intermediate free radicals in the decompositions
of N_2O_5 and of HNO_3, the values of these thermodynamic data are listed in
Table 4.   The entropy of a mole of activated complex in the standard state
is given by Eq. 27.   Similarly, one can evaluate the standard free energy of
formation and the standard enthalpy of formation of the activated complex:

$$\Delta_f H_{\ddagger}^{\circ} = \sum_{\text{reactants}} \Delta_f H° + \Delta H_{\ddagger}^{\circ}$$

$$\Delta_f G_{\ddagger}^{\circ} = \sum_{\text{reactants}} \Delta_f G° + \Delta G_{\ddagger}^{\circ}$$

$$(16\text{–}30)$$

TABLE 16-4

Standard-State (Gas at One Atm.) Thermodynamic Properties
of Individual Reactants and Products in the Laboratory
Reactions: Decomposition of N_2O_5 and Decomposition of HNO_3

Substance	$\Delta_f H^\circ_{298}$ (kcal/mole)	S°_{298} (cal/mole-deg)	$\Delta_f G^\circ_{298}$ (kcal/mole)
NO	21.6	50.3	20.7
NO_2	8.1	57.5	12.4
NO_3	17.1	61	27.6
N_2O_5	3.1	85	27.9
HO	10.0	43.9	8.9
H_2O	−57.8	45.1	−54.6
HNO_3	−29.4	63.6	−15.0
O_2	0	49.0	0
N_2	0	45.8	0
H_2	0	31.2	0

TABLE 16-5

Standard-State Thermodynamic Properties of the Sum of
Reactants, Activated Complex, and Sum of Products for the
Elementary Reactions (298°K)

Reaction	$\Sigma\Delta_f H^\circ_{reactants}$	$\Delta_f H^\circ_\ddagger$	$\Sigma\Delta_f H^\circ_{products}$
A $N_2O_5 \rightarrow NO_2 + NO_3$	3.1	25.2	25.2
k $HNO_3 \rightarrow HO + NO_2$	−29.4	17.9	17.9
m $HO + HNO_3 \rightarrow H_2O + NO_3$	−19.6	−17	−40.7
e $NO_2 + NO_3 \rightarrow NO + O_2 + NO_2$	25.2	29.7	29.7
f $NO + NO_3 \rightarrow 2 NO_2$	38.7	40	14.2

	$\Sigma\Delta_f G^\circ_{reactants}$	$\Delta_f G^\circ_\ddagger$	$\Sigma\Delta_f G^\circ_{products}$
A $N_2O_5 \rightarrow NO_2 + NO_3$	27.9	46.1	40.0
k $HNO_3 \rightarrow HO + NO_2$	−15.0	28.7	21.3
m $HO + HNO_3 \rightarrow H_2O + NO_3$	−6.1	4.9	−27
e $NO_2 + NO_3 \rightarrow NO + O_2 + NO_2$	40.0	48.2	33.1
f $NO + NO_3 \rightarrow 2 NO_2$	48.6	50.2	24.8

Table 5 gives the values of these thermodynamic quantities for reactants, activated complex, and products for the various steps in the decomposition of N_2O_5 and HNO_3.

(iii) Partial Molal Free Energy of Reactants, Activated Complex, and Products at Equilibrium

At equilibrium the reactant, N_2O_5, is reduced to some low value, and thus its actual molal free energy is lower than the standard-state value. The condition for total chemical equilibrium is that reactants, activated complex, and products all have the same partial molal free energy. Under all conditions where the reactants are in equilibrium with the activated complex, their actual molal free energies are equal.

C.   GRAPHICAL REPRESENTATION OF COMPLEX, MULTISTEP REACTIONS

The book by Glasstone, Laidler, and Eyring[33] has a paragraph labeled "successive reactions" (pp. 99 and 100), and a graph (p. 100) that shows five

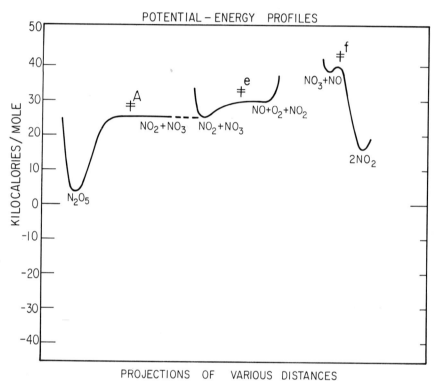

POTENTIAL – ENERGY PROFILES

PROJECTIONS OF   VARIOUS DISTANCES

Fig. 16–1. Potential-energy profiles for reactions A, e, and f in the decomposition of N_2O_5; on a common energy scale (zero for N_2 and O_2 under standard-state conditions).

minima and four maxima. The axes are labelled "reaction coordinate" and "potential energy." In Chapter 10 it was shown, by means of Figs. 10–2 and 10–3, that with suitable projections one can show certain features of a two-dimensional potential-energy contour map in terms of a one-dimensional potential-energy profile. Figure 19 (p. 100) of Glasstone, Laidler, and Eyring looks very much like four profiles, such as Fig. 10–3, hooked together.

The discussion in the text tends to bear out this interpretation. The book seems to say that the highest peak in such a series will be *the* activated complex, and the intermediate steps can be more or less ignored. The discussion asserts that the activation energy will be the difference between the minimum energy for reactants and the height of the highest barrier. It seems worthwhile to take considerable time to explore the meaning of such graphical presentations for a few well-understood complex reactions.

One of the first questions to ask is this: Is it potential energy, standard-state molal free energy, partial-molal free energy, enthalpy, or what, as ordinate? For the decomposition of N_2O_5 and of HNO_3, several different plots will be presented.

For a simple, elementary unimolecular reaction, the complex multi-dimensional potential-energy surface can perhaps be abbreviated by a curve similar to a Morse curve (Fig. 4–1) along the bond being broken. For a bimolecular, atom-transfer reaction, the multidimensional potential-energy surface can be represented in part by a profile like Fig. 10–3. For different reactions in a complex mechanism, an energy scale with a common origin (elements in standard state) can be found in terms of the sum of the enthalpy of reactants, activated complex, and sum of products. Such quantities are given in Table 5 and plotted as potential-energy profiles in Fig. 1 for the decomposition of N_2O_5 and in Fig. 2 for the decomposition of HNO_3. The ordinate is molal standard-state enthalpy of formation from the elements; the abcissa represent distance in the sense of Fig. 10–3 for each elementary reaction; and the various elementary steps of the mechanism are given in order.

The first two elementary reactions in Fig. 1 have the same empirical formula: N_2O_5, $N_2O_5^{\ddagger}$, $NO_2 + NO_3$, $ONOONO_2^{\ddagger}$, $NO + O_2 + NO_2$. Thus one is quite willing to connect these two potential-energy profiles together as indicated by the dotted line. The third elementary reaction has a different empirical formula, N_2O_4. Thus it is impossible to make any meaningful connection between the last two potential-energy profiles. Thus one sees that the linkages shown by Glasstone, Laidler, and Eyring (on p. 100) are restricted to consecutive isomerizations or other processes (such as $N_2O_5 \rightarrow NO_2 + NO_3 \rightarrow NO + O_2 + NO_2$) with identical stoichiometry. In the decomposition of N_2O_5 as illustrated by Fig. 1, there are three activated complexes, for which the enthalpies are (kcal/mole):

$$(A) \quad N_2O_5^{\ddagger} \qquad 25.2$$
$$(e) \quad ONOONO_2^{\ddagger} \quad 29.7 \qquad\qquad (16\text{–}31)$$
$$(f) \quad ON\text{—}ONO_2^{\ddagger} \quad 40$$

It is often stated that in a multistep reaction, the complex of the rate-determining step is that of the highest potential energy. But this statement is quite false: for N_2O_5 alone, the rate-determining step is e at 29.7 kcal/mole, far below the potential energy of the complex of step f at 40 kcal/mole; for N_2O_5 flooded with nitric oxide, the rate-determining step is A (Eq. 9) with an activated complex at 25.2 kcal, whereas step f has a complex at 40 kcal; for N_2O_5 with added NO and flooded with NO_2, the rate-determining step becomes f (Eq. 6). Potential-energy surfaces are the same

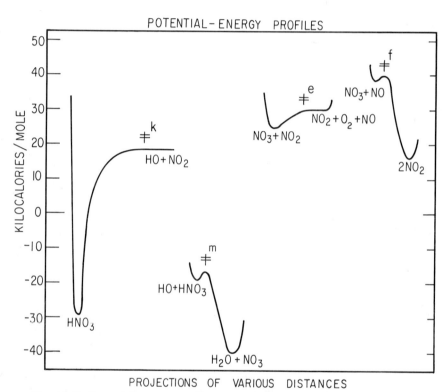

POTENTIAL–ENERGY PROFILES

PROJECTIONS OF VARIOUS DISTANCES

Fig. 16–2. Potential-energy profiles on a common energy scale for the elementary reactions in the decomposition of HNO_3 vapor.

regardless of relative concentration of added reagents. As these examples show, the height of the potential-energy barrier in a complex reaction is not the whole story; the rate-determining step may be either the lowest barrier or the middle-sized barrier, or the highest barrier, depending on concentrations of added nitric oxide and nitrogen dioxide.

The energy (enthalpy) profiles for the four steps (five, counting the reverse of k) in the decomposition of nitric acid vapor are shown in Fig. 2. The empirical formulas for all these steps are different. The four activated complexes and their enthalpy are (kcal/mole):

$$
\begin{array}{lll}
(k) & \text{HNO}_3^{\ddagger} & 17.9 \\
(m) & \text{HO·HNO}_3^{\ddagger} & -17 \\
(e) & \text{ONOONO}_2^{\ddagger} & 29.7 \\
(f) & \text{ONONO}_2^{\ddagger} & 40
\end{array} \qquad (16\text{--}32)
$$

As noted by Eq. 22, the usual rate-determining step is k with an activated complex at 17.9 kcal; but (Eq. 2) if flooded with NO_2, the rate-determining step is m with the lowest-energy activated complex of all.   The reactions

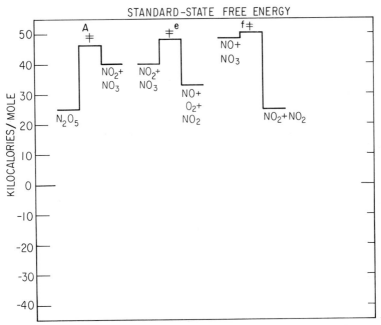

Fig. 16–3. Bar graphs representing standard-state free energy of reactants, activated complexes, and products for the elementary reactions in the decomposition of N_2O_5; on a common free-energy scale (zero for elementary substances under standard-state conditions).

with activated complexes at high energies, 29.7 or 40 kcal are never rate-determining in this system.

On the other hand, some people say it is the free energy, not potential energy, that identifies the rate-determining step of a complex reaction.   It cannot be the actual molal free energy because equilibrium between reactants and activated complex means that reactants and activated complex have equal partial molal free energy.   It is reasonable to postulate that standard-state molal free energy is important.   Table 5 and Figs. 3 and 4 examine this postulate. The activated complexes in the decomposition of N_2O_5 have standard-state free energies of (kcal/mole):

$$(A) \quad N_2O_5^{\ddagger} \qquad 46.1$$
$$(e) \quad NO_2 \cdot NO_3 \qquad 48.2 \qquad (16\text{--}33)$$
$$(f) \quad NO \cdot NO_3 \qquad 50.2$$

These are closer together than the corresponding enthalpy values, but they are in the same order. For pure N_2O_5 the rate-determining step is the middle barrier. With nitric oxide flooding, the rate-determining step is the lowest

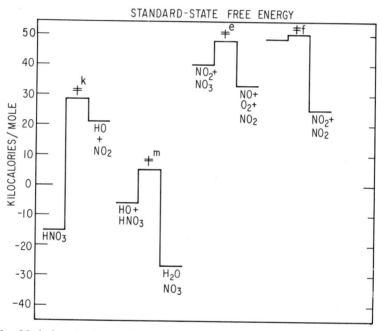

Fig. 16–4. Standard-state free energy of reactants, activated complexes, and products for elementary reactions in the decomposition of nitric acid vapor.

barrier, and with added nitric oxide and excess nitrogen dioxide the rate-determining step becomes the highest barrier.

Similarly, the molal standard-state free energies on a common energy scale for the four elementary reactions in the decomposition of HNO_3 are shown in Fig. 4. The relative heights of the free-energy barriers are the same as the relative heights of enthalpy (potential energy) barriers. With flooded NO_2, the rate-determining step is m, with the lowest free-energy barrier. For the initial rate, the activated complex is k, which is only second from the lowest. In no known reaction do the activated complexes with highest standard-state free energy become rate determining.

Another interpretation can be given to the diagram (pp. 99–100) of Glasstone, Laidler, and Eyring. It could be interpreted as referring to the full stoichiometric composition at all stages of the reaction, $2N_2O_5$ for reaction 1 and $4HNO_3$ for reaction 20. Since the mechanisms of these reactions are known, one can reconstruct the various stages of these reactions, carrying along all products:

$$2N_2O_5 \rightarrow 2\ddagger_A \rightarrow 2NO_2 + 2NO_3 \rightarrow \ddagger_e + NO_2 + NO_3 \rightarrow$$
$$2NO_2 + O_2 + NO + NO_3 \rightarrow \ddagger_f + 2NO_2 + O_2 \rightarrow 4NO_2 + O_2 \quad (16\text{-}34)$$

$$4HNO_3 \rightarrow 2\ddagger_k + 2HNO_3 \rightarrow 2HO + 2NO_2 + 2HNO_3 \rightarrow$$
$$2\ddagger_m + 2NO_2 \rightarrow 2H_2O + 2NO_2 + 2NO_3 \rightarrow \quad (16\text{-}35)$$
$$\ddagger_e + 2H_2O + NO_2 + NO_3 \rightarrow 2NO_2 + NO + O_2 + 2H_2O + NO_3 \rightarrow$$
$$\ddagger_f + 2NO_2 + 2H_2O + O_2 \rightarrow 4NO_2 + 2H_2O + O_2$$

By means of the thermodynamic data in Tables 4 and 5, the total standard-state enthalpy and free energy of each stage of the reaction can be evaluated; such values are given in Table 6 and the free-energy values are plotted in Fig. 5. For N_2O_5 there are three different maxima including one or more activated complexes and (in some cases) other substances, which are either intermediates or products. These maxima are not in the same order as those

TABLE 16–6

Standard-State Thermodynamic Properties of Full Stoichiometric Composition at Various Stages of Reaction *

Stages	$\Sigma\Delta_f H^\circ$	$\Sigma\Delta_f G^\circ$
Reaction: $2N_2O_5 = 4NO_2 + O_2$		
$2N_2O_5$	6.2	55.8
$2\ddagger_A$	50.4	92.2
$2NO_2 + 2NO_3$	50.4	80.0
$\ddagger_e + NO_2 + NO_3$	54.9	88.2
$2NO_2 + O_2 + NO + NO_3$	54.9	73.1
$\ddagger_f + 2NO_2 + O_2$	56.2	75.0
$4NO_2 + O_2$	32.4	49.6
Reaction: $4HNO_3 = 4NO_2 + 2H_2O + O_2$		
$4HNO_3$	−117.6	−60.0
$2\ddagger_k + 2HNO_3$	−40.9	27.4
$2HO + 2NO_2 + 2HNO_3$	−23.0	12.6
$2\ddagger_m + 2NO_2$	−17.8	34.6
$2H_2O + 2NO_2 + 2NO_3$	−65.2	−29.2
$\ddagger_e + 2H_2O + NO_2 + NO_3$	−60.7	−21.0
$2NO_2 + NO + O_2 + 2H_2O + NO_3$	−60.7	−35.8
$\ddagger_f + 2NO_2 + 2H_2O + O_2$	−59.4	−34.2
$4NO_2 + 2H_2O + O_2$	−83.2	−59.6

* kcal/mole.

found by the previous graphical methods. The highest peak includes the activated complex for the step that is rate-determining, if N_2O_5 is flooded with nitric oxide. The middle-height peak includes the activated complex of the reaction that is rate-determining in the decomposition of N_2O_5 alone. The lowest energy peak includes the activated complex of the rate-determining step if N_2O_5 is flooded with NO_2 and some NO is also present.

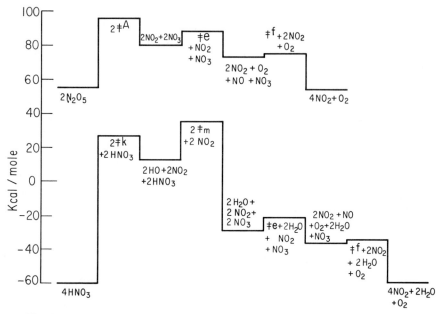

Fig. 16–5. Standard molal free energy of full stoichiometric mixture at various stages of the decomposition of $2\,N_2O_5$ and of $4\,HNO_3$.

By this procedure of carrying along the full stoichiometric composition of the overall reaction, the stages of decomposition of nitric acid vapor are also shown in Fig. 5. In all cases the peaks represent both activated complexes and various other molecules of reactants, intermediates, or products. Once again the highest free-energy peak does *not* identify the rate-determining step in the decomposition of pure nitric acid vapor, although step m may become rate-determining if the system is flooded with NO_2. This system of representing total thermodynamic standard-state functions allows the various stages of the reactions to be joined together in a clear-cut fashion, but the relation to kinetics is very hard to find. The energy steps from a "pool of reactants" to a peak height is often not an activation energy but twice an activation energy in three cases in Fig. 5. As noted repeatedly above, the rate-determining step is a function of relative concentrations and not exclusively energy peak-heights.

The abscissa in Figs. 1 through 5 is sometimes named "reaction coordinate"; the meaning of this term in these cases where the mechanism is understood is discernible but only with very great difficulty.

Even so, one continues to see some chemists represent complex mechanisms by means of graphs analogous to that of Glasstone, Laidler, and Eyring. These peaks are shown to rise and fall with added reagents of various sorts. The present analysis shows that the ordinate in these plots is:

1. Not potential energy.
2. Not standard-state molal enthalpy.
3. Not partial molal free energy.
4. Not standard-state, molal free energy.

It cannot be said that these plots are meaningless. It can be said that they are an artificial, conventional, short-hand notation for complex reactions. Some people are able to communicate with each other using these symbols, even though many are confused by the supposed relation to potential energy or to free energy. It was shown in connection with the decomposition of nitric acid vapor that the observed rate is that for one step if the system consists of (1) pre-equilibria, (2) a rate-determining step, and (3) fast follow reactions. In the false belief that the activated complex with highest energy is the rate-determining step, the convention is that the highest peak on these diagrams represents the rate-determining step. Pre-equilibria are represented by a series of valleys and low peaks to the left of the rate determining step, and fast, follow reactions are symbolized by valleys and low peaks to the right. The various steps are linked together even though different stoichiometry may be involved and even though the energy of the products of one reaction may be different from the reactants of the next reaction. This symbolism is shown for different conditions for N_2O_5 in Fig. 6 and for HNO_3 in Fig. 7.

The graphical code for discussing the decomposition of N_2O_5 is given by Fig. 6 for three experimental conditions: (1) N_2O_5 alone, (2) N_2O_5 plus NO, (3) N_2O_5 plus NO plus large excess of NO_2. In example 1 the high peak for activated complex e symbolizes that e is the rate-determining step (even though f in fact has a complex at higher energy). The pre-equilibrium $N_2O_5 = NO_2 + NO_3$ is symbolized by the A_+ peak and $NO_2 + NO_3$ valley. The valley to the right of the e_+ peak means two things: the products of reaction e and the reactants of reaction f. In this way one represents the forward reaction f to be faster than the reverse of reaction e. In Fig. 6, case 2, the fast, follow reaction f is symbolized directly to the right of peak A_+ and reaction e is omitted. The valley between A_+ and f_+ represents both the products of A and the reactants of f. If to case 2 one adds excess NO_2, the effect is to increase the rate of the back reaction from $NO_2 + NO_3$

through $A_{\ddagger}$ to N_2O_5. This effect is not by virtue of changing any barrier heights, but it is just a mass-action effect. However, with this code, vertical height symbolizes slowness of rate. Thus in curve 3 of Fig. 6, the barrier $A_{\ddagger}$ is lowered and the barrier $f_{\ddagger}$ is raised to show that f is now the slowest step.

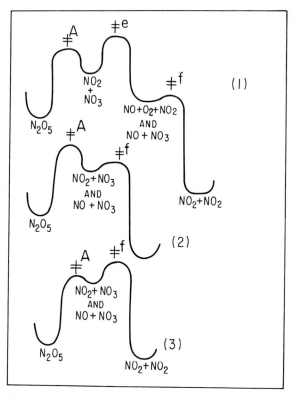

Fig. 16–6. Symbolic, graphical representation of the decomposition of N_2O_5 under various conditions: (1) N_2O_5 alone, (2) N_2O_5 plus NO, (3) N_2O_5 plus NO plus excess NO_2. The ordinate is *not* potential energy or free energy but rather a conventional representation of the relative slowness of reaction. The abscissa is some sort of progress variable for the stages in the mechanism.

By use of this symbolic graphical notation, the mechanism of the decomposition of nitric acid vapor, flooded with NO_2, is shown by Fig. 7. One pre-equilibrium and two fast, follow reactions are illustrated. The peaks represent a single activated complex, but the valleys represent both the products of one reaction and the reactants of the next, which have different stoichiometry. The heights of the peaks represent slowness of reaction, not any sort of energy. The successive valleys give qualitatively relative heats of reaction; however, valleys with two intervening peaks do not give this information, since vertical energy scales are shifted to cause products of one reaction to overlap reactants of the next.

This graphical notation is useful in giving a qualitative discussion of mechanisms that occur by way of successive steps. It does not seem capable of symbolizing chain reactions, and it is inadequate to symbolize other complex mechanisms. Thus use of this symbolic method may lead one to overlook the actual mechanism, because it does not fit the code. There is,

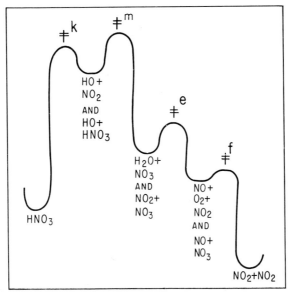

Fig. 16-7. Same as Fig. 5 for the decomposition of HNO_3 vapor, flooded with NO_2. To appreciate the artificiality of this code, one should compare Figs. 2 and 4.

however, a more serious criticism of some of those who use this symbolism: the supposed relation of the ordinate to potential energy or to free energy may lead to great confusion. In justifying a mechanism, one may use energy arguments to explain a rate effect that really depends on concentration of some other species.

If one wishes to do anything quantitative with kinetic data and in particular if one wants to understand rates in terms of molecular properties, molecular structure, and molecular dynamics, then one should avoid vague thermodynamic functions and not use artificial graphical representations of complex mechanisms. It is strongly recommended that complex reactions be treated by the steady-state method (Appendix A) wherever possible. In some cases one must turn to the more difficult methods of simultaneous differential equations. On the other hand, one may sometimes be able to relax into the simpler method, and regard intermediates to be in equilibrium with reactants. Theories of reaction rates should be applied only to the rate constants of elementary reactions. If the complex rate expression found from the steady-state method is a function of elementary constants (for example, Eqs. 3, 10, 13, 17, 18, etc.), then each elementary rate constant in the complex expression should be treated theoretically.

17
Conclusions

In quantum mechanics and in classical mechanics, a two-particle problem can be treated exactly, but a three-particle or larger system requires restraints, approximations, or restrictions to special cases. Even the simplest chemical-physical reactions, such as

$$e^- + H \rightarrow H^+ + 2e^-$$
$$H^+ + D \rightarrow H + D^+$$
$$H + H \rightarrow H_2^+ + e^-$$
$$H_2(v = 0) + Ar \rightarrow H_2(v = 1) + Ar$$

involve three or more fundamental particles; and, of course, chemical reactions involve many particles. For the examples given above, the first reaction may be solved by the Born *approximation* if the kinetic energy of the incoming electron is very large compared to the ionization energy of the hydrogen atom; this approximation *restricts* this theoretical treatment to one range of energy. To regard an argon atom as one particle is to impose a *restraint* that the eighteen electrons and the nucleus move together. The theory of gas-phase chemical kinetics is not a straightforward deductive science; like other fields of "many-body" theory, it is characterized by restraints, restrictions, and approximations. It is no criticism of a chemical theory to call it "approximate" or "limited." The value of a theory is measured by the strength of its predictions within its restricted range of applicability.

It was emphasized in Chapter 1 that the area wherein gas-phase chemical kinetics is most strongly predictive is in its transferability of elementary rate constants from one environment to another. The next fourteen chapters focused on "collision theory" and "activated-complex theory" of chemical reactions and on the nature of the non-kinetic, input data to these theories. Certain highpoints of these developments are discussed below.

A. POTENTIAL-ENERGY SURFACES

The potential-energy function between the "particles" of the microscopic system is a natural starting point of almost any theory of chemistry or physics.   Members of the "activated-complex" school pioneered in developing potential-energy surfaces for three or more atoms, but they have no special claim to nor special responsibility for this subject itself.   One should clearly separate into two compartments: (1) the problem of obtaining the potential energy function and (2) the theory of evaluating a rate expression from a given potential energy function.

(i) Two-Atom Systems

The theoretical treatment of hydrogen-hydrogen interactions is in excellent shape; the theoretical treatment of other atom pairs is only approximate and not quite accurate.   For any atom pairs, the London dispersion forces that contribute to Lennard-Jones bonding can be found by semiempirical methods, or evaluated empirically from transport properties. Chemical bonding and antibonding repulsions can also be treated by semiempirical methods.   The primary tool for empirical determination of chemical bonding is molecular spectroscopy.   Molecular structure determinations and thermodynamic methods also give empirical data concerning chemical bonding.   Attractive and repulsive interactions can be explored by means of attenuation or scattering of molecular beams.

(ii) Three-Atom Systems

It requires at least three atoms to give chemical reactions, and thus for kinetic purposes three-atom potential-energy surfaces play a key role.   The potential energy of a three-atom system depends on two bond lengths and one (for non-linear molecule) or two (linear molecule) bond angles.   For a given angular configuration, the full potential energy of the system can be shown by potential-energy contours on a bond-distance (R_1, R_2) surface. At least five different types of linear, three-atom potential-energy surfaces can be shown (Chapter 4), and these are useful in visualizing various chemical processes.

For three-atom potential-energy surfaces, the H_3 case has been treated theoretically, but the accuracy of the method is not yet satisfying.   Several semiempirical methods for H_3 and for other atoms have been put forward: the original method of London-Polanyi-Eyring has been judged in recent years to be qualitatively incorrect in giving a broad and deep well in the top of the potential-energy pass; the modification of this method by Sato gives a potential-energy surface that has been useful in predicting Arrhenius A-factors, kinetic isotope effects, and trends of activation energy with bond energy.   This London-Polanyi-Eyring-Sato potential-energy surface for bimolecular reactions may be as good as kinetic data.   However, calculated kinetic factors are not very sensitive to the form of the potential-energy surface.   This fact is emphasized by the bond-energy–bond-order method. This method is ludicrously crude in concept, predicts somewhat different *properties* of the activated complex, and yet it predicts chemical kinetic data as well as the much more elaborate London-Polanyi-Eyring-Sato or Karplus methods.

(iii) Polyatomic Systems

There seems to be no significant quantum-mechanical theory of four-atom or more systems of sufficient detail or accuracy to use in kinetic systems. The semiempirical method of London-Polanyi-Eyring-Sato has been applied to reactions such as $CH_3 + H_2 \rightarrow CH_4 + H$, where the process is regarded as a pseudo-three-atom system, that is, the methyl radical is treated as an atom. The simple, inelegant bond-energy–bond-order method has also been applied to polyatomic systems that engage in "three-center" atom-transfer reactions. In some cases, the potential energy of activation follows predictions based on three-center empirical or semiempirical methods; and in some cases one sees departures "explained" then, as non-bonding interactions. At the present stage of knowledge, potential-energy surfaces proposed for polyatomic systems are postulates in an area almost inaccessible to experimental verification. Thus one needs to go very slowly in passing judgement of any kind.

In general, little research has been devoted to constructing potential-energy surfaces for unimolecular isomerizations or decompositions, or for termolecular reactions. Thus both collision theory and activated complex theory lack a starting point in a realistic treatment of such reactions.

B. COLLISION THEORY VERSUS ACTIVATED-COMPLEX THEORY FOR ELEMENTARY REACTIONS

(i) Bimolecular Reactions with Activation Energy

If a bimolecular reaction occurs with activation energy, there is some "ridge" of potential energy between reactants and products and a lowest "saddlepoint" on the ridge. One can discuss three sets of $3N$-dimensional normal coordinates (when N is the total number of atoms in the stoichiometric reaction): those based on reactants, those based on the saddlepoint extremum, and those based on products. If the rate expression is set up in the normal coordinates of reactants (including translational and rotational, zero-frequency normal modes), it is called "collision theory." If the rate expression is set up in the normal coordinates of the saddlepoint, it is called "activated-complex theory." So far, no one seems to have proposed a special name for using the normal coordinates of the products to describe the rate; but if one hurries, perhaps this theory can be named after one's paternal grandfather.

It is very natural to express bimolecular reaction rates in terms of bimolecular collision rates and other factors. Bimolecular collision rates, whether one uses the hard-sphere model or potential-energy functions, are

usually calculated from two-particle mechanics (although structured reactants or reactants with dipole moments call for additional, orientational
variables). For chemical reaction to occur, the two-particle collision
problem must be modified by multidimensional chemical transformations,
that is, changes of bonds and changes of normal coordinates from those of
reactants to those of products. The distribution of reactants over translational and internal energy is of concern; and if reactants have an equilibrium distribution over states, a Boltzmann factor, $\exp(-E/RT)$, and other
factors, may arise. The rate may thus be expressed as *collision rate* times
Boltzmann factor times "*steric factor*," where the "steric factor" includes the
effect of internal degrees of freedom on the reaction yield per collision, over
and above the energy requirement. One naturally examines all of the
potential-energy surface between reactants and products to select those
portions that allow a collision to be a reaction. The potential-energy function
near the saddlepoint may be a "bottleneck" and particularly important in
determining the "steric factor." However, the potential-energy function
between reactants and saddlepoint may "shadow" the pass from certain
states of the reactant, and the potential-energy surface between saddlepoint
and products may "reflect" systems to prevent reaction. Thus a *complete*
collision theory starts with the actual distribution of reactants, and from
considerations of all the potential-energy surface between reactants and
products it calculates the fraction of collisions that lead to products. (Compare Ref. 69.)

It is also very natural to consider bimolecular reactions in terms of the
normal coordinates of the saddlepoint between reactants and products. If
the saddlepoint is indeed the "bottleneck" of the reaction, high in energy or
narrow in configuration, or both, then the "activated complex" may be
"like a normal molecule in all degrees of freedom except one." The rate can
be expressed in terms of the flux of systems from reactant side, the rate of
crossing the saddlepoint region, and the probability of systems that cross
becoming products. The flux of systems from reactant side depends on the
initial distribution of reactants over energy states and also on features of the
potential-energy surface between reactants and complex that may cut off
certain states of the reactant from ever reaching the complex. The rate
of crossing the saddlepoint region depends on the potential-energy surface
there. The probability that a system having crossed reaches products may
depend on all of the potential-energy surface between complex and products.
Thus a *complete* activated-complex theory considers the actual distribution
of reactants and all of the potential-energy surface between reactants and
products.

It is quite clear that the *complete* collision theory described above and the
complete activated complex would give identical predictions (see Table
10–11B). As usually practiced, neither theory is complete in the calculation

of chemical reaction rates. One gets two theories, two schools of thought, two "parties," because the two theories resort to different simplifying approximations in order to calculate rates. Since in practice neither method is complete, neither method is exact, and neither method is "absolute," then it is obvious that both methods (each with its own approximations) should be used; the best theoretical treatment may be a superposition of the two predictions.

When collision theory expresses the rate as *collision rate* times *steric factor* times $\exp(-E/RT)$ with both the activation energy and steric factor as empirical parameters to be fitted to kinetic data, then it is a very empty and unsatisfying theory. Theoreticians in 1935 were properly impatient with this approach.

When activated-complex theory uses the structural and mechanical *properties* of the activated complex as adjustable parameters to be fitted to kinetic data, then indeed the theory can "explain" anything and predict nothing. There are so many bond lengths and force constants in an activated complex and so few independent kinetic observables (Arrhenius **A** and **E** cover most kinetic data) that one should firmly resolve *never under any circumstance* to fit force constants or bond lengths to kinetic data. The inevitable "fit to the data" gives "explanations" or "confirmations of the theory" that are totally devoid of any scientific content. Activated-complex theory has some residue as a predictive science for those methods that fit only one parameter to kinetic data, such as f of London-Polanyi-Eyring, Δ of London-Polanyi-Eyring-Sato, or the scale factor to Sato's repulsion term (Eq. 4–21) in the bond-energy–bond-order method. Any further fitting of parameters or pulling and twisting the activated complex must be strictly forbidden. One does not expect activated-complex theory to give a precise prediction to any kinetic data, and thus forcing a fit by fixing parameters spoils the value of the theory as a reasonable first approximation to some kinetic problems.

(ii) Unimolecular Reactions

Unimolecular reaction rates involve not one theoretical function but rather three: b_i, the translational-vibrational energy-transfer function; P_i, the Boltzmann factor for internal energy states of a molecule; and c_i, the microscopic, molecular rate constant for unimolecular decomposition of an excited polyatomic molecule.

The function P_i is needed either for a dynamic theory or for a statistical theory of unimolecular reactions, but it is not a rate function. It is purely a problem in equilibrium statistical mechanics.

The energy-transfer function b_i has been solved for low-energy diatomic molecules by Herzfeld and co-workers by a straightforward, quantum-mechanical, collisional theory. The theoretical problem for highly excited polyatomic molecules has not been solved; but experiments on the quenching of fluorescence and deactivation of chemically activated radicals indicate that a fairly large amount of vibrational energy (variable from one foreign gas to another) is transferred upon each collision.   An important area of future research is to decide what collision rate is important here: hard sphere, close collision subject to attractive potential, or more detailed models.   The process, vibrational-translational energy transfer, does not involve any uniquely important structure.   There is no potential-energy barrier between reactants and products.   There is no "activated complex" or "transition state" for this process.

The unimolecular rate constant for activated molecules c_i has been treated by activated-complex ideas by Rice, Ramsperger, Kassel, Marcus, Rosen-stock $et\ al.$, Wahrhaftig, and others.   The essence of activated-complex theory is that rate phenomena reside in one and only one reaction coordinate, and then all other coordinates contribute "density of states," or "parallel paths," or "partition functions" (compare Eq. 29.12, p. 193, in Schiff's $Quantum\ Mechanics$, Ref. 23).   Kassel proposed that the decomposition rate of activated molecules vary as the number of quantum states that are consistent with supplying the reaction coordinate with a certain minimum energy.   Thus he reduced the function c_i to an undetermined rate constant D and the problem of density of states in the excited molecule.   Marcus and later Rosenstock $et\ al.$ in effect pointed out how to evaluate Kassel's rate constant D from activated-complex theory.   Recent experiments by Rabinovitch have demonstrated that these statistical theories are perhaps as good as experimental data on unimolecular reactions.   Thus the activated-complex methods developed between Rice and Ramsperger (1928) through Kassel (1928–32) and Marcus (1951) provide a sensible and useful theory of chemical reaction rates.

Collision theory starts with normal coordinates of the reactants and expresses the rate of reaction in terms of the dynamics of the reactant molecules.   For the decomposition of activated molecules, N. B. Slater set up just such a dynamic theory and averaged over phases and amplitudes of the reactant normal modes.   Slater's theory involves elegant mathematics and an unrealistic model.   This work has little value as a realistic chemical theory, but it is very significant as an important, though inadequate, step toward a dynamical theory of unimolecular reaction rates.

(iii) Termolecular Atom Recombinations

Atom recombination reactions are the limiting two-body case of the low-pressure limit of unimolecular reactions.   As such, vibrational-trans-lational energy transfer is the essence of the process, and this phenomenon is not completely understood for very high energies.   A consideration of potential-energy surfaces shows that there is no saddlepoint and no narrow channel that gives any significance to "activated-complex" notation. The reaction occurs over a wide range of the potential-energy surface, and by way of both classical "mechanisms" (A·M intermediate and excited A_2 intermediate). This case, then, is most naturally and properly treated from a collisional point of view. The ultrasimple collision theory considered in Chapter 14 gives fair agreement with the data for iodine atoms, over wide ranges of catalysts and temperature.

C.   COMPLEX REACTIONS AND ACTIVATED-COMPLEX THEORY

Over the years, some chemists have asserted that activated-complex theory can be applied directly to complex chemical reactions, without the necessity of analyzing the steps in the mechanism.   It has been stated that the "rate-determining step" can be identified by an energy criterion, the activated complex with the highest potential energy (or was it free energy?). Some believe that the "entropy of activation" for the overall, unresolved, complex mechanism has some value in interpreting the mechanism itself.

In Chapter 16, two complex, non-chain reactions of understood mechanism were examined in great detail.   The complex rate is a known function of several elementary rate constants.   Each of these elementary rate constants was interpreted in terms of activated-complex theory, both in the partition-function form and in the more vague "thermodynamic" form. From this theoretical treatment of all the elementary rate constants in the complex rate expression, it was shown that many claims about the power of activated-complex theory to handle complex reactions are false.   There is no energy criterion sufficient to find the rate-determining step.   In many reactions there is no rate-determining step.   There is no "reaction coordinate" in complex reactions, except for a sequence of isomerizations.

D.   THE TOOL KIT OF THEORETICAL CHEMICAL KINETICS

Insofar as fundamental nuclei and electrons are concerned, chemical kinetics is an extremely complicated subject.   Quantum-mechanical treatments can be carried through for simple chemical-physical processes, and fundamental theory can be used to set up several different approximate theories and semiempirical theories.   Extensive model calculations by means of computers can answer certain fundamental questions about reaction dynamics, and this information can be fed back into theories of more complex systems.   Molecular beam kinetics is a field in itself, "translational spectroscopy," and also provides experimental answers to dynamical questions that can be utilized by theories of chemical reaction rates.   It is unrealistic (extravagant) to think that fundamental theory, computer science, or molecular beam studies will completely solve all rate problems of interest to chemists.   Thus there remain the important (though now narrowed) fields of laboratory investigation of macroscopic rates and the formulation of chemists' theories of thermal rate constants.

Theories designed to predict chemical kinetic data deal with such abstractions as: chemical species, chemical bonds, bond energies, bond force constants, molecular distribution functions. At best, these theories utilize empiricism from the fields of molecular structure, molecular spectroscopy, and chemical thermodynamics. At second best, these theories also fit one parameter to some form of kinetic data. The immediate goal of chemical kinetics is to understand (predictions as well as explanations) chemical reaction rates in terms of empirical molecular properties, that is, bond lengths, bond energies, etc. Gas-phase, theoretical chemical kinetics is a small domain of physical science that operates at this level of abstraction. It has several tools (but, alas, no "powerful apparatus") with which to work on various problems. These tools include such things as: hard-sphere collision theory; Boltzmann's relation for independent particles; Eyring's activated-complex theory; Herzfeld's theory of translational-vibrational energy transfer; Rice-Ramsperger-Kassel-Marcus theory of molecular reaction rates; new ideas from quantum mechanics, model computations, and molecular beam studies; various potential-energy functions (Morse, Lennard-Jones, London-Polanyi-Eyring-Sato, and others); models for one-dimensional tunneling factors (Eckart, Bell, and others). Each of these methods has some value and some shortcomings; and all should be thoroughly understood, both by the experimenter who wants to interpret his data and by the theorist who wants to construct more powerful and more generally applicable tools.

Finally, it should be emphasized that with this "tool kit" gas-phase chemical kinetics is a vital, constructive, predictive science. At this time, theoretical kinetics has a number of specific contributions to pass on to the chemical engineer. Also, it contains enough incompletely solved and unsolved problems to challenge the imagination of vigorous young chemists.

Appendix

A. RELATION OF STEADY-STATE APPROXIMATION TO EXACT SOLUTIONS OF RATE EQUATIONS

(i) Exact Solutions

In view of the extensive use of the steady-state approximation in resolving complex reactions into elementary steps, it is worthwhile to give a detailed evaluation of the steady-state method for a particular complex reaction.

The mechanism to be considered is

$$A \underset{b}{\overset{a}{\rightleftarrows}} B \overset{c}{\longrightarrow} C \tag{A-1}$$

The rate expressions are

$$\frac{d[A]}{dt} = -a[A] + b[B]$$

$$\frac{d[B]}{dt} = a[A] - (b + c)[B] \tag{A-2}$$

$$\frac{d[C]}{dt} = c[B]$$

As is shown in many textbooks and repeatedly in many journal articles, any system of coupled first-order reactions such as Eqs. 1 and 2 can be solved exactly. The general solution to the set of differential equations, Eq. 2, is given by

$$[A] = \frac{[A_0]}{\lambda_2 - \lambda_3} [(a - \lambda_3) \exp(-\lambda_2 t) - (a - \lambda_2) \exp(-\lambda_3 t)]$$

$$[B] = \frac{[A_0]a}{\lambda_2 - \lambda_3} [-\exp(-\lambda_2 t) + \exp(-\lambda_3 t)] \tag{A-3}$$

$$[C] = [A_0] \left[1 + \frac{\lambda_2 \lambda_3}{(\lambda_2 - \lambda_3)} \frac{\exp(-\lambda_2 t)}{\lambda_2} - \frac{\exp(-\lambda_3 t)}{\lambda_3} \right]$$

where $\lambda_2 \lambda_3 = ac$, $\lambda_2 + \lambda_3 = a + b + c$, and $(a - \lambda_2)(a - \lambda_3) = -ab$. Depending on the values of the rate constants a, b, c, the build-up and decay of B, and the build-up of C can take on a large variety of forms.

(ii) Steady-State Approximation

The primary purpose of this analysis is to explore the nature of the steady-state approximation. The mechanism Eq. 1 is now considered to involve reactant A, transient intermediate B for which the steady-state approximation will be made, and product C. The observed rate of loss of reactant is

$$\mathbf{R} = -\frac{d[\mathrm{A}]}{dt} = a[\mathrm{A}] - b[\mathrm{B}] \tag{A-4}$$

The net change in the concentration of the intermediate is approximately zero relative to the large gross rates of its formation and destruction:

$$\frac{d[\mathrm{B}]}{dt} = a[\mathrm{A}] - (b+c)[\mathrm{B}] \approx 0 \tag{A-5}$$

Thus the steady-state concentration of intermediate B is

$$\frac{[\mathrm{B}]_{\mathrm{ss}}}{[\mathrm{A}]} = \frac{a}{b+c} \tag{A-6}$$

But the concentration of intermediate must be very much less than that of reactant. Thus the steady-state approximation places the following assumption on rate constants:

$$a \ll (b+c) \tag{A-7}$$

Substituting the steady-state relation, Eq. 6, in the rate equation 4, one obtains the easily integrated relation

$$-\frac{d[\mathrm{A}]}{dt} = \frac{ac}{b+c}[\mathrm{A}] \tag{A-8}$$

$$[\mathrm{A}] - [\mathrm{A}_0]\exp\left(-\frac{ac}{b+c}t\right) \tag{A-9}$$

$$[\mathrm{C}] = \mathrm{A}_0\left[1 - \exp\left(-\frac{ac}{b+c}t\right)\right] \tag{A-10}$$

These integrated expressions are to be compared with Eq. 3, with the approximation of Eq. 7 included:

$$[\mathrm{A}] = [\mathrm{A}_0]\frac{1}{b+c}\left[\frac{ab}{b+c}\exp\{-(b+c)t\} + (b+c)\exp\left\{-\frac{ac}{b+c}t\right\}\right]$$

$$[\mathrm{B}] = [\mathrm{A}_0]\frac{a}{b+c}\left[-\exp\{-(b+c)t\} + \exp\left\{-\frac{ac}{b+c}t\right\}\right] \tag{A-11}$$

$$[\mathrm{C}] = [\mathrm{A}_0]\left[1 + \frac{ac}{b+c}\left(\frac{\exp\{-(b+c)t\}}{b+c} - \frac{\exp\left\{-\frac{ac}{b+c}t\right\}}{\frac{ac}{b+c}}\right)\right]$$

It is seen that Eqs. 11 reduce to the steady-state Eqs. 6, 9, and 10 only after a time long enough so that

$$(b + c)t \gg 1 \tag{A-12}$$

Equations 7 and 12 are the answers to this inquiry: the steady-state assumption implies that certain rate constants are very much smaller than others, Eq. 7, and it requires a time scale not too short, Eq. 12.   A direct

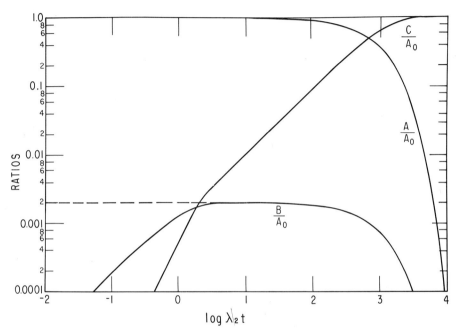

Fig. A-1. Comparison of exact integrated function (solid curve) with steady-state solution (dashed curve) for the mechanism $A \underset{b}{\overset{a}{\rightleftharpoons}} B \overset{c}{\longrightarrow} C$. The rate constants are $a = 0.002$, $b = c = 0.5$.

comparison of the exact integrated equations and the steady-state approximation for two sets of conditions is given by Figs. 1 and 2.   The exact solution is given by the solid line, and the steady-state approximation by the dashed line.   For Fig. 1, the steady-state condition as given by Eq. 7 is realized in that a is 0.002 and $b = c = 0.5$.   Time is plotted in dimensionless form as $\lambda_2 t$, and ratios of concentrations are given.   In agreement with Eq. 12, the steady-state result agrees with the exact result when $\lambda_2 t$ becomes equal to about 4 or 5.   The reactant and product never deviate significantly from the steady-state result.   The situation is different in Fig. 2; here all three rate constants are equal, $a = b = c = 1$.   The concentration of the intermediate departs markedly from the steady-state value, at all values except the one point where B goes through a maximum (then, of course, dB/dt is truly zero). The final product lags very considerably behind the value predicted by the steady-state hypothesis.

(iii) Equilibrium Approximation

For a mechanism such as Eq. 1, one often assumes the reactant and intermediate to be in chemical equilibrium:

$$K = [B]/[A] = a/b \qquad\qquad \text{(A–13)}$$

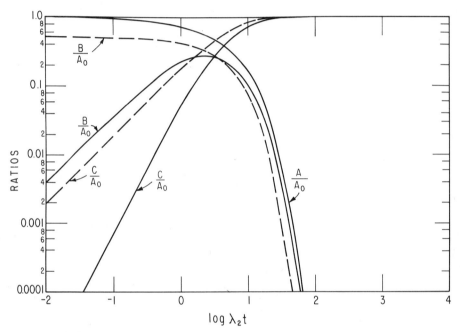

Fig. A–2. The same as Fig. I, except that the rate constants are $a = b = c = 1.0$.

From Eq. 6, it can be seen that the equilibrium assumption requires that the rate constant for conversion of intermediate to product is small compared to the rate constant for reconversion of the intermediate to reactant, that is,

$$c \ll b \qquad\qquad \text{(A–14)}$$

The equilibrium assumption is a special, more restricted case under the steady-state method, and it should not be made until the steady-state treatment shows it to be valid. Subject to restrictions of Eqs. 7, 12, and 14, the integrated expressions for reactant and product are

$$[A] = [A_0] \exp(-Kct)$$
$$[C] = [A_0][1 - \exp(-Kct)] \qquad\qquad \text{(A–15)}$$
$$[B] = K[A_0] \exp(-Kct)$$

B. EVALUATION OF STRETCHING- AND BENDING-FORCE CONSTANTS FOR A THREE-ATOM SYSTEM FROM A POTENTIAL-ENERGY SURFACE

To evaluate the stretching-force constants from a potential energy surface, one finds the extremum 0, and graphically or numerically obtains three appropriate curvatures through 0. The force constant F_{11} is given by $2\Delta V = F_{11}r_1^2$ for a line through 0, parallel to the R_1 axis so that $r_2 = 0$. The force constant F_{22} is given by $2\Delta V = F_{22}r_2^2$ for a line through 0 parallel to the R_2 axis so that $r_1 = 0$. To obtain F_{12}, one must find a curvature through some line not parallel to R_1 or R_2; either COD or EOF of Fig. 4–3 is convenient, although other lines through 0 of slope c may be used. If $c = dR_2/dR_1$, the general expression for changes of potential energy very close to the saddlepoint is

$$2\,dV = (F_{11} + c^2 F_{22} + 2c F_{12})\,dR_1^2 \tag{B–1}$$

The square of the distance along this line is

$$(d\rho)^2 = (dR_1)^2 + (dR_2)^2 = (1 + c^2)(dR_1)^2 \tag{B–2}$$

The force constant along a line of slope c is

$$F_c = 2\,dV/(d\rho)^2 = (F_{11} + c^2 F_{22} + 2\,c F_{12})/(1 + c^2) \tag{B–3}$$

The value of the interaction constant is

$$F_{12} = [F_c(1 + c^2) - F_{11} - c^2 F_{22}]/2c \tag{B–4}$$

A potential-energy function is often expressed in terms of the distances R_1, R_2, and R_3. The relation between R_3 and Φ is given by the cosine law:

$$R_3^2 = R_1^2 + R_2^2 - 2R_1 R_2 \cos \Phi \tag{B–5}$$

for which the first and second derivatives are

$$\left(\frac{\partial R_3}{\partial \Phi}\right)_{R_1, R_2} = \frac{R_1 R_2}{R_3} \sin \Phi \tag{B–6}$$

$$\left(\frac{\partial^2 R_3}{\partial \Phi^2}\right)_{R_1, R_2} = \frac{R_1 R_2}{R_3} \cos \Phi - \frac{R_1^2 R_2^2}{R_3^3} \sin^2 \Phi \tag{B–7}$$

The first derivative of the potential-energy surface with respect to angle evaluated at an extremum is zero, and the second derivative is

$$F_\Phi = \left(\frac{\partial V}{\partial R_3}\right)\left(\frac{\partial^2 R_3}{\partial \Phi^2}\right) + \left(\frac{\partial R_3}{\partial \Phi}\right)^2 \left(\frac{\partial^2 V}{\partial R_3^2}\right) \tag{B–8}$$

Therefore, for a linear molecule or complex, the bending-force constant is

$$F_\Phi = - \frac{R_1 R_2}{R_3}\left(\frac{\partial V}{\partial R_3}\right)_{R_1, R_2} \tag{B–9}$$

and for a nonlinear three-atom complex it is

$$F_{\Phi} = \frac{R_1 R_2}{R_3}\left[\left(\cos\Phi - \frac{R_1 R_2}{R_3^2}\sin^2\Phi\right)\left(\frac{\partial V}{\partial R_3}\right) + \frac{R_1 R_2}{R_3}\sin^2\Phi\left(\frac{\partial^2 V}{\partial R_3^2}\right)\right] \quad \text{(B–10)}$$

C. SEPARATE DIAGONALIZATION OF KINETIC ENERGY OR POTENTIAL ENERGY

(i) Removal of Cross-Product Terms in a General Quadratic Expression in Two Dimensions

In two cartesian dimensions, X and Y, the general quadratic expression is

$$g(X, Y) = A_{11}X^2 + 2A_{12}XY + A_{22}Y^2 \quad \text{(C–1)}$$

The origin of the function is at $X = 0$, $Y = 0$, and first derivatives are zero at the origin.

The function g may be left completely unchanged, but it may be described by another set of cartesian axes, ξ and η, rotated by an angle Θ about the origin. A given point in space may be located by the two distances, X, Y, or by the two distances, ξ, η. From Fig. 1, the following relations between these four distances and the angle Θ are evident:

$$X = \xi/\cos\Theta + Y\tan\Theta \quad \text{(C–2)}$$
$$\eta = Y/\cos\Theta + \xi\tan\Theta \quad \text{(C–3)}$$

From these relations one readily solves for either pair of variables in terms of the other pair:

$$X = \eta\sin\Theta + \xi\cos\Theta$$
$$Y = \eta\cos\Theta - \xi\sin\Theta \quad \text{(C–4)}$$

$$\eta = X\sin\Theta + Y\cos\Theta$$
$$\xi = X\cos\Theta - Y\sin\Theta \quad \text{(C–5)}$$

The relative scale of the axes ξ and η may be changed, and this distorts the original function g. The change in scale may be accomplished by replacing η by $\alpha\zeta$:

$$X = \alpha\zeta\sin\Theta + \xi\cos\Theta$$
$$Y = \alpha\zeta\cos\Theta - \xi\sin\Theta \quad \text{(C–6)}$$

Equations 6 may be substituted in Eq. 1 and the coefficients of ξ^2, $2\xi\zeta$, and ζ^2 collected:

$$g = \xi^2[A_{11}\cos^2\Theta - 2A_{12}\sin\Theta\cos\Theta + A_{22}\sin^2\Theta]$$
$$+ 2\alpha\xi\zeta[A_{11}\sin\Theta\cos\Theta + A_{12}(\cos^2\Theta - \sin^2\Theta) - A_{22}\sin\Theta\cos\Theta]$$
$$+ \alpha^2\zeta^2[A_{11}\sin^2\Theta + 2A_{12}\sin\Theta\cos\Theta + A_{22}\cos^2\Theta]$$
$$= B_{11}\xi^2 + 2B_{12}\xi\zeta + B_{22}\zeta^2 \quad \text{(C–7)}$$

If α is unity, the function g is undistorted, and the only change is the orientation of the cartesian axes describing the function. Regardless of the value of the scale factor α, the condition on Θ that sets B_{12} to zero is

$$\frac{A_{11} - A_{22}}{A_{12}} = \tan\Theta - \cot\Theta \tag{C-8}$$

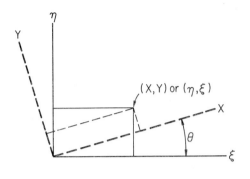

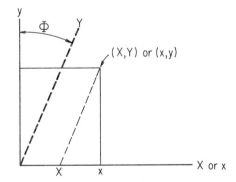

Fig. C-I. Coordinate transformations.

With this value of Θ, the further condition on the scale factor α that makes B_{11} equal to B_{22} is

$$\alpha^2 = \frac{A_{11}\cos^2\Theta - 2A_{12}\sin\Theta\cos\Theta + A_{22}\sin^2\Theta}{A_{11}\sin^2\Theta + 2A_{12}\sin\Theta\cos\Theta + A_{22}\cos^2\Theta} \tag{C-9}$$

Thus by a simple rotation of cartesian axes the general quadratic expression, Eq. 1, may be diagonalized; by a change of scale factor, it may be put in the form

$$g = B(\xi^2 + \zeta^2) \tag{C-10}$$

There are other transformations that can diagonalize Eq. 1: for example, the original cartesian axes may be skewed, with or without a change of scale factor. From Fig. 1, one readily sees the relation between the new axes, x and y, and the original axes X and Y subjected to the transformations

$$X = x - y \tan \Phi$$
$$Y = \beta y \sec \Phi \tag{C-11}$$

where Φ is the skew angle between original and final y axes and β is the scale factor. Eqs. 11 may be substituted in Eq. 1, and the coefficients of x^2, $2xy$, and y^2 collected:

$$\begin{aligned} g &= A_{11}x^2 + 2xy[A_{12}\beta \sec \Phi - A_{11} \tan \Phi] \\ &+ y^2[A_{11}\tan^2 \Phi - 2\beta A_{12} \sec \Phi \tan \Phi + \beta^2 A_{22} \sec^2 \Phi] \\ &= C_{11}x^2 + 2C_{12}xy + C_{22}y^2 \end{aligned} \tag{C-12}$$

The condition that sets C_{12} to zero is

$$\sin \Phi = \beta A_{12}/A_{11} \tag{C-13}$$

The further condition on the scale factor that makes C_{11} equal to C_{22} is

$$\beta = (A_{11}/A_{22})^{1/2} \tag{C-14}$$

The condition on the skew angle Φ that both diagonalizes Eq. 1 and equates the coefficients is

$$\sin \Phi = A_{12}/(A_{11}A_{22})^{1/2} \tag{C-15}$$

Thus by skewing the cartesian axes and by changing the scale, Eq. 1 may be put in the form

$$g = C(x^2 + y^2) \tag{C-16}$$

(ii) Separate Diagonalization of Internal Kinetic Energy of Linear Triatomic Complex

Relative to a fixed center of mass, the kinetic energy of a linear triatomic complex

(a)————(b)————(c)
R_1　　　R_2

is given the expression

$$T = \frac{1}{2M}[m_a(m_b + m_c)\dot{R}_1^2 + 2m_a m_c \dot{R}_1\dot{R}_2 + m_c(m_a + m_b)\dot{R}_2^2] \tag{C-17}$$

where $\dot{R}_1$ is dR_1/dt, and M is the molecular mass. This may be regarded as a general quadratic expression in the two-dimensional cartesian coordinates, $\dot{R}_1$ and $\dot{R}_2$. In another set of cartesian axes, ξ and ζ, rotated by an angle Θ with respect to $\dot{R}_1$ and $\dot{R}_2$, the kinetic energy is diagonalized if (compare Eq. 9)

$$\tan \Theta = \frac{m_b(m_a - m_c)}{2m_a m_c} \pm \left[\left(\frac{m_b(m_a - m_c)}{2m_a m_c}\right)^2 + 1\right]^{1/2} \tag{C-18}$$

For the special case of equal mass of the end atoms, $m_a = m_c$, $\tan \Theta = \pm 1$, or the axes are rotated by $\pm 45°$. For this special case, the scale factor that equates B_{11} and B_{22} is $\alpha = (m_b/M)^{1/2}$, and the kinetic energy is

$$T = \frac{m_a m_b}{2M}\, (\xi^2 + \zeta^2) \qquad\qquad (\text{C--19})$$

In a third cartesian system, x and y, relative to which the axis Y is skewed by an angle Φ, the kinetic energy is diagonalized if

$$\sin \Phi = \beta m_c/(m_b + m_c) \qquad\qquad (\text{C--20})$$

The coefficient of x^2 is equal to that of y^2 if the scale factor is

$$\beta = \left[\frac{m_a(m_b + m_c)}{m_c(m_a + m_b)}\right]^{1/2} \qquad\qquad (\text{C--21})$$

The inclusion of this scale factor in Eq. 20 gives

$$\sin \Phi = \left[\frac{m_a m_c}{(m_b + m_a)(m_b + m_c)}\right]^{1/2} \qquad\qquad (\text{C--22})$$

For the special case of equal mass of the end atoms, $m_a = m_c$, the scale factor is unity and the skew angle is given by

$$\sin \Phi = \frac{m_a}{m_a + m_b} \qquad\qquad (\text{C--23})$$

The kinetic-energy expression for this special case is

$$T = \frac{m_a(m_a + m_b)}{2M}\, (x^2 + y^2) \qquad\qquad (\text{C--24})$$

Thus there are (at least) two transformations that diagonalize the internal kinetic energy of the linear triatomic complex and that also make the "mass" independent of direction of motion in some two-dimensional plane representing the system. As will be noted from Eqs. 19 and 24, the constant "mass" is different for the two transformations. At first sight, this appears as a contradiction; however, the transformed coordinates themselves depend on mass, and the "effective mass" in the sense of Chapter 3 does depend on the type of motion being executed. It is often useful to apply a coordinate transformation to a potential-energy surface in order to explore the classical trajectory during a collision; in this case the classical motion is given by a ball rolling on the transformed potential energy surface. It must be remembered, however, that the transformations depend on mass, and a different potential energy surface must be constructed for different isotopes as reactants.

(iii) Potential Energy

Near the saddlepoint, the potential energy is given by Eq. 4–35, a general quadratic expression in r_1 and r_2, deviations from the saddlepoint. From Eqs. 7 and 8 one is assured that there is some angle of rotation Θ that puts the potential energy in the form

$$V - V_0 = \tfrac{1}{2}[F_\xi \xi^2 + F_\eta \eta^2] \tag{C-25}$$

That is, there are orthogonal coordinates ξ and η along which there are no interaction terms. Along the "reaction path," the energy depends on the making and breaking of bonds, and the complex is by no means "like a normal molecule." Perpendicular to the reaction path ρ is the direction σ with zero component "along the reaction path." Increase or decrease of σ stretches or compresses bonds of the complex as if in a normal molecule. Thus the force constants in these two directions depend on entirely different physical considerations.

(iv) Simultaneous Diagonalization of Kinetic Energy and Potential Energy

For the linear three-atom complex, the kinetic energy is given by Eq. 17 and the potential energy near the saddlepoint by Eq. 4–35. The kinetic energy is in terms of time derivatives of coordinates, $\dot{r}_1$, $\dot{r}_2$, and the potential energy in terms of displacement coordinates from equilibrium structure, r_1, r_2. The diagonalization of either kinetic or potential energy in general leaves the other non-diagonal. The transformation of variables that simultaneously diagonalizes both kinetic energy and potential energy is unique; these unique coordinates are the "normal coordinates."

D.   CONSTANTS AND CONVERSION FACTORS

Avogadro number n_A	6.02×10^{23}
Planck's constant h	6.63×10^{-27} erg-sec.
Boltzmann constant k	1.38×10^{-16} erg deg.$^{-1}$
Molar gas constant R	8.31×10^7 ergs mole^{-1} deg.$^{-1}$
	1.987 cal. mole^{-1} deg.$^{-1}$
Velocity of light c	3.00×10^{10} cm. sec.$^{-1}$
Electronic charge ε	4.80×10^{-10} e.s.u.
Radius of Bohr orbit a_0	0.529×10^{-8} cm.
1 electron volt $=$	1.602×10^{-12} ergs
$=$	8066 cm.$^{-1}$
$=$	23062 cal. mole^{-1}

De Broglie wavelength (Eqs. 2–2 and 2–3, Table 2–1):

$\Lambda = h/(2\pi mkT)^{1/2} = 17.45/(MT)^{1/2}$

$\alpha = 2\pi V/h\nu = 2.20\ V/\omega$ (Eq. 2–16 and 2–32), ω in cm.$^{-1}$

$h\nu/kT = 1.439\ \omega/T$, ω in cm.$^{-1}$

$kT/h = 2.083 \times 10^{10}T$ sec.$^{-1}$

Translational partition function (Eq. 6–19):
$$f_t^3 = 1.88 \times 10^{20}(MT)^{3/2}V$$

Rotational partition function (Eqs. 6–20 and 6–21):
$$f_r^2 = 0.0412IT/\sigma$$
$$f_r^3 = 0.0148(I_1I_2I_3)^{1/2}T^{3/2}/\sigma$$

Vibrational partition function (Eq. 6–22):
$$f_v = (1 - e^{-u})^{-1} \qquad u = h\nu/kT$$

Classical vibrational amplitude (Eq. 6–23, Table 12–1):
$$1 = (2\pi kT/F)^{1/2} = 0.00931(T/F)^{1/2}$$

Quantum correction factors for vibrations (Eq. 6–28, Table 10–13):
$$\Gamma = (u/2)/\sinh(u/2)$$
$$\Theta = d\ln\Gamma/d\ln T$$

Eckart tunneling corrections (Eq. 2–31, Table 2–2)

Hard-sphere collision rates (Eqs. 9–21 to 28)

Jacobian factors for molecular coordinates (Table 6–1)

Algebraic equations for vibration frequencies of linear three-atom molecule:

$$\text{a}\!-\!\!-\!\!-\!\!x\!-\!\!-\!\!-\text{b}$$
$$R_1 \qquad R_2$$

$$\lambda_\alpha = \tfrac{1}{2}[B + (B^2 - 4C)^{1/2}]$$
$$\lambda_\beta = \tfrac{1}{2}[B - (B^2 - 4C)^{1/2}]$$
$$B = \frac{F_{11}}{m_a} + \frac{F_{22}}{m_b} + \frac{F_{11} + F_{22} - 2F_{12}}{m_x}$$
$$C = \frac{(F_{11}F_{22} - F_{12}^2)(m_a + m_x + m_b)}{m_a m_b m_x}$$
$$\lambda_\Phi = F_\Phi\left[\frac{1}{R_1^2 m_a} + \frac{1}{R_2^2 m_b} + \left(\frac{1}{R_1} + \frac{1}{R_2}\right)^2\frac{1}{m_x}\right]$$
$$\omega = 1301.9\lambda^{1/2} \text{ cm}^{-1}$$

F in units of 10^5 dynes/cm

F_Φ in units of 10^{-11} ergs/radian^2

R in angstrom units

m in gram-molar mass units

E. BOND-ENERGY–BOND-ORDER METHODS

(i) Hydrogen Transfer Reactions: Activation Energies,

Force Constants, and Rate Constants[41a]

(a) Bond-Energy–Bond-Order (BEBO) Method for Three-Atom Model of Reaction. For the reaction $AH + B \rightarrow A \cdots H \cdots B \rightarrow A + HB$, the following model and notation are used:

Model	A $\cdots$ H $\cdots$ B		
Bond length	R_1	R_2	$R_3 = R_1 + R_2$
Bond order	n	m	
Bond energy index	p	q	
Single-bond length	R_{1s}	R_{2s}	R_{3s}
Single-bond force constant	F_{1s}	F_{2s}	F_{3s}
Single-bond energy	E_{1s}	E_{2s}	E_{3s}
Morse parameter	β_1	β_2	β_3
$R - R_s$	r_1	r_2	r_3

$$\Delta R_s = R_{1s} + R_{2s} - R_{3s}$$
$$\gamma = 0.26\beta_3$$
$$B = \tfrac{1}{2}\exp\left(-\beta\Delta R_s\right)$$

This method, as presented here, is used only where the transferred atom is hydrogen. The energy of the system V along the locus of the line of constant bond order, $m = 1 - n$, is

$$
\begin{aligned}
V &= E_{1s} - E_{1s}n^p - E_{2s}m^q + E_{3s}(\tfrac{1}{2}e^{-\beta r_3})(1 + \tfrac{1}{2}e^{-\beta r_3}) \\
&= E_{1s}(1 - n^p) - E_{2s}(1 - n)^q + E_{3s}B(n - n^2)^\gamma[1 + B(n - n^2)^\gamma] \quad \text{(E–1)}
\end{aligned}
$$

To avoid undue accumulation of algebra in the derivation of force constants the last term is neglected, or the expression used for V is

$$V = E_{1s}(1 - n^p) - E_{2s}(1 - n)^q + E_{3s}B(n - n^2)^\gamma \quad \text{(E–2)}$$

At the maximum energy along this line, $\mathbf{V^*}$, the first derivative of V with respect to order n is zero:

$$
\begin{aligned}
\frac{dV}{dn} &= -E_{1s}pn^{p-1} + E_{2s}q(1 - n)^{q-1} + E_{3s}B\gamma(n - n^2)^{\gamma-1}(1 - 2n) \\
&= 0 \text{ at } \mathbf{V^*}
\end{aligned}
\quad \text{(E–3)}
$$

This expression can be solved numerically for the orders, n^* and $1 - n^*$, at the maximum. These orders substituted into Equation 1 for V give directly the potential energy of activation $\mathbf{V^*}$, or V can be evaluated point by point for a series of values of n from 1 to 0. The second derivative of V with respect to the progress variable n is

$$\frac{\partial^2 V}{\partial n^2} = -\frac{E_{1s}p(p-1)}{n^{2-p}} - \frac{E_{2s}q(q-1)}{m^{2-q}} - \frac{E_{3s}2B\gamma}{(nm)^{1-\gamma}}\left[1 + \frac{(1-\gamma)(1-2n)^2}{2nm}\right] \quad \text{(E–4)}$$

where $m = 1 - n$. Distance along the path of constant order from the saddlepoint is the variable ρ. For any small displacement along ρ,

$$(d\rho)^2 = (dR_1)^2 + (dR_2)^2 \quad \text{(E–5)}$$

From Pauling's Eq. 4-49, the distances along ρ are

$$R_1 = R_{1s} - 0.26 \ln n$$
$$R_2 = R_{2s} - 0.26 \ln (1 - n) \qquad \text{(E-6)}$$

and differential changes of these distances along ρ

$$dR_1 = -0.26 \, dn/n$$
$$dR_2 = 0.26 \, dn/(1 - n) \qquad \text{(E-7)}$$

Thus displacement along ρ is given by

$$(d\rho)^2 = (0.26)^2[1/n^2 + 1/m^2](dn)^2 \qquad \text{(E-8)}$$

and the ratio of differentials is

$$\left(\frac{dn}{d\rho}\right)^2 = 14.8 \, \frac{n^2 m^2}{n^2 + m^2} \qquad \text{(E-9)}$$

The second derivative of V with respect to ρ can be written as

$$V = V(n)$$
$$\frac{dV}{d\rho} = \frac{dV}{dn} \frac{dn}{d\rho} \qquad \text{(E-10)}$$
$$\frac{d^2V}{d\rho^2} = \frac{d^2V}{dn^2}\left(\frac{dn}{d\rho}\right)^2 + \frac{dV}{dn} \frac{d^2n}{d\rho^2}$$

The force constant along the reaction path F_ρ is the second derivative evaluated at the point of maximum $\mathbf{V^*}$, where dV/dn is zero:

$$F_\rho = \left(\frac{d^2V}{dn^2}\right)\left(\frac{dn}{d\rho}\right)^2_* \qquad \text{(E-11)}$$

The two factors in this expression are given above. The numerical value of this force constant is

$$-F_\rho = \frac{10.27}{\dfrac{1}{n^2} + \dfrac{1}{m^2}} \left\{ \frac{E_{1s}p(p-1)}{n^{2-p}} + \frac{E_{2s}q(q-1)}{m^{2-q}} \right.$$
$$\left. + \frac{E_{3s}2B\gamma}{(nm)^{1-\gamma}}\left[1 + \frac{(1-\gamma)(1-2n)^2}{2nm}\right] \right\} \qquad \text{(E-12)}$$

where F_ρ is in dynes/cm. and E_s in calories/mole.

In general, around a saddlepoint on a rectilinear R_1-R_2 potential-energy surface, the potential energy for small displacements is (Eq. 4-35)

$$V - V^* = \tfrac{1}{2}F_{11}r_1^2 + F_{12}r_1r_2 + \tfrac{1}{2}F_{22}r_2^2 \qquad \text{(E-13)}$$

Some rotation of axes (Eqs. C-2 to C-10) will locate two variables in which the potential-energy function will contain only square terms, no cross product terms.   It is assumed in the BEBO method that one of these two directions is along the reaction path through the saddlepoint, ρ, and therefore the other is perpendicular to ρ and is called σ.   The complex falls apart along the path ρ, and one does not expect Badger's rule (Fig. 4–11) for force constants to be applicable to motions along ρ.   On the other hand, motion perpendicular to ρ is a motion like the stretching of a normal molecule, and Badger's rule as given by Eq. 4–55 should be applicable, $F = F_s n$.   Thus the potential energy along σ, perpendicular to ρ, is assumed to be

$$(V - \mathbf{V^*})_\sigma = \frac{1}{2}\left\{ F_{1s}n(dR_1)_\sigma^2 + F_{2s}m(dR_2)_\sigma^2 + \left(\frac{\partial^2 V_T}{\partial R_3^2}\right)(dR_3)_\sigma^2 \right\} \quad \text{(E–14)}$$

As shown above, along the path ρ

$$(dR_2/dR_1)_\rho = -n/m \quad \text{(E–15)}$$

From the condition for the slope of the normal to a curve

$$\left(\frac{dR_2}{dR_1}\right)_\sigma = -\frac{1}{\left(\dfrac{dR_1}{dR_2}\right)_\rho} = \frac{m}{n} \quad \text{(E–16)}$$

For a motion along σ, the force constant is given by

$$(V - \mathbf{V^*})_\sigma = \tfrac{1}{2}F_\sigma(d\sigma)^2 \quad \text{(E–17)}$$

For a displacement along the distance σ

$$(d\sigma)^2 = (dR_1)^2 + (dR_2)^2 = (dR_1)^2[1 + (m/n)^2] \quad \text{(E–18)}$$

Along σ both dR_2 and dR_3 can be expressed in terms of dR_1 and thus $d\sigma$:

$$dR_2 = (m/n)\,dR_1 \quad \text{(E–19)}$$

$$dR_3 = dR_1 + dR_2 = dR_1(1 + m/n) = dR_1/n \quad \text{(E–20)}$$

Thus the potential energy along σ is

$$V - \mathbf{V^*} = \frac{1}{2}\left\{ \frac{F_{1s}n^3 + F_{2s}m^3 + \dfrac{\partial^2 V_T}{\partial R_3^2}}{n^2 + m^2} \right\} \quad \text{(E–21)}$$

The approximate expression for V_T is

$$V_T = \frac{E_{3s}}{2}\exp\left[-\beta(R_3 - R_{3s})\right] = \frac{E_{3s}}{2}\exp\left(-\beta r_3\right) \quad \text{(E–22)}$$

$$\frac{\partial^2 V_T}{\partial R_3^2} = \frac{2E_{3s}\beta^2}{4}\exp\left(-\beta r_3\right)$$

$$= \frac{F_{3s}(nm)^\gamma}{4}\exp\left(-\beta\Delta R_s\right) = \frac{F_{3s}(nm)^\gamma B}{2} \quad \text{(E–23)}$$

Thus the force constant along σ evaluated at the saddlepoint is

$$F_\sigma = \frac{F_{1s}n^3 + F_{2s}m^3 + (F_{3s}/2)(nm)^\gamma B}{n^2 + m^2} \tag{E–24}$$

For normal-mode analysis it is convenient to have force constants in valence-bond coordinates, with interaction constant, that is F_{11}, F_{22}, and F_{12}. In the cartesian axes r_1 and r_2 the potential-energy function (for small displacements) is given by Eq. 13. In cartesian axes ρ and σ with the same origin as r_1 and r_2 but rotated through an angle whose tangent is m/n, there is no cross-product term so that (Eq. C–8) one has a relation between F_{11}, F_{22}, and F_{12}

$$\frac{F_{22} - F_{11}}{F_{12}} = \frac{m}{n} - \frac{n}{m} \tag{E–25}$$

and the potential energy is

$$V - V^* = \tfrac{1}{2}F_\rho(d\rho)^2 + \tfrac{1}{2}F_\sigma(d\sigma)^2 \tag{E–26}$$

For zero displacement along σ, combination of Eqs. 26, 13, and 15 gives

$$F_\rho[1 + (n/m)^2] = F_{11} + (n/m)^2 F_{22} - 2(n/m)F_{12} \tag{E–27}$$

For zero displacement along ρ, combination of Eqs. 26, 13, and 16 gives

$$F_\sigma = [1 + (m/n)^2] = F_{11} + (m/n)^2 F_{22} + 2(m/n)F_{12} \tag{E–28}$$

Simultaneous solution of Eqs. 25, 27, and 28 gives the desired relations

$$F_{11} = \frac{F_\rho m^2 + F_\sigma n^2}{n^2 + m^2}$$

$$F_{22} = \frac{F_\rho n^2 + F_\sigma m^2}{n^2 + m^2} \tag{E–29}$$

$$F_{12} = \frac{(-F_\rho + F_\sigma)nm}{n^2 + m^2}$$

For a linear triatomic complex, the general expression for the bending force constant was derived in Appendix B and given as

$$F_\Phi = \frac{-R_1R_2}{R_3}\left(\frac{\partial V}{\partial R_3}\right)_{R_1,R_2} \tag{E–30}$$

The derivative of Eq. 2 with respect to R_3 at constant R_1 and R_2 is

$$\left(\frac{\partial V}{\partial R_3}\right)_{R_1,R_2} = -\frac{E_{3s}\beta}{2}\exp(-\beta r_3)$$

$$= -\frac{F_{3s}}{4\beta}\exp(-\beta r_3)$$

$$= -\frac{F_{3s}}{4\beta}(nm)^\gamma \exp(-\beta \Delta R_s) \tag{E–31}$$

The bending-force constant can be expressed in any of the forms of Eq. 31

$$F_\Phi = \frac{R_1 R_2 F_{3s}}{4\beta_3 R_3}(nm)^\gamma \exp(-\beta \Delta R_s) \qquad \text{(E–32)}$$

If F_{3s} is expressed in usual units of 10^5 dynes/cm. and R_1 and R_2 in Å, then the bending force constant is a multiple of 10^{-11} ergs/radian².

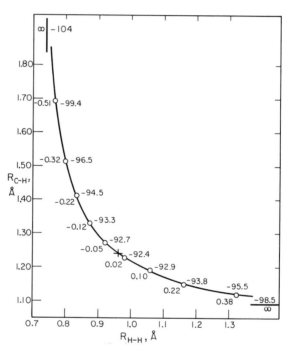

Fig. E–I. Line of constant order for the reaction $CH_3 + H_2$. Numerical values of energies in kcal and distances from the maximum in Å are indicated.

This method does not give a complete potential energy surface but only a narrow curving parabolic channel between reactants and products, for example, Fig. E–1. With a complete potential-energy surface as provided by the LEPS method, one can almost imagine that the locus of most probable tunneling can be found. On the LEPS surface one can clearly see that the base from which tunneling occurs must lie much higher than the minimum energy of reactants, and it may even be higher than the zero-point-energy of the reactant. With the BEBO method the only step that can be taken in this direction is to place the base for tunneling at the zero point energy of reactant. Specifically, one uses the Eckart function, and the parameters for Eqs. 2–12 to 2–17 are

$$V_1 = \mathbf{V}^* - ZPE \text{ (reactant)}$$
$$V_2 = \mathbf{V}^* - ZPE \text{ (product)}$$
$$\nu^* = \tfrac{1}{2}\pi\left(\frac{-F_\rho}{m_\rho}\right)^{1/2}$$

(E–33)

where ZPE stands for "zero-point energy," F_ρ is given by Eq. 12, and the effective mass is given by Eq. 3–23 and Eq. 15:

$$m_\rho = \frac{m_A m_c(1 - n/m) + m_c m_B(n/m)^2 + m_A m_B}{M[1 + (n/m)^2]}$$

(E–34)

When the zero-point energy of reactant is greater than the potential energy of activation, no tunneling correction is made; although quantum effects are surely operable, one does not know how to account for them. Tunneling factors are obtained from Table 2–2. The range of validity of this method and its expected range of error in computing the tunneling correction is not known. The arbitrary rule has been used of continuing these calculations until a tunneling factor as high as 10 is encountered, and then the method is discontinued.

(b) Rate Constant Expressions. From the force constants, bond lengths, and masses, one finds the vibrational frequencies by the methods of Chapter 5. The rate constant for a three-atom complex is given by Eq. 12–13, for example. For complexes that have more than three atoms, one calculates the rate by the three-atom model and multiplies by the ratio of $\mathbf{B}'$ (real model)/$\mathbf{B}'$(three-atom model); where the $\mathbf{B}'$ factors are given in Chapter 12 or similar ones are readily derived for any model. As a simple example, suppose the real reaction involved 4 atoms, but the rate was calculated by use of the three atom model. The ratio of $\mathbf{B}'$ term is given by Eqs. 12–15 and 13:

$$\frac{\mathbf{B}_4'}{\mathbf{B}_3'} = \left(\frac{R_\ddagger}{R}\right)_3^2 \left(\frac{F}{F_\ddagger'}\right)_3^{1/2} \frac{l_\beta^2}{4\pi} \approx \frac{l_\beta^2}{4\pi}$$

(E–35)

Thus the rate constant is evaluated by use of the simple 3-atom model and corrected to the real model by use of the proper number of vibrational amplitudes and constant terms from the Jacobian factors, J, such as 4π, $8\pi^2$, etc. The quantum corrections are made for the three-atom model and no further quantum corrections are made. This procedure is followed because it has been seen that $\mathbf{A}$ or $\mathbf{B}$ factors are sensitive to model but the kinetic isotope effect, which depends almost exclusively on the quantum corrections, does not depend strongly on model so long as a self-consistent one is used between reactants and complex.

(ii) Kinetic Isotope Effect

To use the BEBO method for calculating the kinetic isotope effect, it is recommended that q be set equal to p and that p be fitted to the observed activation energy. Since the activation energy cancels out from the calculated isotope effect, this procedure avoids distorting the isotope effect by

TABLE E–I

Relation of Index p to Relative Bond Strengths of
Reactant and Product and Potential Energy of Activation, and
Order of Bond Number One in the Complex

$\dfrac{V_{act}}{E_1}$	E_2/E_1								
	1.00	1.05	1.10	1.2	1.3	1.5	1.7	2.0	
0.01	1.012	1.03	1.054	1.087	1.112	1.155	1.180	1.226	p
	0.500	0.83	0.850	0.890	0.914	0.935	0.950	0.995	n^x
	0.064	0.08	0.10	0.11	0.12	0.12	0.13	0.13	$-F_\rho/E_1^{(a)}$
0.02	1.025	1.057	1.078	1.110	1.141	1.188	1.220	1.274	p
	0.500	0.700	0.775	0.841	0.869	0.897	0.918	0.925	n^x
	0.128	0.18	0.22	0.23	0.24	0.25	0.26	0.27	$-F_\rho/E_1$
0.04	1.055	1.088	1.112	1.153	1.187	1.240	1.290	1.335	p
	0.500	0.636	0.706	0.766	0.803	0.842	0.860	0.890	n^x
	0.286	0.37	0.44	0.49	0.51	0.53	0.55	0.58	$-F_\rho/E_1$
0.07	1.105	1.130	1.162	1.207	1.244	1.305	1.350	1.414	p
	0.500	0.596	0.643	0.708	0.746	0.790	0.819	0.842	n^x
	0.551	0.65	0.76	0.84	0.88	0.95	0.96	1.0	$-F_\rho/E_1$
0.10	1.152	1.186	1.212	1.260	1.300	1.367	1.420	1.487	p
	0.500	0.566	0.613	0.669	0.706	0.750	0.778	0.805	n
	0.805	0.97	1.07	1.21	1.30	1.38	1.45	1.53	$-F_\rho/E_1$
0.15	1.233	1.269	1.295	1.350	1.392	1.465	1.525	—	p
	0.500	0.546	0.580	0.628	0.660	0.705	0.735	—	n
	1.25	1.46	1.59	1.80	1.9	2.1	2.2	—	$-F_\rho/E_1$
0.20	1.322	1.357	1.387	1.442	1.473	—	—	—	p
	0.500	0.534	0.560	0.602	0.635	—	—	—	n
	1.74	1.98	2.15	2.4	2.5	—	—	—	$-F_\rho/E_1$

(a) In dimensions of (dynes/cm.) ÷ (calories/mole).

errors in the activation energy. After p is fitted to the observed activation energy, the operations given in section i above can be followed to evaluate force constants and vibration frequencies. This procedure gives results that are very close to those calculated by the LEPS method, and it is very much simpler.

(iii) Atom Transfer Reactions Other than Hydrogen[41b]

Because of core polarization of the atom being transferred (among other reasons), one cannot apply the above model for transfer of atoms other than hydrogen. However, a modification of Eq. 1 can be used as a semi-empirical theory to calculate pre-exponential factors, kinetic isotope effects, or to predict trends of activation energy for series of similar reactions (Eq. 11–3 and Figs. 11–1 and 11–2). The method has one empirical parameter, p, to be adjusted to one activation energy. The energy expression is

$$V = E_1(1 - n^p) - E_2(1 - n)^p \qquad \text{(E–36)}$$

In dimensionless form, this expression is simply

$$\frac{V}{E_1} = (1 - n^p) - \frac{E_2}{E_1}(1 - n)^p \qquad \text{(E–37)}$$

The maximum energy V^*, the bond order at the maximum n^*, and the curvature along the reaction path at the maximum F_ρ are derived as given above. For this simple case these quantities are simply expressed in terms of the ratios V^*/E_1, and E_2/E_1, as in Table 1. From this table one may read off the value of p to use in Eq. 11–3 to predict how the activation energy will change for other values of E_2. Stretching-force constants are evaluated from Eq. 4–56.

This method is extremely simple and easy to use; and its results for kinetic isotope effects, A-factors, and E-trends are very nearly the same as the full BEBO method or the LEPS method. By virtue of the very great simplicity of this method, it may be preferable to the full BEBO method, even for hydrogen-transfer reactions—except when one is calculating activation energy.

References

1. WADE L. FITE and SHELDON DATZ, "Chemical Research with Molecular Beams," *Ann. Rev. Phys. Chem.*, **14**, 61 (1963).

2. SHELDON DATZ and E. H. TAYLOR, "Ionization on Platinum and Tungsten Surfaces. I. The Alkali Metals," *J. Chem. Phys.*, **25**, 389 (1956).

3. I. AMDUR and H. PEARLMAN, "Helium Repulsive Potential from Collision Cross Section Measurements," *J. Chem. Phys.*, **9**, 503 (1941).

4. R. B. BERNSTEIN, "Quantum Mechanical Analysis of Differential Elastic Scattering of Molecular Beams," *J. Chem. Phys.*, **33**, 795 (1960).

5. D. R. BATES (ed), *Atomic and Molecular Processes*, Academic Press, Inc., New York (1962).

6. D. R. HERSHBACH, "Reactive Collisions in Crossed Molecular Beams," *Disc. Faraday Soc.*, **33**, 149 (1962).

7. F. W. SCHNEIDER and B. S. RABINOVITCH, "The Thermal Unimolecular Isomerization of Methyl Isocyanide," *J. Am. Chem. Soc.*, **84**, 4215 (1962).

8. FARRINGTON DANIELS and E. H. JOHNSTON, "The Thermal Decomposition of Gaseous Nitrogen Pentoxide. A Monomolecular Reaction," *J. Am. Chem. Soc.*, **43**, 53 (1921).

9. H. S. JOHNSTON and D. M. YOST, "Kinetics of the Rapid Gas Reaction Between Ozone and Nitrogen Dioxide," *J. Chem. Phys.*, **17**, 386 (1949).

10a. H. J. SCHUMACHER and G. SPRENGER, "Die Reaktion zwischen Stickstoffpentoxyd und Ozon. II.", *Z. Physik. Chem.*, **B2**, 267 (1929).

10b. G. SPRENGER, "Die Spektrographische Identifizierung intermediar auftretenden Stickoxydes," *Z. Elektrochem.*, **37**, 674 (1931).

11. J. H. SMITH and F. DANIELS, "A Study of the Kinetics of the Reaction between Nitrogen Pentoxide and Nitric Oxide," *J. Am. Chem. Soc.*, **69**, 1735 (1947).

12. I. C. HISATSUNE, BRYCE CRAWFORD, Jr., and R. A. OGG, Jr., "The Kinetics of the NO—N_2O_5 Reaction," *J. Am. Chem. Soc.*, **79**, 4648 (1957).

13. Decomposition of N_2O_5 at extremely low pressure:
    J. H. HODGES and E. F. LINHORST, *J. Am. Chem. Soc.*, **56**, 836 (1934);
    H. C. RAMSPERGER and R. C. TOLMAN, *Proc. Natl. Acad. Sci.*, **16**, 6 (1930);
    H. C. RAMSPERGER and R. C. TOLMAN, *ibid*, **15**, 453 (1929).

14. R. L. MILLS and H. S. JOHNSTON, "Decomposition of Nitrogen Pentoxide in the Presence of Nitric Oxide," *J. Am. Chem. Soc.*, **73**, 938 (1951).

15. H. S. JOHNSTON, "Effect of Foreign Gases," *J. Am. Chem. Soc.*, **75**, 1567 (1953).

16. H. S. JOHNSTON and YU-SHENG TAO, "Thermal Decomposition of Nitrogen Pentoxide at High Temperature," *J. Am. Chem. Soc.*, **73**, 2948 (1951).

17. GARRY SCHOTT and N. DAVIDSON, "The Decomposition of N_2O_5 at High Temperatures," *J. Am. Chem. Soc.*, **80**, 1841 (1958).

18. H. S. JOHNSTON, "Four Mechanisms Involving Nitrogen Pentoxide," *J. Am. Chem. Soc.*, **73**, 4542 (1951).

19. H. S. JOHNSTON and J. HEICKLEN, "Photochemical Oxidations," *J. Am. Chem. Soc.*, **86**, 4249, 4254 (1964).

20. L. PAULING and E. B. WILSON, Jr., *Introduction to Quantum Mechanics*, McGraw-Hill Book Co., Inc., New York (1935).

21. K. S. PITZER, *Quantum Chemistry*, Prentice-Hall, Inc., New York, (1953).

22. H. EYRING, J. WALTER, and G. E. KIMBALL, *Quantum Chemistry*, John Wiley and Sons, Inc., New York (1944).

23. L. I. SCHIFF, *Quantum Mechanics*, McGraw-Hill Book Company, Inc., New York (1949).

24. R. P. BELL, "The Tunnel Effect Correction for Parabolic Potential Barriers," *Trans. Faraday Soc.*, **55**, 1, (1959).

25. C. ECKART, "The Penetration of a Potential Barrier by Electrons," *Phys. Rev.*, **35**, 1303 (1930).

26. H. S. JOHNSTON and J. HEICKLEN, "Tunneling Corrections for Unsymmetrical Eckart Potential Energy Barriers," *J. Phys. Chem.*, **66**, 532 (1962).

27. H. S. JOHNSTON and D. RAPP, "Large Tunneling Corrections in Chemical Reaction Rates," *J. Am. Chem. Soc.*, **83**, 1 (1961).

28. E. B. WILSON, Jr., J. C. DECIUS, and P. C. CROSS, *Molecular Vibrations*, McGraw-Hill Book Co., Inc., New York (1955).

29. J. O. HIRSCHFELDER, C. F. CURTISS, and R. B. BIRD, *Molecular Theory of Gases and Liquids*, John Wiley and Sons, Inc., New York (1954).

30. K. S. PITZER, "Electronic Correlation in Molecules. II. The Rare Gases," *J. Am. Chem. Soc.*, **78**, 4565 (1956).

31. G. HERZBERG, *Spectra of Diatomic Molecules*, D. Van Nostrand Co., New York (1950).

32. P. M. MORSE, "Diatomic Molecules According to the Wave Mechanics. II. Vibrational Levels," *Phys. Rev.*, **34**, 57 (1929).

33. S. GLASSTONE, K. J. LAIDLER, and H. EYRING, *The Theory of Rate Processes*, McGraw-Hill Book Company, Inc., New York (1941).

34. S. SATO, "Potential Energy Surface of the System of Three Atoms," *J. Chem. Phys.*, **23**, 2465 (1955).

35. B. MAHAN, "Perturbation of Molecular Distribution Functions by Chemical Reactions," *J. Chem. Phys.*, **32**, 362 (1960).

36. D. R. HERSCHBACH and V. W. LAURIE, "Anharmonic Potential Constants and Their Dependence upon Bond Lengths," *J. Chem. Phys.*, **35**, 458 (1961).

37. H. S. JOHNSTON, "Continuity of Force Constants between Normal Molecules and Lennard-Jones Pairs," *J. Am. Chem. Soc.*, **86**, 1643 (1964).

38. T. L. COTTRELL, *The Strength of Chemical Bonds*, Butterworths Scientific Publications, London, 2nd ed., (1958).

39. J. W. LINNETT, "A Modification of the Lewis-Langmuir Octet Rule," *J. Am. Chem. Soc.*, **83**, 2643 (1961).

40. L. PAULING, "Atomic Radii and Interatomic Distances in Metals," *J. Am. Chem. Soc.*, **69**, 542 (1947).

41a. H. S. JOHNSTON and C. PARR, "Activation Energies from Bond Energies," *J. Am. Chem. Soc.*, **85**, 2544 (1963).

41b. H. S. JOHNSTON, *Advances in Chemical Physics*, **3**, 131 (1960).

42. G. HERZBERG, *Infrared and Raman Spectra*, D. Van Nostrand Company, Inc., New York (1945).

43. J. E. and M. G. MAYER, *Statistical Mechanics*, John Wiley and Sons, Inc., New York (1940), pp. 213–217.

44. R. C. TOLMAN, *The Principles of Statistical Mechanics*, Oxford University Press, Oxford, England, 1938.

45. G. S. RUSHBROOKE, *Introduction to Statistical Mechanics*, Clarendon Press, Oxford (1949).

46. W. J. MOORE, *Physical Chemistry*, Prentice-Hall, Inc., New York (1962), 3rd ed.

47. D. R. HERSCHBACH, H. S. JOHNSTON. and D. RAPP, "Molecular Partition Functions in Terms of Local Properties," *J. Chem. Phys.*, **31**, 1652 (1959).

48. O. REDLICH, "Eine allgemeine Beziehung zwischen den Schwingungsfrequenzen isotoper Molekeln," *Z. Physik. Chem.*, **B28**, 371 (1935).

49. E. B. WILSON, Jr., "The Present Status of the Statistical Method of Calculating Thermodynamic Functions," *Chem. Rev.*, **27**, 17 (1940).

50. R. D. PRESENT, *Kinetic Theory of Gases*, McGraw-Hill Book Co., Inc., New York (1958).

51. E. WIGNER, "On the Penetration of Potential Barriers in Chemical Reactions," *Z. Physik. Chem.*, **B19**, 203 (1932).

52. E. GORIN, *Acta Physicochem. U.R.S.S.*, **9**, 661 (1938).

53. B. MAHAN, "Gaseous Ion Recombination Rates," *J. Chem. Phys.*, **40**, 392 (1964).

54. H. S. JOHNSTON and P. GOLDFINGER, "Theoretical Interpretation of Reactions Occurring in Photochlorination," *J. Chem. Phys.*, **37**, 700 (1962)

55. A. SHEPP, "Rate of Recombination of Radicals. A General Sector Theory," *J. Chem. Phys.*, **24**, 939 (1956).

56. R. ECKLING, P. GOLDFINGER, G. HUYBRECHTS, G. MARTENS, L. MEYERS, and S. SMOES, "Kinetische Studie über die Konkurrenz bei Photochlorierungsreaktionen," *Chem. Ber.*, **93**, 3014 (1960).

57. G. C. FETTIS, J. H. KNOX, and A. F. TROTMAN-DICKENSON, "The Transfer Reactions of Halogen Atoms," *Canad. J. Chem.*, **38**, 1643 (1960); J. H. KNOX, "Competitive Chlorinations. II. Chloromethanes," *Trans. Faraday Soc.*, **58**, 275 (1962).

58. F. W. LAMPE, J. L. FRANKLIN, and F. H. FIELD, "Kinetics of Reactions of Ions with Molecules," *Progress in Reaction Kinetics*, **1**, 69 (1961).

59a. B. H. Mahan, and J. C. Person, "Gaseous Ion Recombination Rates. II,"
      J. Chem. Phys., **40**, 2851 (1964).

59b. T. S. Carlton and B. Mahan, "Gaseous Ion Recombination Rates. III,"
      J. Chem. Phys., **40**, 3683 (1964).

·60. Experimental data for HHH reactions:
      a. A. Farkas, *Z. Physik. Chem.*, **B10**, 419 (1930);
      b. K. H. Geib and P. Harteck, *Z. Physik. Chem., Bodenstein Festband*,
          849 (1931);
      c. M. van Meersche, *Bull. Soc. Chim. Belg.*, **60**, 99 (1951);
      d. A. Farkas and L. Farkas, *Proc. Roy. Soc.* (London), **A152**, 124 (1935).
      e. G. Boato, G. Careri, A. Cimino, E. Molanari, and G. G. Volpi, *J.
          Chem. Phys.*, **24**, 783 (1956).
      f. W. R. Schulz and D. J. LeRoy, *J. Chem. Phys.*, **42**, 3869 (1965).
      g. W. R. Schulz and D. J. LeRoy, *Can. J. Chem.* **42**, 2480 (1964).
      h. W. L. Fite and R. T. Brackman, *Proc. Third International Conf. on
          Atomic Collision Processes*, M. R. C. McDowell, ed. John Wiley and
          Sons, Inc., New York, 1964, p. 955.
      i. S. Datz and E. H. Taylor, *J. Chem. Phys.*, **39**, 1896 (1963).

61.   F. London, *Probleme der modernen Physik, Sommerfeld Festschrift*, S.
      Hirzel, Leipzig, p. 104 (1928); *Z. Elektrochem.*, **35**, 552 (1929).

62.   L. S. Kassel, *Kinetics of Homogeneous Gas Reactions*, The Chemical
      Catalog Co., Inc., New York (1932).

63.   Term paper by Phillip Dow in Chemistry 219, University of California,
      Berkeley (1963); independently discovered by J. C. Polanyi, private
      communication (1964). It appears that in the preceding thirty years
      no one bothered to make this computation.

64.   S. F. Boys and I. Shavitt, "A Fundamental Calculation of the Energy
      Surfaces for the System of Three Hydrogen Atoms," Technical Report
      WIS-AF-13, (1959); I. Shavitt, "A Calculation of the Rates of the
      Ortho-Para Conversions and Isotope Exchanges in Hydrogen," *J. Chem.
      Phys.*, **31**, 1359 (1959).

65.   A. S. Coolidge and H. M. James, "The Approximations Involved in
      Calculations of Atomic Interactions and Activation Energies," *J. Chem.
      Phys.*, **2**, 811 (1934).

66a. R. Weston, "H_3 Activated Complex and the Rate of Reaction of Hydrogen
      Atoms and Hydrogen Molecules," *J. Chem. Phys.*, **31**, 892 (1959).

66b. R. N. Porter and M. Karplus, *J. Chem. Phys.*, **40**, 1105 (1964).

67.   L. Farkas and E. Wigner, "Calculation of the Rate of Elementary
      Reactions of Light and Heavy Hydrogen," *Trans. Faraday Soc.*, **32**,
      708 (1936).

68.   Early calculations of HHH reaction rates:
      H. Pelzer and E. Wigner, *Z. Physik. Chem.*, **15B**, 445 (1932);
      E. Wigner, *ibid.*, **19B**, 203 (1932);
      H. Eyring and M. Polanyi, *Z. Physik. Chem.*, **B12**, 279 (1931);
      J. Hirschfelder, H. Eyring and B. Topley, *J. Chem. Phys.*, **4**, 170 (1936).

69.   Classical-mechanical computations of reaction dynamics for HHH system:
      a. F. T. Wall, L. A. Hiller, Jr., and J. Mazur, *J. Chem. Phys.*, **29**, 255
          (1959); **35**, 1284 (1961). F. T. Wall and R. N. Porter, *J. Chem.
          Phys.*, **36**, 3256 (1962); **39**, 3112 (1963).

b. M. KARPLUS, R. N. PORTER, and R. D. SHARMA, *J. Chem. Phys.*, **40**, 2033 (1964); **43**, 3259 (1965).

70. A series of articles over a ten-year period, with references and a summary given by J. BIGELEISEN and M. WOLFSBERG, *Advances in Chemical Physics*, **1**, 15 (1958).

71. M. G. EVANS and M. POLANYI, "Inertia and Driving Force of Chemical Reactions," *Trans. Faraday Soc.*, **34**, 11 (1938).

72. N. N. SEMENOV, *Some Problems in Chemical Kinetics and Reactivity*, Vol. I (translated by M. BOUDART), Princeton University Press, Princeton, N.J. (1958).

73. K. S. PITZER and W. D. GWINN, "Energy Levels and Thermodynamic Functions for Molecules with Internal Rotation. I. Rigid Frame with Attached Tops," *J. Chem. Phys.*, **10**, 428 (1942).

74. D. R. HERSCHBACH, H. S. JOHNSTON, K. S. PITZER, and R. E. POWELL, "Theoretical Pre-exponential Factors for Twelve Bimolecular Reactions," *J. Chem. Phys.*, **25**, 736 (1956).

75. A. F. TROTMAN-DICKENSON, *Gas Kinetics*, Academic Press, Inc., New York (1955).

76. a. T. E. SHARP and H. S. JOHNSTON, "Hydrogen-Deuterium Kinetic Isotope Effect, an Experimental and Theoretical Study over a Wide Range of Temperature," *J. Chem. Phys.*, **37**, 1541 (1962);
    b. H. S. JOHNSTON and E. TSCHUIKOW-ROUX, *J. Chem. Phys.*, **36**, 463 (1962).

77. P. B. AYSCOUGH, J. C. POLANYI, and E. W. R. STEACIE, "Mechanism and Data for Reactions of CF_3 Radicals," *Canad. J. Chem.*, **33**, 743 (1955); P. B. AYSCOUGH, *J. Chem. Phys.*, **24**, 944 (1956).

78. J. G. DAVY, C. R. GUERRA, H. S. JOHNSTON, C. F. WEAVER and C. E. YOUNG, "Hydrogen-Deuterium Kinetic Isotope Effect," *J. Chem. Phys.*, **41**, 1517 (1964).

79. J. R. MCNESBY, "Kinetic Isotope Effects in the Reaction of Methyl Radicals with Ethane, Ethane-d_6, and Ethane-1,1,1-d_3," *J. Phys. Chem.*, **64**, 1671 (1960).

80. G. CHILTZ, R. ECKLING, P. GOLDFINGER, G. HUYBRECHTS, H. S. JOHNSTON L. MEYERS, and G. VERBEKE, "Kinetic Isotope Effect in Photochlorination of H_2, CH_4, $CHCl_3$, and C_2H_6," *J. Chem. Phys.*, **38**, 1053 (1963).

81. J. BIGELEISEN, F. S. KLEIN, R. E. WESTON, Jr., and M. WOLFSBERG, "Deuterium Isotope Effect in the Reaction of Hydrogen Molecules with Chlorine Atoms and the Potential Energy of the H_2Cl Transition Complex," *J. Chem. Phys.*, **30**, 1340 (1959).

82. Data for iodine atom recombination rates:
    a. E. RABINOWITCH and W. C. WOOD, *J. Chem. Phys.*, **4**, 497 (1936);
    b. R. G. W. NORRISH and G. PORTER, *Nature*, **164**, 658 (1949);
    c. N. DAVIDSON, R. MARSHALL, A. E. LARSH, Jr., and T. CARRINGTON, *J. Chem. Phys.*, **19**, 1311 (1951);
    d. K. E. RUSSELL and J. SIMONS, *Proc. Roy. Soc.*, **A217**, 271 (1953);
    e. M. I. CHRISTIE, A. J. HARRISON, R. G. W. NORRISH, and G. PORTER, *Proc. Roy. Soc.*, **A231**, 446 (1955);
    f. R. L. STRONG, J. C. W. CHIEN, P. E. GRAF, and J. E. WILLARD, *J. Chem. Phys.*, **26**, 1287 (1957);

g. D. L. BUNKER and N. DAVIDSON, *J. Am. Chem. Soc.*, **80**, 5085 (1958);
h. D. BRITTON, N. DAVIDSON, W. GEHMAN, and G. SCHOTT, *J. Chem. Phys.*, **25**, 805 (1956).

83. E. RABINOWITCH, "The Recombination-Velocity of Free Atoms," *Trans. Faraday Soc.*, **33**, 283 (1937).

84. D. L. BUNKER and N. DAVIDSON, "On the Interpretation of Halogen Atom Recombination Rates," *J. Am. Chem. Soc.*, **80**, 5090 (1958).

85. E. WIGNER, "Calculation of the Rate of Elementary Association Reactions," *J. Chem. Phys.*, **5**, 720 (1938).

86. J. C. KECK, "Statistical Theories of Chemical Reaction Rates," *J. Chem. Phys.*, **29**, 410 (1958).

87. J. C. LIGHT, "Dissociation of Gaseous Diatomic Molecules," *J. Chem. Phys.*, **36**, 1016 (1962).

88. D. L. BUNKER, "Mechanics of Atomic Recombination Reactions," *J. Chem. Phys.*, **32**, 1001 (1960).

89. G. PORTER, Z. G. SZABO, and M. G. TOWNSEND, "The Recombination of Atoms. V," *Proc. Roy. Soc.* (London), **A270**, 493 (1962).

90. F. A. LINDEMANN, "Discussion on 'Radiation Theory of Chemical Action'," *Trans. Faraday Soc.*, **17**, 598 (1922); C. N. HINSHELWOOD, *The Kinetics of Chemical Change*," Oxford University Press, Oxford (1940).

91. H. S. JOHNSTON and J. R. WHITE, "Statistical Interpretations of Unimolecular Reaction Rates," *J. Chem. Phys.*, **22**, 1969 (1954); H. S. JOHNSTON, *J. Chem. Phys.*, **20**, 1103 (1952).

92. F. BUFF and D. J. WILSON, "Some Considerations of Unimolecular Rate Theory," *J. Chem. Phys.*, **32**, 677 (1960).

93. B. N. SLATER, *Theory of Unimolecular Reactions*, Cornell University Press, Ithaca, N.Y. (1959).

94. R. C. TOLMAN, "Statistical Mechanics Applied to Chemical Kinetics," *J. Am. Chem. Soc.*, **42**, 2506 (1920); *ibid.*, **47**, 2652 (1925).

95. G. Z. WHITTEN and B. S. RABINOVITCH, "Accurate and Facile Approximation for Vibrational Energy-Level Sums," *J. Chem. Phys.*, **38**, 2466 (1963).

96. M. VESTAL, A. L. WAHRHAFTIG, and W. H. JOHNSTON, "Improved Rate Expression in the Quasi-Equilibrium Theory of Mass Spectra," *J. Chem. Phys.*, **37**, 1276 (1962).

97. T. L. COTTRELL and J. C. McCOUBREY, *Molecular Energy Transfer in Gases*, Butterworths, London (1961).

98. K. F. HERZFELD and T. A. LITOVITZ, *Absorption and Dispersion of Ultrasonic Waves*, Academic Press, Inc., New York (1959); R. N. SCHWARTZ, A. I. SLAWSKY, and K. F. HERZFELD, *J. Chem. Phys.*, **20**, 1591 (1952).

99. M. Boudart and J. T. Doubois, "Stabilization of Energy-Rich Molecules," *J. Chem. Phys.*, **23**, 223 (1955); this article includes a re-interpretation of data by N. S. NEPORENT, *Zhur. Fiz. Khim.*, **21**, 1111 (1947); **24**, 1219 (1950).

100. G. H. KOHLMAIER and B. S. RABINOVITCH, "Collisional Transition Probabilities for Vibrational Deactivation of Chemically Activated *sec*-Butyl Radicals," *J. Chem. Phys.*, **38**, 1692, 1709 (1963).

101. R. A. MARCUS and O. K. RICE, "Kinetics of the Recombination of Methyl Radicals," *J. Phys. Colloid Chem.*, **55**, 894 (1951); R. A. MARCUS, *J. Chem. Phys.*, **21**, 359 (1952).

102. H. M. ROSENSTOCK, M. B. WALLENSTEIN, A. L. WAHRHAFTIG, and H. E. EYRING, "Absolute Rate Theory for Isolated Systems and the Mass Spectra of Polyatomic Molecules," *Proc. Nat. Acad. Sci. (U.S.)*, **38**, 667 (1952).

103. M. POLANYI and E. WIGNER, "Über die Interferenz von Eigenschwingungen als Ursache von Energieschwankungen und chemischer Umsetzungen," *Z. Physik. Chem.*, **A139**, 439 (1928).

104. S. W. BENSON, *The Foundations of Chemical Kinetics*, McGraw-Hill Book Company, Inc., New York (1960), pp. 39–42.

105. R. RYASON and M. K. WILSON, "Vibrational Spectrum and Structure of Nitryl Choride," *J. Chem. Phys.*, **22**, 2000 (1954).

106. V. N. KONDRAT'EV, *Chemical Kinetics of Gas Reactions* (translated from the Russian by J. M. CRABTREE and S. N. CARRUTHERS), Addison-Wesley Publishing Company, Inc., Reading, Mass. (1964).

107. H. S. JOHNSTON, L. FOERING, J. R. WHITE, "Kinetics of the Thermal Decomposition of Nitric Acid Vapor. III. Low Pressure Results," *J. Am. Chem. Soc.*, **77**, 4208 (1955); also article II in this series.

108. "Selected Values of Chemical Thermodynamic Properties," Circular of the National Bureau of Standards 500, Govt. Printing Office, Washington, D.C. (1952).

Index